THE
AROMATIC DIAZO-COMPOUNDS
AND THEIR
TECHNICAL APPLICATIONS

The first man knew her not perfectly,
And in like manner the last hath not traced her out.
—Ecclesiasticus.

THE
AROMATIC DIAZO-COMPOUNDS
AND THEIR
TECHNICAL APPLICATIONS

BY

K. H. SAUNDERS

M.C., M.A.(Cantab.), B.Sc.(Lond.), F.I.C.

CHEMIST, IMPERIAL CHEMICAL INDUSTRIES, LTD.

WITH A FOREWORD BY

PROFESSOR A. G. GREEN

F.R.S., M.Sc., F.I.C.

NEW YORK

LONGMANS, GREEN & CO.

LONDON: EDWARD ARNOLD & CO.

Printed in Great Britain by
Richard Clay & Sons, Ltd., Bungay, Suffolk.

FOREWORD

By Professor A. G. Green, F.R.S., M.Sc., F.I.C.

Since the publication of the second edition of Cain's " Chemistry and Technology of the Diazo-Compounds " in 1920, great advances in the chemistry and technical application of this group of compounds have occurred. A new text-book embracing the present position of our knowledge has therefore become a serious necessity, not only for the theoretical chemist, but also for the dyestuff technologist, to whom an intimate acquaintance with diazo-chemistry is essential. No other reaction in organic chemistry exhibits such an extraordinary versatility and generality as the diazo-reaction. No other series of chemical changes occur with such quantitative accuracy, ease and rapidity as those of which diazo-compounds are capable. In the field of dyestuff manufacture the diazo-reaction has afforded the means of preparing an endless array of colouring matters of all shades and the greatest variety of properties. Many of these dyes are capable not only of being produced in substance, but can also be formed with equal ease within the fibre itself or upon any desired substratum. There has thus arisen a new technique for the production of fast colours on textile materials and of new pigments for paints, lithography and lacquers. Furthermore, through their remarkable adaptability as synthetic agents, diazo-compounds afford a prolific means for the economical production of new compounds, many of which would be otherwise unobtainable or only producible by reactions incapable of technical realisation. Many products which are thus obtained serve as valuable intermediates for dyestuff production, whilst others find employment in medicine. At the present time over 80% of the dyestuffs in commerce owe their formation, one way or another, to the diazo-reaction. In the photographic industry also, the diazo-reaction has become during recent years widely employed for the reproduction of architectural and engineering drawings, and many patents have been taken for this purpose. It is only in regard to the theory of the diazo-compounds and the remarkable isomerism they exhibit that but little recent advance can be recorded. This matter remains in much the same position as it was left after the controversy between Hantzsch and Bamberger, and there is here much scope for re-examination of the question from modern points of view.

In presenting a clear and concise account of diazo-chemistry, Mr.

Saunders has fulfilled a task which should be of equal value to the student and the technologist. Together with the earlier work of Cain, it will form a lasting tribute to the memory of Peter Griess, whose services to chemical science and the dyestuff industry, so poorly appreciated or recompensed during his lifetime, can scarcely be over-estimated.

PREFACE

One might hazard the guess that if all the papers and patents which have been published on diazo-compounds in English, French and German were printed seriatim, a volume of some fifteen thousand quarto pages would result. The present writer has attempted to condense such a mass into some two hundred and fifty pages, not for the benefit of chemists who have had wide experience of diazo-compounds and have cut their own paths through the jungle, but for the larger number who seek an introduction to this field of academic and industrial activity, or who wish to be informed of the directions in which progress is taking place.

This volume is not therefore a comprehensive treatise, for such would become so unwieldy as to defeat its own end, but the author hopes that he has omitted no reference of major importance, so that those wishing to go further in the matter should have no difficulty in tracing the original sources in the literature, and he hopes that he has earned a small measure of gratitude from readers by not giving way to the temptation to bedevil the subject further by throwing up another theory of the constitution of the isomeric diazo-compounds. As regards the patent literature, the author has perforce used English scripts as the basis of discussion, and given the foreign equivalents where known to him, but he has not made search to ascertain that the list of foreign equivalents is complete. The fact that no foreign equivalent is given to an English patent does not mean that one does not exist, nor are the equivalents given necessarily entirely congruent, owing to the differing requirements of the patent laws of the various countries.

In compiling this work the author has been much indebted in the first place to Prof. A. G. Green, F.R.S., for encouragement and guidance, particularly on points pertaining to the history of the development of the diazo-compounds. His thanks are also due to the Directors of the Dyestuffs Group of Imperial Chemical Industries, both for permission to undertake the work and for the privilege of using the facilities of the Group Library, including the use of translations of Russian papers not available *in extenso* in *British Chemical Abstracts* or the *Centralblatt*.

K. H. S.

Hale, Cheshire.
  September, 1936.

CONTENTS

CHAP.
                                                           PAGE

I.   THE FORMATION OF DIAZO-COMPOUNDS 1

II.   STABILISED DIAZO-COMPOUNDS 28

III.   ELIMINATION AND INTERCHANGE OF GROUPS IN DIAZO-COMPOUNDS 52

IV.   THEORY OF THE DIAZOTISATION REACTION: HETEROCYCLIC DIAZO-COMPOUNDS: STABILITY: ANALYSIS: THERMO-CHEMISTRY OF DIAZO-COMPOUNDS 61

V.   REACTIONS OF THE DIAZO-COMPOUNDS. CLASS A. DERIVATIVES IN WHICH THE DIAZO-GROUP REMAINS FUNCTIONALLY INTACT 80

VI.   REACTIONS OF THE DIAZO-COMPOUNDS. CLASS B. DERIVATIVES IN WHICH THE DIAZO-FUNCTION DISAPPEARS, BUT THE DIAZO-NITROGEN ATOMS REMAIN IN THE NEW MOLECULE 102

VII.   REACTIONS OF THE DIAZO-COMPOUNDS. CLASS B (continued) 125

VIII.   REACTIONS OF THE DIAZO-COMPOUNDS. CLASS C. DERIVATIVES FORMED BY REPLACEMENT OF THE DIAZO-GROUP . 144

IX.   THE ACTION OF LIGHT ON DIAZO-COMPOUNDS . . . 164

X.   THEORIES OF THE CONSTITUTION OF THE DIAZO-COMPOUNDS . 173

AUTHOR INDEX 216

SUBJECT INDEX 222

LIST OF ABBREVIATIONS

A	British Chemical Abstracts A.
Agfa . . .	Aktiengesellschaft für Anilinfabrikation in Berlin.*
Amer. Chem. J. .	American Chemical Journal.
Amer. J. Pharm. .	American Journal of Pharmacy.
Angew. Chem. .	Angewandte Chemie. Changed from Z. angew. Chem. 1932.
Anilinokras. Prom.	Anilinokrasotschnaja Promischlennosti.
Anm. . . .	Deutsches Reichs-Patent Anmeldung.
Ann. . . .	Justus Liebig's Annalen der Chemie.
Ann. Chim. Appl.	Annali di Chimica Applicata.
B . . .	British Chemical Abstracts B.
B.A.S.F. . . .	Badische Anilin- und Soda-Fabrik, Ludwigshaven a/Rhein.*
Bayer . . .	Farbenfabriken vorm. Friedr. Bayer & Co., Elberfeld.*
Ber.	Berichte der Deutschen Chemischen Gesellschaft.
Bull. Soc. chim.	Bulletin de la Société Chimique de France.
Bull. Soc. Mulhouse	Bulletin de la Société industrielle de Mulhouse.
Cain . . .	The Chemistry and Technology of the Diazo-compounds. Arnold, London, 1920.
Cassella . . .	Cassella & Co., Mainkur.*
Cent. . . .	Centralblatt.
Chem. Abs. .	Chemical Abstracts.
Chem. and Ind. . .	Chemistry and Industry.
Chem. Listy .	Chemické Listy pro Vědu a Průmysl.
Chem. News .	Chemical News.
Chem. Revs. .	Chemical Reviews.
Chem. Wkbld. .	Chemisch Weekblad.
Chem. Zeit. .	Chemiker Zeitung.
Compt. rend. . .	Comptes rendus hebdomadaires des Séances de l'Académie des Sciences.
Deut. Arch. Klin. Med.	Deutsches Archiv für Klinische Medizin.
D.R.P. . . .	Deutsches Reichs-Patent.
E.P. . . .	English Patent.
F.P. . . .	French Patent.
Fr. . . .	Friedländer's Fortschritte der Teerfarbenfabrikation.
Gazz. . . .	Gazzetta chimica italiana.
Griesheim . .	Farbwerk Griesheim Electron, Offenbach am Main.*
Helv. Chim. Acta	Helvetica Chimica Acta.
I.C.I. . . .	Imperial Chemical Industries, Ltd., London.
I.G. . . .	Interessen Gemeinschaft, A.-G., Frankfort.
Ind. Eng. Chem.	Industrial and Engineering Chemistry.
J. Am. C.S. .	Journal of the American Chemical Society.
J. appl. Chem. Russ. .	Journal of Applied Chemistry, Russia.
J.C.S. . . .	Journal of the Chemical Society, London.
J. Indian C.S. .	Journal of the Indian Chemical Society.
J. Physical Chem.	Journal of Physical Chemistry.
J. pr. Chem. .	Journal für praktische Chemie.
J. Roy. Tech. Coll.	Journal of the Royal Technical College, Glasgow.
J.S.C.I. . .	Journal of the Society of Chemical Industry.
J.S.D.C. . .	Journal of the Society of Dyers and Colourists.
J. Wash. Acad. Sci.	Journal of the Washington Academy of Sciences.
Kuhlmann . .	Compagnie National de Matières Colorantis et Manufacture de Produits Chimiques du Nord Reunis Établissements Kuhlmann.

Lectures . . . R. Robinson, Two Lectures on an "Outline of an Electrochemical Theory of the Course of Organic Reactions." Institute of Chemistry of Great Britain and Ireland, London, 1932.

M.L.B. . . . Farbwerke Höchst, vorm. Meister, Lucius and Bruning.*

Monats. . . . Monatshefte für Chemie.

Phil. Trans. . . Philosophical Transactions of the Royal Society.

Phot. Journ. . . Photographic Journal.

Proc. . . . Proceedings of the Chemical Society.

R.A.L. . . . Atti della Reale Accademia dei Lincei.

Rec. trav. chim. . Recueil des travaux chimiques des Pays-Bas.

Rocz. Chem. . . Roczniki Chemji organ Polskiego Towarzystwa Chemicznego.

S.C.I. . . . Society of Chemical Industry in Basle.

St. Denis . . . Société anonyme des Matière Colorantes et Produits Chimiques de Saint-Denis.

Sw.P. . . . Swiss Patent.

Textilber. . . . Melliand's Textilberichte.

Weiler-ter-Meer . . Weiler-ter-Meer & Co., Uerdingen.

Z. anal. Chem. . . Zeitschrift für analytische Chemie.

Zeit. angew. Chem. .   „   angewandte Chemie.

Zeit. anorg. Chem. .   „   anorganische und Allgemeine Chemie.

Zeit. Elektrochem. .   „   Elektrochemie.

Zeit. Farb. Ind. . .   „   Farben-Industrie.

Zeit. physiol. Chem. . Hoppe-Seyler's Zeitschrift für physiologische Chemie.

Zeit. wiss. Phot. . Zeitschrift für wissenschaftliche Photographie.

U.S.P. . . . United States Patent.

* Firms marked with an asterisk are now constituents of the I.G.

NOMENCLATURE

The diazo-compounds are tautomeric substances, and in this book the following conventions with regard to nomenclature are observed :—

The name " diazo " or " diazo-compound " is used as a generic name to cover all the tautomeric forms.

" Diazonium " and " diazonium salts " refer to tautomers functioning as strong salt-forming bases.

" Diazotate " refers to derivatives of the acidic tautomers of which the free acids are the diazohydroxides.

The evolution of the system of nomenclature and the structures by which the tautomers are differentiated is explained in Chapter X.

GENERAL REFERENCES TO THE LITERATURE OF THE DIAZO-COMPOUNDS

A. W. v. Hofmann, *Ber.*, 1891, **24**, 1007 *Ref.* An account of the Life and Work of Griess.

Hantzsch, " Die Diazoverbindungen," Ahren's Sammlung, 1903, **8**, 1.

Morgan, " Our Present Knowledge of Aromatic Diazo-compounds." Report to the British Association, 1902.

Eibner, " Zur Geschichte der aromatischen Diazoverbindungen." Oldenburg, 1903.

Watson-Smith, *J.S.C.I.*, 1907, **26**, 134. History of the first application of diazo-compounds to the manufacture of azo-dyes.

Cain, " Chemistry and Technology of the Diazo-compounds." Arnold, London, 1920.

Hantzsch, Reddelien, " Die Diazoverbindungen." Springer, Berlin, 1921.

Moore, the Hantzsch Memorial Lecture, *J.C.S.*, **1936**, 1051.

Concerning technical methods of making diazo-compounds see :—

Groggins, " Unit Processes in Organic Synthesis." Chapter on " Diazotisation," contributed by H. E. Woodward, pp. 111 *et seq.* McGraw-Hill Book Co., London, 1935.

CHAPTER I

THE FORMATION OF DIAZO-COMPOUNDS

In the whole realm of Organic Chemistry there is no reaction the occurrence of which can be relied upon with more certainty than the formation of a diazo-compound by the action of nitrous acid on a primary aromatic amine. The certainty and smoothness with which this reaction can be accomplished under appropriate conditions, coupled with the high reactivity of the resulting diazo-compound, make it one of the utmost value, alike to the manufacturer of chemicals on a large scale and to the chemist engaged in research. The initiating ripple of the whole tide of human energy which has since been expended in the study of these compounds was released at Marburg in the year 1858, when Peter Griess first had in hand a specimen of diazotised picramic acid and recognised it as a member of a hitherto unknown class of chemical compounds.[1]

This discovery, like all others, did not arise by chance out of nothing. Some knowledge of the reaction of nitrous acid on the amino-group was already in existence, and it was known that aminobenzoic acid could be converted into hydroxybenzoic acid by the action of warm nitrous acid, for which reason Kolbe had suggested to Griess that in like manner picramic acid might be converted into hydroxypicramic acid. Griess, however, altered the experimental conditions slightly by using nitrous acid in the cold, and so obtained a substance which had none of the properties to be expected from the substance sought, and by acting on other amines in the same way he was soon convinced that he had discovered a reaction of general applicability. Griess thought that the previous investigators had failed to detect the new substances because they had worked in aqueous solutions, whereas he, by employing alcohol as solvent, had isolated them in a crystalline state.[2]

At the time of Griess's discovery the labours of organic chemists were directed towards elucidating the nature of radicals and the effect of substitution on such entities, and he gave to his new compounds the name " diazo " because he believed that they owed their genesis to the replacement of two hydrogen atoms by two atoms of nitrogen in the aromatic radicals from which they were derived. Griess soon laid down the main lines of the chemistry of the diazo-compounds, but as his method of performing the operation of diazotisation was cumbersome (see p. 15), and as his view as to the structure of the diazo-compounds

B

was erroneous, it is not expedient to describe the early work in detail at this point. Instead, the more profitable course will be followed of setting out the various means now known by which the diazo-compounds may be formed, and in the course of so doing the contribution made by

TABLE I

Methods of Producing Diazo-Compounds Based on the Fundamental Reaction :—

$$ArNH_2 + HX + HNO_2 = ArN_2X + 2H_2O$$

Reaction Technique.	Sphere of Employment.
1. A solution of a metallic nitrite is added to a cold solution of the amine in mineral acid :— $ArNH_2 + 2HX + NaNO_2 = ArN_2X + NaX + 2H_2O$ The " Direct Method."	i. Strongly basic amines giving salts readily soluble in aqueous mineral acids. ii. Amines sulphonated sufficiently to be soluble in acid solution.
2. Mixed alkaline solutions of a metallic nitrite and a salt of a sulphonated or carboxylated amine are run into excess of cold mineral acid :— $Ar{\diagdown}^{NH_2}_{SO_3Na} + NaNO_2 + 3HX = Ar{\diagdown}^{N_2X}_{SO_3H} + 2NaX + 2H_2O$ The " Inverted Method."	i. Amino - acids such as sulphanilic acid, naphthionic acid, aminobenzoic acid. ii. Some weakly basic amines.
3. The amine is dissolved in a concentrated acid (sulphuric acid, phosphoric acid, glacial acetic acid) and diazotised with nitrosylsulphuric acid :— $ArNH_2 + NOHSO_4 = ArN_2HSO_4 + H_2O$	For weakly basic amines.
4. The amine is dissolved in nitric acid and metabisulphite added, thus producing nitrous acid, which diazotises the amine. The method of Witt.	For weakly basic amines not easily nitrated or oxidised.
5. The amine salt is suspended or dissolved in a little water or alcohol and treated with nitrogen trioxide. The method of Griess.	For effecting diazotisation so that the solid diazo-salts may be subsequently isolated.
6. The amine salt is dissolved in water, or acids, or alcohol, or suspended in an inert solvent and treated with an alkyl nitrite :— $ArNH_2HX + Alk.NO = ArN_2X + Alk.OH + H_2O$ The method of Knoevenagel.	As for 5 above.

Griess will be seen in its proper relationship to the chemistry of the aromatic diazo-compounds, which will alone be the theme of this book.

A number of distinct ways of producing the diazo-compounds are known, but one of them so dominates the others that they are of trifling importance by comparison, and will be discussed later. The basic reaction by which the diazo-compounds are formed is expressed in its simplest and most general way as follows :—

$$ArNH_2 + HX + HNO_2 = ArN_2X + 2H_2O$$

where Ar is a mono- or poly-nuclear aromatic radical which may carry substituents and HX is a monobasic acid or its equivalent.

The exigencies arising from the differing properties of amines and the purposes to which the reaction products are to be put have caused the evolution of a number of variations in the operating technique. The nitrous acid may arise from different sources, the association of amine and acid may be altered, while the reaction may be carried out in aqueous solution or in solution or suspension in solvents. But whatever device may be employed the fundamental sequence of chemical changes will be found to be expressed by the above equation.

An attempt has been made in Table I to bring into a small compass a survey of methods of diazotisation which will afterwards be enlarged in detail, but it will be realised that the size of this volume forbids any attempt to cover every example of diazotisation mentioned in the literature. For that purpose such works as that of Beilstein must be consulted. Nor will any attempt be made to discuss or describe special details in the conduct of diazotisation on the manufacturing scale. Suffice it to remark that this is effected substantially in the same manner as in the laboratory, except that wooden vessels or vessels having linings such as tiles or rubber are employed. The high pitch of efficiency necessary in technical working is reached by attention in the case of each amine to the details of temperature, speed of agitation, presence of metals, and so forth. A number of works dealing with this aspect of the matter are included in the list of general references (page xii).

METHOD 1. THE DIRECT METHOD

The selection of this method to occupy the foremost place and the bestowal upon it of the name " direct " are both entirely arbitrary, but may be justified by the consideration that this is the method which it is always preferable to employ if circumstances permit. Ease, speed, and cheapness are the advantages to be gained by its use, but it is not suitable when isolation of the diazo-compound in the solid state is in view, except when stable diazo-compounds (see p. 30) are to be made.

This is the method, therefore, on which extensive manufacturing processes are based, and in which, on account of the instability of the diazo-compounds, their isolation is neither desirable nor necessary, as the synthetic reactions for which they are employed are carried out in the same solution in which diazotisation has previously taken place. Of the scores of tons of diazo-compounds manufactured daily by this reaction, not one solid particle is seen by the workers.

Martius was the chemist to whom the introduction of sodium nitrite as the source of nitrous acid was due.[3] The liberation of nitrous acid by the action of a mineral acid and its attack on an amine salt, provided the latter is in solution and so able to react, occur with great rapidity (see p. 61). If the solubility of the amine salt is insufficient for all to be dissolved at the commencement of the reaction, then it is important that the portion remaining as a solid phase should be as finely divided as possible, so that it can dissolve as fast as that in solution is converted into the diazo-salt. The necessary fineness can usually be attained by dissolving the base in one equivalent of hot weak acid, then cooling and adding the remainder of the acid, when the salt is precipitated in a sufficiently fine form, provided lumps are prevented from forming. The use of dispersing agents which do not react with nitrous acid has been patented for the purpose of obtaining amines, ordinarily difficult to diazotise, in the finest possible state of division.[4]

There is nothing to be gained by conducting the diazo-reaction any slower than the maximum rate at which the amine is found to react with nitrous acid. The reaction takes place with liberation of heat, and this prevents the reaction speed being utilised to the full, as it may not be possible to withdraw the heat quickly enough to prevent undue rise in temperature. On the other hand, to proceed too slowly is to run the risk of a product contaminated with decomposition products. There are cases, too, where delay results in the appearance of diazo-amino-compounds due to the diazo-compound first formed combining with the unreacted amine. When once formed some diazoamino-compounds cannot be split even by the addition of much extra acid, and to prevent their formation the nitrite is added all at once to the amine solution, which is cooled by floating ice. Cooling by ice in this manner is often known as internal cooling. p-Nitroaniline and α-naphthylamine are common examples where retarded reaction by the slow addition of nitrite results in the formation of diazoamino-compounds.

Diazotisation can rarely be brought about with only the theoretical two equivalents of acid indicated by the equation, because there is always risk that diazoamino-compounds may appear unless the solution remains fully acid until completion of the reaction. Two and a quarter to two and a half equivalents is the usual amount allowed, and more is required as the amine diminishes in basicity. If an organic acid is used, more is necessary than the amount which will suffice if a highly ionised mineral acid is employed in the same reaction. Altschul [5] examined this point, and found that in diazotising aniline eleven equivalents of acetic acid are needed before diazotisation becomes complete. He also discovered that if only one equivalent of mineral acid is used, the formation of the diazo-compound is related to the concentration of the solution of amine salt and increases rapidly as the concentration of the latter becomes greater.

The above remarks may be better appreciated by a few examples.

Diazotisation of 4-Chloro-o-toluidine. (" *Fast Red KB Base.*")—
The hydrochloride of the base (17·7 g. = 0·1 mol.) is dissolved in hot water (50 c.c.) and the contents of the beaker are allowed to cool with stirring. Concentrated hydrochloric acid (12 c.c.) is then added to precipitate the hydrochloride as a sludge. The beaker is surrounded by ice and stirring continued until the temperature falls to below 5°. Then a solution made by dissolving dry technical sodium nitrite (7 g. = 0·1 mol.) in water (11 c.c.) is run in slowly either down the side or under the surface, at such speed that the temperature does not rise above 5°. The hydrochloride during this time passes smoothly into solution as diazotisation proceeds. When all the nitrite has been added, a drop of the pale yellow solution should still show mineral acidity on Congo paper and a pale blue spot on starch-iodide paper. If the spot on starch iodide is negative, extra nitrite solution must be added drop by drop; if so strong as to indicate excess of nitrous acid, a solution of the hydrochloride of the base must be added until the excess has been removed. This final operation is frequently spoken of as " balancing." The chlorodiazotoluene solution so obtained should be clear, pale yellow, though the technical product may be darker and need filtering from flocculent impurities.

The following points should be noticed :—

1. The molecular weight of sodium nitrite is 69, but analysis of good-quality material usually shows its molecular weight to lie between 70 and 71.

2. The end-point of the reaction is detected with starch-iodide paper. Cadmium iodide is usually considered the iodide which affords the most sensitive papers. It must not be forgotten that strong mineral acid also causes the paper to turn blue, and when diazotising in strongly acid solution, care must be taken not to confound the mark left by acid with that left by nitrous acid. The colour left by the latter develops more sharply and is richer than that left by acid, but a few blanks will soon give a working comparison in any case where doubt has arisen. Spotting the paper through a pinch of salt is a device also used to ensure a clear mark; a better mark is sometimes shown on paper which has been wetted.

While starch iodide is universally used to detect the end-point of the reaction, another method has been described by Tscherwinski.[6] The method is applicable to strongly basic amines which are dissolved in aqueous acid, and a dilute solution of a dye containing a secondary amino-group is added as an indicator. " Methylene Yellow " will serve the purpose. Excess of sodium nitrite is then added and the excess of nitrous acid is then back-titrated with more amine solution until the indicator turns pink. On the face of it there is no advantage over the usual direct determination of the end-point.

The procedure described above is the standard process for the simple strongly basic monoamines such as aniline, the toluidines, xylidines, aminophenols, and their ethers, also monochloro-derivatives of the benzenoid amines where the chlorine atom is *meta* to the amino-group. The diamines of the benzidine series and α- and β-naphthyl-amine also belong to this group. The optimum temperature is 0—2° for the simple bases, 0—5° for the *m*-halogenated bases, and 10—12° for the benzidine bases and naphthylamines.

When negative groups are in the *ortho* or *para* position to the amino-group, diazotisation becomes more difficult. *p*-Nitroaniline is the representative member of this type, and owing to its importance for dyeing Para Red, a considerable literature relating to its diazotisation exists.[7] For diazotising this amine both the direct method and the inverted method to be described later can be used. The process published by Schwalbe is as follows :—

p-Nitroaniline (21·0 g. = 0·15 mol.) is dissolved by warming with 10*N*-hydro-chloric acid (50 c.c.) diluted with water (100 c.c.). When dissolved the solution is cooled to 5—10° by pouring on ice (200 g.). A solution of sodium nitrite (11·5 g.) in water (80 c.c.) is then poured in all at once and the mixed solutions are stirred until a clear solution is obtained.

Amines which can be dealt with in the above way are those having *ortho*- or *para*-nitro- or halogen groups and the various chloronitro-amines used in ice colour work. As the basicity becomes less the amount of acid must be increased, until just the concentration can be found at which the amine will dissolve in the hot acid. If that point is overshot, then the acid salts out the hydrochloride, and lumps very resistant to the action of nitrous acid are formed. 2 : 5-Dichloroaniline, which falls in this category, can be smoothly diazotised as follows :— [8]

10*N*-hydrochloric acid (50 c.c.) is diluted to 210 c.c. and brought to the boil, when 2 : 5-dichloroaniline (16·5 g. = 0·1 mol.) is added and boiling continued until the molten base has dissolved. The solution is cooled with stirring, the thick white mass of crystals being cooled to 10°. A solution of sodium nitrite (7 g.) is then added over thirty seconds, when almost all the solid passes into solution. A slight permanent reaction on starch-iodide paper must remain, or the stable diazoamino-compound will form. After five minutes the pale yellow solution is filtered from a little flocculent matter, and is ready for use.

Schaarschmidt has shown that 1-aminoanthraquinone may be diazo-tised in the direct manner, as its great stability permits the temperature to be raised to 40°, at which temperature the hydrochloride is sufficiently soluble.[9]

The amine is obtained first in a finely-divided state by dissolving in strong sulphuric acid, pouring into water, collecting, and washing the base (liberated by hydrolysis of the sulphate) free from acid. By treating with concentrated hydro-chloric acid it is converted to the greyish-white hydrochloride, and diazotised by running an equivalent of sodium nitrite solution under the surface with stirring at 30—40°. Completion of reaction is detected by diluting a drop of the reaction solution with water, all the amine being diazotised when red flocks, due to hydro-lysis of the unchanged amine salt, no longer appear. The crude diazo-chloride is poured into 15 times its volume of water at 85—90°, the solution filtered, and salt added to throw out the pure chloride in shining, pale brownish-yellow plates.

When the diazo-compound is insoluble as well as the amine, a circumstance which sometimes occurs among the aminoazo-bases, then there is no avoidance of a prolonged reaction time. p-Aminoazobenzene is typical of this group, and its diazotisation is described by Erban and Mebus :— [10]

Aminoazobenzene (19·7 g. = 0·1 mol.) is ground in a warm mortar with boiling water (40 c.c.), and then with the addition of 10N-sulphuric acid (40 c.c.) until the mass is Bordeaux red. 50 c.c. more of water can be added before dis-sociation sets in. The contents are washed out of the mortar with water (200 c.c.), which cools the suspension to 28°, and diazotisation is then performed with sodium nitrite (7·8 g.) dissolved in water (50 c.c.) and dropped in so slowly that no nitrous acid is lost. After twenty hours' stirring the vessel is filled with a red crystalline mass of the diazosulphate. (For directions for diazotisation of o-aminoazotoluene in hydrochloric acid, see p. 34.)

In a recent patent the diazotisation of a large number of o-aminoazo-compounds has been described.[11]

Nitrous acid can behave as an oxidising agent, and on this account may cause destruction of sensitive amines instead of the formation of their diazo-derivatives. This difficulty was first encountered in the case of the 1 : 2- and 2 : 1-aminonaphtholsulphonic acids, though 2 : 3-aminonaphthol-6-sulphonic acid behaves in the same way as the o-aminophenols of the benzene series.[12] The 1 : 2-aminonaphthol acids are particularly valuable as chrome dyestuff components, and a variety of ways of surmounting the difficulty have been described. One way is to acetylate the hydroxy-group and remove the acetyl group by alkaline hydrolysis after diazotisation.[13] The more direct methods are, however, better, and utilise the fact that the oxidising influence of nitrous acid is diminished by the presence of copper sulphate, which permits of diazotisation in the normal way both for 2 : 1- and 1 : 2-aminonaphthols,[14] 1 : 2-aminonaphthol-4-sulphonic acid,[15] and of the recently discovered 1 : 2-aminonaphthol-8-sulphonic acid.[16]

The diazotisation of 1-amino-2-naphthol-4-sulphonic acid with the aid of copper is carried out as follows :—

The acid (30 g.) is pasted with water (200 c.c.) and cooled to 5°; then in sequence there are added solutions of copper sulphate (2·5 g.) and sodium nitrite (9 g.). After diazotisation has taken place the solution is filtered, and concen-trated hydrochloric acid added to the orange-yellow filtrate. The yellow needles of the diazo-oxide which separate are collected, washed with dilute hydrochloric acid, and dried in the air. The yield is 30 g.

The stable diazo-oxide (see p. 180) can be further purified if quickly crystallised from hot water.

With the free sulphonic acids no addition of mineral acid is necessary for diazotisation, as the sulphonic acid group serves to decompose the sodium nitrite. In other patents the diazotisation media are strong solutions of zinc sulphate or other heavy metal salt [17] or alkali metal salts.[18] In a further patent excess of organic acid such as oxalic acid is used.[19] This difficulty, due to oxidation, has arisen again in recent years in the diazotisation of some of the aminodiphenylamines, now so much used for blue ice colours, and from current patents it would appear that the success of the older methods depended on the fact that they controlled the p_H value of the diazotisation medium. If such control is not exercised in the case of the aminodiphenylamines, scission can occur, the products being a quinone and a diazo-compound. Buffer solutions of definite p_H value are now specified in carrying out the diazotisation process.[20] Salts of zinc, copper, iron, and aluminium are useful for these buffers by which the p_H is adjusted to lie between 1 and 4. According to the patents, 4-amino-3-methoxydiphenylamine is diazotised as follows :—

214 parts of the base are finely dispersed in 3000 parts of water containing 3000 parts of zinc chloride at 30°. 76 parts of sodium nitrite dissolved in 500 parts of water are then dropped in over 3 hours. On completion of diazotisation the whole is filtered and the insoluble residue extracted with cold water. This solution is added to the filtrate and the zinc chloride double salt of the diazo-compound salted out with sodium chloride.

While it is the amine on which interest is usually fixed in this reaction, it must not be forgotten that both the acid and the nitrite are variables which can sometimes be employed to effect. Most of the diazo-salts to be described later can be obtained by double decomposition of the sulphate or chloride, but when the bromide is required for Sandmeyer reactions (see p. 154) it is often best to ensure its formation by using hydrobromic acid for diazotisation. Instead of sodium nitrite, both calcium nitrite [21] and barium nitrite [22] have been used, the latter because by diazotising with the exact amount of sulphuric acid the barium and sulphuric acid are both removed from the solution as barium sulphate, leaving only the diazo-salt. Lastly the amine nitrite may be formed, and then treated with a mineral acid.[23]

REFERENCES

[1] Griess, *Ann.*, 1858, **106**, 123.
[2] Griess, *ibid.*, 1860, **113**, 201; *ibid.*, p. 334.
[3] Martius, *J. pr. Chem.*, 1866, **98**, 94.
[4] S.C.I., E.P. 439,569; D.R.P. 615,744; F.P. 769,591; Sw.P. 165,829.
[5] Altschul, *J. pr. Chem.*, 1896, ii, **54**, 508.
[6] Tscherwinski, Russ. Pat. 39,775. *Cent.*, 1935, **106**, ii, 3440.
[7] Schwalbe, *Zeit. Farb. Ind.*, 1905, **4**, 433. Erban, Mebus, *Chem. Zeit.*, 1907, **31**, 663, 678, 687.
[8] Rohner, D.R.P. 193,211 (Fr., **9**, 336). Noelting, Kopp, *Ber.*, 1905, **38**, 3506.
[9] Schaarschmidt, *Ber.*, 1916, **49**, 2678.

[10] Erban, Mebus, *Chem. Zeit.*, 1907, **31**, 1013.
[11] I.G., E.P. 434,416; D.R.P. 609,334; F.P. 768,098.
[12] Cassella, E.P. 28,107/97.
[13] S.C.I., E.P. 10,022/95; D.R.P. 181,714 (Fr., **8**, 678); U.S.P. 797,441, 806,415; F.P. 351,125.
[14] Geigy, E.P. 10,235/04; D.R.P. 171,024, 172,446 (Fr., **8**, 640, 656); U.S.P. 793,743; F.P. 349,989.
[15] Geigy, E.P. 10,234/04.
[16] I.C.I., E.P. 417,861. Schmidt, Maier, *Ber.*, 1931, **64**, 772.
[17] Kalle, E.P. 23,034/05; D.R.P. 175,593, 178,936, 807,422 (Fr., **8**, 648, 649, 650).
[18] B.A.S.F., E.P. 10,323/06; D.R.P. 189,179 (Fr., **8**, 654); F.P. 365,919.
[19] Weiler-ter-Meer, D.R.P. 155,083 (Fr., **7**, 405).
[20] I.G., E.P. 434,725; D.R.P. 604,278, 611,399; U.S.P. 2,013,180; F.P. 769,810; Sw.P. 174,648.
[21] Griess, Caro, E.P. 1956/66; F.P. 73,286.
[22] Witt, *Ber.*, 1903, **36**, 4388.
[23] Wallach, *Ann.*, 1907, **353**, 322.

METHOD 2. THE "INVERTED METHOD"

Schmitt, who discovered diazobenzene p sulphonic acid,[1] obtained it by Griess's method, but as many of the monoaminosulphonic and carboxylic acids are insoluble in water, and so can be acted on but slowly by nitrous acid, and the diazo-salts themselves are also sparingly soluble, reaction may soon come to a halt. The reactivity of the acid can be increased by precipitating it in a fine state of division by adding acid to a solution of its salt, but a better alternative is to add the nitrite to the alkaline solution of the amino-acid and then run the mixture steadily into the chilled acid. Diazotisation takes place instantly, and the insoluble substance which separates is the diazo-compound.

Diazotisation of sulphanilic acid :— [2]
Sodium sulphanilate (23 g. = 0·1 mol.) and sodium nitrite (7 g.) are dissolved in water (120 c.c.) cooled with ice and then poured with stirring into sulphuric acid (17 c.c., sp. gr. 1·81) diluted with water (100 c.c.). The diazo-compound is precipitated and reaction is complete almost as soon as the last of the solution is added to the acid.
Another convenient method of diazotising sulphanilic acid is to stir the ground acid into a solution of one equivalent of sodium nitrite, when it dissolves almost completely. Upon the addition of one equivalent of hydrochloric acid the diazo-compound is precipitated.
The diazobenzene-p-sulphonic acid can be collected and dried, but it is a dangerous substance (see p. 67).

Naphthionic acid and the aminobenzoic acids can be diazotised in the same way, and the inverted method is also serviceable for weakly basic amines of the p-nitroaniline group and is carried out thus :—

p-Nitroaniline (14 g. = 0·1 mol.) is pasted with water (28 c.c.) and sodium nitrite (7·5 g.) to a smooth slurry and poured on ice (30 g.) and concentrated hydrochloric acid (30 c.c.). The whole is stirred vigorously and filtered after ten minutes.

This method has the advantage over the direct one that it gives a more concentrated solution and can be carried out more quickly, as no heating is required, while the acid requirement can be cut down to 0·1 mol. excess over the theoretical.[3]

REFERENCES

[1] Schmitt, *Ann.*, 1859, **112**, 118; 1861, **120**, 144.
[2] *Rev. Prod. Chim.*, 1917, **20**, 21.
[3] C. and H. Sunder, *Bull. Soc. Ind. Mulhouse*, 1923, **89**, 237.

METHOD 3. STRONG ACID SOLVENTS FOR WEAKLY BASIC AMINES

When the basicity of an amine is so much reduced that it is no longer soluble in aqueous acids because its salts suffer complete hydrolytic dissociation, the use of such media for diazotisation becomes impossible.   Weakly basic amines are soluble only in highly concentrated or anhydrous acids, and diazotisation must perforce be carried out in such solutions. As a number of technically valuable amines fall in this class, of which 2 : 4-dinitroaniline is probably the most important, a considerable amount of experimental work has been conducted in this field, in which Claus and his co-workers were among the pioneers.[1] They successfully diazotised such amines as the tetrabromoanilines, the dibromonitroanilines and the dinitrotoluidines. Another weakly basic amine to which much attention has been given is picramic acid, its diazo-derivative being much used for chrome dyestuffs,[2] while it has also been proposed as an explosive (see p. 67).

Strong sulphuric acid is the solvent which is most commonly employed, on account of its convenience both in the laboratory and on the large scale.   40% hydrochloric acid is also used when the diazochloride is the salt desired, but this acid is much less pleasant to handle than sulphuric acid.   The nitrous acid is introduced either by powdering in the solid nitrite or as a nearly saturated aqueous solution, or it may be first dissolved in concentrated sulphuric acid so as to form a solution of nitrosylsulphuric acid, which is then slowly added to the amine dissolved in sulphuric acid.   Glacial acetic acid may also be used mixed with a mineral acid such as hydrobromic acid.

The progress of diazotisation can be followed by allowing drops of the reaction solution to fall into water, the reaction being complete when flocks of the free base no longer appear.   Starch-iodide paper is rarely useful in these cases. The reaction mixture is finally diluted either by pouring on ice or by adding lumps of ice until sufficiently diluted to pour into water without undue rise in temperature.

Diazotisation of 2 : 4-Dinitroaniline :—
Dry sodium nitrite (7·0 g.) is slowly added with stirring to sulphuric acid

(150 c.c., sp. gr. 1·80), allowing the temperature to rise to 40°. When solution is complete, the dinitroaniline (16·7 g. = 0·1 mol.) is slowly added at 30—35°, and then the mixture stirred for two hours while the temperature is allowed to fall. When a test drop with water shows only a slight precipitate of base, the mixture is poured on ice, allowed to stand for impurities to settle, and filtered.

Misslin,[3] in his study of the diazotisation of highly substituted amines, such as 4-chloro-2 : 6-dinitroaniline, used a variant of the above method in which the amine is dissolved in glacial acetic acid and then treated with nitrosylsulphuric acid. He also showed that only 20% diazotisation is attained by pouring the sulphuric acid solution of the base into water followed by treatment of the finely divided suspension with nitrous acid. Picramide, 2 : 4 : 6-trinitroaniline, can also be smoothly diazotised in sulphuric acid,[4] although the method of Griess fails with this very weak base.[5] Schoutissen failed to diazotise p-amino-benzaldehyde by the above method, and came to the conclusion that the nitrosylsulphuric acid does not at all easily give up its nitrogen, and in order to weaken the attachment he diluted the solution with a weak acid such as phosphoric acid.[6] This is an improvement which has rendered possible the smooth diazotisation of the most intractable of amines, including p-aminobenzaldehyde.[7]

Diazotisation of 2 : 6-Dibromo-4-nitroaniline (Schoutissen) :—
The base (3 g.) is dissolved in sulphuric acid (15 c.c., sp. gr. 1·84) and cooled to 0°. To this is added nitrosylsulphuric acid made by dissolving sodium nitrite (0·9 g.) in sulphuric acid (15 c.c.). Then with stirring there is run in phosphoric acid (60 c.c., sp. gr. 1·70) at 0°. After half an hour urea (2 g.) is added and the reaction mixture poured on ice, when a clear diazo-solution is obtained directly.
2 : 6-Dichloro-4-nitroaniline and 2 : 4 : 6-trinitro-5-amino-anisol and -phenetol can be diazotised in the same way.

There is evidence for the soundness of Schoutissen's modification, for when diazotisation is performed in completely anhydrous sulphuric acid the indications are that the reaction does not proceed to completion in that medium, but that the dilution stage plays a considerable part. For example, nitrous acid will make its presence evident if the dilution is carried out too quickly or too soon after mixing the components. Schoutissen found that after aniline and nitrosylsulphuric acid have been allowed to remain in contact for some time, the addition of strong nitric acid causes the product on dilution to be m-nitrodiazo-benzenesulphate. But, as Griess discovered, diazobenzene cannot be nitrated in the cold, and therefore Schoutissen argues that aniline must be present unchanged in the sulphuric acid solution with the nitrosyl-sulphuric acid, and therefore it nitrates normally in the *meta* position, while diazotisation does not occur until the subsequent dilution. The 2- and 4-nitro- and 2 : 4-dinitro-1-naphthylamines are three other amines difficult to diazotise, but their diazosulphates can be obtained without by-products by pouring their solution in glacial acetic acid into nitrosylsulphuric acid.   The reverse process causes precipitation of the insoluble sulphate of the base and no diazo-compound is formed.[8]

This method is also frequently used to diazotise the amines of the anthraquinone series.[9]

Nitrosyl chloride and bromide can be used instead of nitrosyl sulphate, both reagents having been employed in early researches on diazo-compounds by Konink and by Pabst and Girard.   The latter workers also showed that nitrosulphonic acid can be used.[10]   These reagents are nearly always used to diazotise an amine salt suspended in alcohol or in a non-hydroxylic solvent when isolation of the diazo-salt is required (see p. 15).   If the free amine is used instead of a salt, mixtures of diazo-salts with diazoamino-compounds or double salts of amine salt and diazo-salt result.[11]

REFERENCES

[1] Claus, Wallbaum, *J. pr. Chem.*, 1897, ii, **56**, 48.   Claus, Beysen, *Ann.*, 1891, **266**, 224.
[2] Agfa, E.P. 10,294/00.
[3] Misslin, *Helv. Chim. Acta*, 1920, **3**, 626.
[4] Blangey, *ibid.*, 1925, **8**, 780.
[5] Meyer, Stuber, *Ann.*, 1873, **165**, 187.
[6] Schoutissen, *J.Am.C.S.*, 1933, **55**, 4531.
[7] Schoutissen, *Rec. trav. chim.*, 1935, **54**, 97.
[8] Hodgson, Walker, *J.C.S.*, 1923, **124**, 1620.
[9] Diazotisation of amines of the anthraquinone series :—
    Schultz, Eber, *J. pr. Chem.*, 1906, ii, **74**, 275.   α- and β-Aminoalizarine.
    Bayer, D.R.P. 152,661 (Fr., **7**, 468).   1-Diazo- and 1 : 8-tetrazo-anthra-quinone.
    Kacer, Scholl, *Ber.*, 1904, **37**, 4185.   1-Diazo- and 1 : 5-tetrazo-anthra-quinone.
    I.G., E.P. 262,119;   U.S.P. 1,700,790.   1-Diazoanthraquinone-2-carb-oxylic acid.
    Amines of the anthracene series :—
    Battegay, Boehler, *Compt. rend.*, 1936, **202**, 769.   α- and β-Anthramine.
[10] Konink, *Ber.*, 1869, **2**, 122.   Pabst, Girard, *ibid.*, 1879, **12**, 365.   D.R.P. 6034 (Fr., **1**, 545).
[11] Bamberger, *ibid.*, 1894, **27**, 670.   Kastle, Keiser, *Amer. Chem. J.*, 1895, **17**, 91.

METHOD 4.   THE METHOD OF WITT

The principle of this method is to use concentrated nitric acid as the solvent for the amine and at the same time by the action of a reducing agent to derive from it the nitrous acid necessary for diazotisation.[1]   The reducing agent most appropriate for this purpose is a metabisulphite, the requisite quantity of the sodium salt being derived from the equation :—

$$Na_2S_2O_5 + 2HNO_3 = Na_2S_2O_7 + 2HNO_2$$

The metabisulphite may be either added to the nitric acid solution of the amine or the amine and the metabisulphite may be mixed and slowly stirred into the nitric acid. For example, 3 : 5-dinitro-*o*-toluidine is diazotised by this method as follows :—

The dinitrotoluidine (9·8 g. = 0·05 mol.) is mixed with sodium metabisulphite (5·9 g.) and added with cooling to fuming nitric acid (50 c.c.). The solution is allowed to stand for at least half an hour, and then poured into water (100 c.c.) mixed with ice (200 g.). The solution is filtered and is ready for use.

The method is not suitable for technical purposes, but it is sometimes useful for experimental purposes, and has been studied from that viewpoint. It is useless for easily oxidised amines (see below), while there is, of course, danger of nitration, which Elion encountered when diazotising 4-amino-3 : 5-dibromobenzoic acid and similar compounds, from all of which the product isolated was 3 : 5-dinitrobenzene.[2] Fuchs pointed out that such results are due to departure from the rigid conditions laid down by Witt,[3] but Elion replied that the determining factor is the concentration of the nitric acid.[4]

The amino-compound can act as the reducing agent for the nitric acid, being thus in part destroyed and in part diazotised. Thus Stenhouse obtained a good yield of the diazo-derivative of picramic acid by acting on it with strong nitric acid alone.[5]

Before leaving this method mention should be made that Möhlau showed that diazobenzene chloride can be made by reducing aniline nitrate with zinc and hydrochloric acid :— [6]

$$Ph·NH_2·HNO_3 + Zn + 3HCl = PhN_2Cl + ZnCl_2 + 3H_2O$$

Knecht brought about diazotisation in a similar way using titanous chloride as the reducing agent :— [7]

$$ArNH_2·HCl + HNO_3 + 2HCl + 2TiCl_3 = ArN_2Cl + 2TiCl_4 + 3H_2O$$

The latter reaction fails when reducible groups such as the nitro-group are present in the aromatic nucleus.

REFERENCES

[1] Witt, *Ber.*, 1909, **42**, 2953.
[2] Elion, *Rec. trav. chim.*, 1923, **42**, 145.
[3] Fuchs, *ibid.*, p. 511.
[4] Elion, *ibid.*, p. 513.
[5] Stenhouse, *J.C.S.*, 1868, **21**, 150.
[6] Möhlau, *Ber.*, 1883, **16**, 3080. D.R.P. 25,146 (Fr., **1**, 545).
[7] Knecht, *J.C.S.*, 1924, **125**, 1537.

METHOD 5. THE METHOD OF GRIESS

Griess in his early work conducted the operation of diazotisation by pasting up a salt of an amine, usually the nitrate or sulphate, with a little water or alcohol, and then passing into the mixture nitrous acid gases, generated by reducing nitric acid of specific gravity 1·35 with starch or arsenious anhydride.   The mixture of gases generated in the foregoing way and passing under the above name behaves as if composed solely of nitrous anhydride, and therefore dissolves in water to form two molecules of nitrous acid :—

$$N_2O_3 + H_2O = 2HNO_2$$

The end-point of the diazotisation reaction was determined by adding a drop of the reaction mixture to weak alkali from time to time until unchanged base could no longer be detected.   The diazo-salt then sometimes crystallised, or could be precipitated by adding ether to an alcoholic solution or by adding sufficient alcohol to an aqueous solution to ensure homogeneity on subsequently adding ether as a precipitant. The method served Griess well, for his object was usually to isolate, analyse, and characterise the diazo-compounds as such, rather than to use them as intermediates in a synthesis.   By this method he was the first to obtain most of the common diazo-salts in the solid state, and it is applicable to many weakly basic amines, because water, which would hydrolyse the amine salts, can be reduced to a minimum quantity or replaced by alcohol.   Indeed, but for this method the diazo-compounds, owing to their extreme solubility in water, might have remained longer unknown.   A variant of the method, practised by Schmitt, consisted in saturating alcohol with nitrous acid gases and then pouring the solution over the amine salt.[1] Sulphuric acid has been used as solvent for diazotising the amines of the anthraquinone series by this method.[2]

At the present day the reaction is rarely used, though from time to time experiments have been made on the use of nitrogen oxides in various ways.

Seidler proposed to effect diazotisation by means of nitrite and acid under air pressure so as to prevent the escape of oxides of nitrogen from the liquid beneath.[3] Briner and Jones carried out diazotisation by condensing nitrogen trioxide in a tube with the amine hydrochloride, sealing off, and allowing the temperature to rise.   Dinitroaniline and tribromoaniline were thus diazotised, but picramide was resistant to the reagent.[4] Houston and Johnson used nitrogen tetroxide to react on amines in benzene solution, bringing about diazotisation according to the equation :— [5]

$$ArNH_2 + N_2O_4 = ArN_2O \cdot NO_2 + H_2O$$

REFERENCES

[1] Schmitt, *Ann.*, 1861, **120**, 144.
[2] Scholl, Schneider, Eberle, *Ber.*, 1904, **37**, 4435.
[3] Seidler, D.R.P. 143,450 (Fr., **7**, 359).
[4] Briner, Jones, *Helv. Chim. Acta*, 1920, **3**, 366.
[5] Houston, Johnson, *J.Am.C.S.*, 1925, **27**, 3011.   Compare Ladenburg, *Ber.*,
     1875, **6**, 1212.

METHOD 6. THE METHOD OF KNOEVENAGEL

Thirty-two years elapsed before Knoevenagel modified the original cumbersome method of Griess by replacing the nitrous acid gases by the more accurately controllable alkyl nitrites as the source of nitrous acid. This is the method now commonly employed when a water-soluble diazo-compound is to be prepared pure in the solid state.[1] Knoevenagel did not discover the use of alkyl nitrites, which had already been used by Schmitt to obtain the diazo-chlorides of the aminophenols,[2] but he established the general utility of the reagent. He suspended the dry amine salt in alcohol, and so brought it into reaction with the alkyl nitrite, but Hantzsch found it better to use glacial acetic acid when working on a larger scale.[3]

The operation can be carried out still more expeditiously if the amine is dissolved in alcohol and the salt prepared immediately before adding the nitrite.   Schoutissen prepares diazobenzene sulphate thus :—[4]

Aniline (15 g.) is dissolved in 96% alcohol (140 c.c.). The solution is cooled to below 10°, and enough sulphuric acid, sp. gr. 1·84, added to redissolve the precipitated sulphate at 0—10°. This requires about 30 g. Amyl nitrite (20 g.) is then added drop by drop while the solution is stirred at 0—5°. After 15—30 minutes the diazo-sulphate crystallises in white needles. An equal volume of ether is added and the diazo-salt collected, washed with alcohol ether (1—1), and dried in vacuo.

While this method is valuable as a laboratory means of diazotising amines such as the aminoanthraquinones,[5] not easily dealt with by the direct method, it is not likely to compel an amine of low reactivity to yield its diazo-derivative. For example, only monodiazotisation results with 2 : 7-naphthylenediamine.[6] It will be noted from the equation given in Table I that a molecule of water is produced in the reaction, and therefore a solvent should be employed in which this water is miscible, or the diazo-salt will be sticky, but as diazo-salts need ether to cause their separation from hydroxylic solvents, attempts have been made in recent years to use non-hydroxylic solvents, such as carbon tetrachloride, acetic ester, benzene, and others, and to bind the water produced in the reaction by adding a water-binding salt such as calcined sodium sulphate.[7] According to a still more recent patent the above products are still sticky, owing to incomplete removal of water, but if the water-binding agent is put in at the beginning of diazo-tisation, then granular products result. The diazo-sulphates are the salts most satisfactory for employment here, on account of their stability, some being fit for direct introduction into commerce (see p. 32). Diazotisation can be brought about not only with alkyl nitrites in such solvents as those mentioned, but also with liquid nitrogen trioxide, nitrosyl chloride, or nitrosylsulphuric acid. Morgan in his researches on the diazo-derivatives of the acyl-*p*-phenylenediamines (see p. 19) used nitrogen trioxide in acetone with great success. Bamberger also diazotised *p*-nitroaniline in a mixture of acetic ester and ether with liquid nitrogen trioxide.[8]

There is one important point first disclosed by Hirsch [9] in making diazo-salts of analytical purity by Knoevenagel's method—namely, that the amine salt must be free from any excess acid, because diazo-salts have a strong tendency to form addition compounds, and such, if once formed, are eliminated with difficulty.

REFERENCES

[1] Knoevenagel, *Ber.*, 1890, **23**, 2995.
[2] Schmitt, *ibid.*, 1868, **1**, 67. See also V. Meyer, Stuber, *Ann.*, 1873, **165**, 187. Cameron, *Amer. Chem. J.*, 1898, **20**, 229.
[3] Hantzsch, Jochem, *Ber.*, 1901, **34**, 3337.
[4] Schoutissen, *Rec. trav. chim.*, 1921, **40**, 763.
[5] Kaufler, *Zeit. Farb. Ind.*, 1903, **2**, 469.
[6] Kaufler, Karrer, *Ber.*, 1907, **40**, 3263.
[7] S.C.I., D.R.P. 575,832 (Fr., **19**, 1812); F.P. 727,293; Sw.P. 152,611.
[8] Bamberger, *Ber.*, 1894, **27**, 1948.
[9] Hirsch, *ibid.*, 1897, **30**, 1148.

THE ACTION OF NITROUS ACID ON DIAMINES

Mention of diamines has been purposely avoided as far as possible up to the present point because they are best discussed as a group distinct from the simple monamines. When two or more amino-groups are attached to different aromatic nuclei forming part of the same molecule, the whole can be considered for purposes of diazotisation as an assemblage of two or more different aromatic amines, in which the diazotisation of one amino-group will not greatly affect the reactivity of the others. Examples of such polyamines are those of the benzidine and stilbene series, 1 : 5-diaminoanthraquinone and triaminotriphenyl-methane. So equally do both groups diazotise in the benzidine series by the direct method that it is difficult to prevent tetrazotisation, though two methods of obtaining the monodiazo-compounds have been described. One consists in mixing the diamine hydrochloride with the tetrazo-salt and allowing the solution to stand at 10—20° for some days, when interchange occurs and a solution of 4-amino-4'-diazodi-phenyl chloride is obtained.[1] The other method consists in diazotising with one equivalent of nitrite and acid, whereupon the diazoamino-compound is formed, and this on treatment with more acid is split to the desired aminodiazo-compound.[2] Occasionally preferential diazo-tisation can be observed among diaminoazo-compounds, as in the case

of 4 : 4′-diaminobenzeneazonaphthalene, where the first equivalent of
nitrite diazotises the amino-group attached to the benzene ring.

When, however, two amino-groups are attached to the same benzene
ring, the tetrazo-compounds are not to be obtained without careful
attention to reaction conditions, and in some cases such compounds
cannot be formed at all, either by reason of the occurrence of secondary
reactions or by sheer inability of one amino-group to react. Morgan
and Davies found that it is impossible for one benzene ring to carry
more than two diazo-groups.[3]

The o-diamines, together with their acyl and alkyl derivatives, are
sharply differentiated from the m- and p-diamines because, except
under very special conditions, the action of nitrous acid leads to the
formation of exceedingly stable substances, the azimines, which are
really internal diazoamino-compounds, and may result directly from
the action of nitrous acid or through the monodiazo-compound.[4]

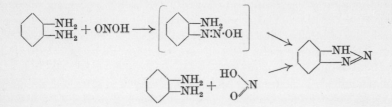

Whether the reaction proceeds directly or through an intermediate
diazo-compound it is impossible to say in the case of o-phenylenedi-
amine, but the existence of the intermediate diazo-compound has been
demonstrated in the case of o-tolylenediamine.[5] Being a general
reaction of diamines, it occurs with 2 : 3-naphthylenediamine,[6] 1 : 2-
naphthylenediamine, which gives two isomeric azimines,[7] the o-diamino-
anthraquinones,[8] and also with 1 : 8-naphthylenediamine.[9]

Tetrazotisation naturally cannot occur if one or both of the amino-
groups are substituted unless nitrous acid can eject a substituent.
The diaminodisulphamic acids, obtained by the action of chlorosulphonic
acid on diamines, contain such a removable substituent, and when they
react with nitrous acid one sulphamic acid group is ejected giving the
sulphaminodiazo-compound :— [10]

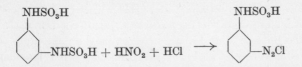

Other examples of the removal of an inorganic acid radical attached
to the nitrogen of an amino-group are to be found on p. 51. One acetyl

C

group in nitrodiacetyl-*p*-phenylenediamine is also easily removed, the amino-group *meta* to the nitro-group being diazotised :— [11]

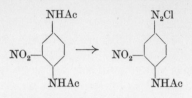

On the other hand, the presence of a substituted amino-group which is indifferent to nitrous acid may have a pronounced effect on the diazotisation of the remaining primary amino-group. Among *meta*- and *para*-diamines acylation in most cases effectually cancels the action of the acylated amino-group, and such diamines behave as ordinary primary monamines. *p*-Aminoacetanilide, for example, in aqueous solution diazotises as smoothly as aniline, as does also acetyl-1 : 4-diaminonaphthalene-2-sulphonic acid.[12] Nevertheless, among the diazo-derivatives of the acylated *p*-diamines azimines exist, but they are of much less stability than those derived from the *o*-diamines and, like diazoimino-compounds in general, are split by acids back into diazo-salt and imine. They are frequently described under the name of "diazo-imines." These *para*-diazoimines were first detected among the benzene sulphonyl-*p*-diamines, and have been thoroughly studied by Morgan and his co-workers.[13] Treatment of the diazo-salt with acetate or alkalis is sufficient to produce the yellow insoluble azimine :—

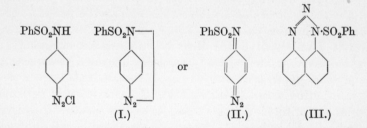

The azimine is not produced if the imine hydrogen is substituted by an alkyl group, and the question as to whether their structure is benzenoid (I) or quinonoid (II) has been settled in favour of the former, one strong supporting argument being that benzenesulphonyl-1 : 8-naphthylenediamine gives an azimine (III), which cannot possibly have a quinonoid structure.[14] The reaction also occurs with benzene-sulphonylbenzidine,[15] but for a considerable time attempts to prepare azimines from formyl-, acetyl-, and benzoyl-*p*-phenylenediamine and their congeners failed.[16] The failure was due to the attempts having been made in aqueous solution when the azimine ring does not close, but success was attained when recourse was had to diazotisation by nitrogen trioxide in acetone.[17] Failure has attended attempts to isolate the p-azimines free from acyl groups by acting on 3-nitro- and 2 : 6-dichloro-p-phenylenediamines with nitrogen trioxide.[18] Similarly the parent p-diazoimine derived from the diazotisation of p-phenylenediamine itself is unknown, though p-aminodiazobenzene hydrochloride can be obtained crystalline by diazotising acetyl-p-phenylenediamine and hydrolysing the acetyl group.[19]

The removal of the acetyl group by the above means frees the amino-group to exert its influence on the diazo-group in the *para* position, and p-aminodiazobenzene is the prototype of a class of substances entirely different in their behaviour to the p-acylaminodiazobenzene salts. The amino-group, alone or substituted by alkyl or aryl radicals, has on the diazo-group the opposite effect of negative substituents, and so causes it to be sluggish in reaction and unstable. p-Aminodimethylaniline is one compound of this type which can only be diazotised by careful attention to detail,[20] while Hantzsch failed to bring about the satisfactory diazotisation of methyl-p-phenylenediamine.[21]

The p-aminodiphenylamines, some of which have already been mentioned in connexion with their susceptibility to oxidation by nitrous acid, are also to be included here. The more negative nature of the aromatic nucleus as compared with that of an alkyl residue increases the stability of the diazo-compounds over those mentioned above, until among the halogenated aminodiphenylamines outstanding stability is reached.[22] 3-Aminocarbazole is another closely related compound, the behaviour of the diazo-compound of which is comparable with the p-aminodiphenylamines.[23]

p-Aminodiphenylamine itself, which was first diazotised by Ikuta,[24] has become of considerable importance in recent years because of its employment for producing blue dyeings in the Ice Colour series (see p. 31) and also for its use in diazotype papers (see p. 167). Rowe has shown that 4-amino-4'-ethoxydiphenylamine can be diazotised as follows without oxidation or nitrosamine formation :—[25]

The base (11·4 g. = 0·05 mol.) is dissolved at the boil in water (150 c.c.) and 10N-hydrochloric acid (6 c.c.). On cooling to 80° further acid (25 c.c.) is added and at 45° a solution of sodium nitrite (3·5 g.) in water (25 c.c.). Diazotisation is immediate and, after filtering from some dark, flocculent material, a clear orange-yellow solution of the diazo-compound is obtained.

Before passing to the tetrazotisation of the diamines, it must be remarked that their reactivity can be greatly influenced by substituents both favourably and unfavourably. Among p-diamines tetrazotisation is by no means a general reaction, even where both amino-groups are free, and a negative substituent often prevents diazotisation of the amino-group to which it stands *ortho* unless special means are employed.

The following is a list of diamines of which it has been recorded that only one amino-group can be diazotised by the direct method :—

p-Diaminobenzoic acid.[26]
Nitro-p-phenylenediamine.[27]
p-Phenylenediaminesulphonic acid.[28]
2 : 6-Dichloro-p-phenylenediamine.
p-Diaminophenylarsinic acid.[29]
1 : 4-Diaminonaphthalene-3-sulphonic acid.[30]
1 : 4-Diamino-2-hydroxynaphthalene.[31]

m-Phenylenediamine can be tetrazotised by the direct method in small quantity by thorough cooling and sudden mixing of the two solutions (but see also p. 22), but the product obtained by the method as ordinarily carried out is the brown basic dyestuff, Bismarck Brown, which is bisbenzeneazophenylenediamine. Griess, who first achieved the tetrazotisation, prevented the formation of the unwanted dyestuff by keeping nitrous acid in excess of the diamine.[32]

A more detailed direction for the procedure is the following :—

Fuming hydrochloric acid (80 c.c.) is poured on ice (400 g.) and the whole cooled by a freezing mixture. To this is added a cold solution of sodium nitrite (15 g.). Into the solution of nitrous acid thus prepared is immediately poured an already prepared solution of m-phenylenediamine (9 g.) acidified with concentrated hydrochloric acid (10 c.c.). A yellow solution of the tetrazo-compound is produced forthwith.[33]

An early patent was taken for tetrazotisation by the direct method using a large excess of acid,[34] and also for the inverted method both for m-phenylenediamine and m-tolylenediamine.[35]

When *meta*-diamines are substituted, tetrazotisation is so much facilitated that it can be brought about by the direct method, as in the case of 2 : 6-diaminotoluene-4-sulphonic acid,[36] or, if desired, only one of the amino-groups in a sulphonated m-diamine may be diazotised by using one equivalent of nitrite and applying the inverted method.[37] Step-wise tetrazotisation through the monoacetyl diamine can also be carried out with 2 : 6-diaminophenol-4-sulphonic acid, as the diazo-group is not affected during the hydrolysis of the acetyl group to give the intermediate aminodiazo-compound.[38] 2 : 4-Diaminophenol is also the parent of a family of easily tetrazotised diamines,[39] which comprises diaminosalicylic acid,[40] 2 : 4-diaminophenol-6-sulphonic acid,[41] and the 2 : 4-diaminophenol ethers.[42]

Griess tetrazotised p-phenylenediamine by the same method he used for the *meta*-diamine, his first attempt by the direct method [43] having been shown by Nietzki to have given a mixture of the diazo- and tetrazo-compounds,[44] while 1 : 4-naphthylenediamine belongs to the class of amines which suffer destructive oxidation by nitrous acid.

Recently Schoutissen has applied his technique of phosphoric acid and nitrosylsulphuric acid to p-diamines, and so succeeded in tetrazo-tising not only p-phenylenediamine, but also 2 : 5-dichloro-, 2 : 6-di-bromo-, 2 : 6-dichloro-, and trichloro-p-phenylenediamine, as well as the nitro- and sulpho-p-phenylenediamines—in fact, all those diamines which have been noted as refusing to pass beyond the monodiazo-stage by the direct method. Schoutissen has also obtained evidence of the tetrazotisation of o-phenylenediamine, as he was able to obtain a small yield of o-di-iodobenzene.[45]

Hantzsch and Borghaus made an important contribution when they showed that the solid tetrazosulphate is much more stable than the hydrochloride in the case of both *meta-* and *para*-tetrazobenzene.[46] Hence tetrazotisation by nitrosylsulphuric acid is often an advantageous way of dealing with diamines, and can be used for 2 : 7-naphthylene-diamine where Knoevenagel's method fails.[47] In a recent patent the art of manufacturing the solid tetrazosulphate of p-phenylenediamine is disclosed, utilising the nitrosylsulphuric acid method :— [48]

p-Phenylenediamine (108 g.) is charged into a solution of nitrosylsulphuric acid (265 g.) in 78% sulphuric acid (800 g.) at 20—25°. The solution is stirred at 25° until tetrazotisation is complete, after which the tetrazosulphate may be isolated :—

1. By cooling to −15° and collecting on an acid-proof filter.
2. By pouring on 600 g. of ice with strong cooling and collecting at −15°.
3. By pouring into 1600 g. of methanol, ethanol, or acetone and collecting at a low temperature.

Lastly, Hodgson and Walker have tetrazotised all three diamines as well as m-tolylenediamine by dissolving in glacial acetic acid and adding the solution below 30° to well-stirred nitrosylsulphuric acid (32 g. of sodium nitrite to 320 c.c. of sulphuric acid, sp. gr. 1·82). On carrying out the Sandmeyer reaction a 70% yield of o-dichlorobenzene can be obtained from o-phenylenediamine.[49]

REFERENCES

[1] Tauber, *Ber.*, 1894, **27**, 2627.
[2] Vaubel, Scheuer, *Zeit. Farb. Ind.*, 1906, **5**, 61.
[3] Morgan, Davies, *J.C.S.*, 1923, **123**, 228.
[4] Ladenburg, *Ber.*, 1876, **9**, 221. See also Hofmann, *Ann.*, 1860, **115**, 249; Griess, *Ber.*, 1872, **5**, 200; 1882, **15**, 1878; Kekulé, *Lehrbuch*, II, 739; Zincke, Lawson, *Ann.*, 1887, **240**, 119; Zincke, Arzberger, *ibid.*, 1888, **249**, 350.
[5] Nölting, Abt, *Ber.*, 1887, **20**, 2999.
[6] Friedländer, Zakrewski, *ibid.*, 1894, **27**, 765.
[7] Morgan, Godden, *J.C.S.*, 1910, **97**, 1702.
[8] Bayer, E.P. 17,829/12; D.R.P. 254,745 (Fr., **11**, 648); U.S.P. 1,065,440; F.P. 453,313.
[9] de Aguiar, *Ber.*, 1874, **7**, 315.
[10] I.G., E.P. 266,388; D.R.P. 473,217 (Fr., **16**, 444); U.S.P. 1,750,057; F.P. 534,199.
[11] Bülow, Mann, *Ber.*, 1897, **30**, 978.
[12] Levinstein, E.P. 17,064/96.
[13] Morgan, Micklethwait, *J.C.S.*, 1905, **87**, 1302; *Ber.*, 1906, **39**, 2867. Morgan, Pickard, *J.C.S.*, 1910, **97**, 48.

[14] Morgan, Micklethwait, *J.C.S.*, 1906, **89**, 4.
[15] Morgan, Hird, *ibid.*, 1907, **91**, 1505.
[16] Morgan, Micklethwait, *ibid.*, 1905, **87**, 921.
[17] Morgan, Upton, *ibid.*, 1917, **111**, 187.
[18] Morgan, Cleague, *ibid.*, 1918, **113**, 588.
[19] Kalle, E.P. 418,011.
[20] Stollé, *Ber.*, 1912, **45**, 2681.
[21] Hantzsch, *ibid.*, 1902, **35**, 896.
[22] Jacobsen, *Ann.*, 1909, **367**, 332.
[23] Morgan, Reid, *J.C.S.*, 1922, **120**, 2709.
[24] Ikuta, *Ann.*, 1893, **272**, 282.
[25] Rowe, *J.S.D.C.*, 1930, **47**, 229.
[26] Griess, *Ber.*, 1884, **17**, 603.
[27] Bülow, *ibid.*, 1896, **29**, 2284.
[28] Agfa, E.P. 27,498/04; D.R.P. 160,170 (Fr., **8**, 138).
[29] Benda, *Ber.*, 1911, **44**, 3300.
[30] Levinstein, E.P. 2946/96.
[31] S.C.I., E.P. 82/05.
[32] Griess, *Ber.*, 1886, **19**, 317.
[33] Täuber, Walder, *ibid.*, 1897, **30**, 2901.
[34] E.P. 1593/88.
[35] Epstein, D.R.P. 103,660, 103,685 (Fr., **5**, 634).
[36] Oehler, E.P. 17,546/92.
[37] M.L.B., D.R.P. 152,879 (Fr., **7**, 75).
[38] Kalle, D.R.P. 182,853 (Fr., **8**, 599).
[39] S.C.I., E.P. 18,624/00; D.R.P. 168,299 (Fr., **8**, 629).
[40] Cassella, D.R.P. 68,303 (Fr., **3**, 638).
[41] M.L.B., D.R.P. 128,619 (Fr., **6**, 916); U.S.P. 693,670; F.P. 313,748.
[42] B.A.S.F., D.R.P. 258,653 (Fr., **11**, 392).
[43] Griess, *Ber.*, 1884, **17**, 697.
[44] Nietzski, *ibid.*, p. 1350.
[45] Schoutissen, *J.Am.C.S.*, 1935, **55**, 4535.
[46] Hantzsch, Borghaus, *Ber.*, 1897, **30**, 93.
[47] Morgan, Micklethwait, *J.C.S.*, 1910, **97**, 2557.
[48] I.G., E.P. 440,424; D.R.P. 611,463; F.P. 775,038.
[49] Hodgson, Walker, *J.C.S.*, **1935**, 530.

FAILURE OF THE DIAZOTISATION REACTION

With the means at their disposal the early workers failed to diazotise a number of amines, chiefly those containing many negative substituents, but very few have since proved entirely resistant when all resources of the methods now known have been brought to bear. Schmidt and Schall failed to diazotise o-aminodiphenic acid by any method known to them,[1] as did also Benda with 4-amino-3 : 5-dinitrophenyl-1-arsinic acid,[2] and Nijk failed with m-carbethoxyaminophenyl-phosphinic acid.[3] Sometimes failure to obtain a diazo-compound occurs because nitrous acid attacks some other part of the molecule in preference to the amino-group. Thus if one equivalent of nitrite is added suddenly to one of m-phenylenediamine with two of hydrochloric acid, yields of nitroso-m-phenylenediamine as high as 20% may result.[4] Nitroso- instead of diazo-compounds are produced when the attempt is made to diazotise meta-substituted amines such as m-toluidine or m-anisidine, or ethers of the latter, with nitrosylsulphuric acid.[5] A ring in the 5 : 6-positions, as in α-naphthylamine, or 1-amino-5 : 6 : 7 : 8-

tetrahydronaphthalene, has the same effect as does the substitution of both the 2- and the 5-position in the benzene ring by alkyl groups. As the result of this reaction it is possible to produce 1 : 4-naphthoquinone oximes from α-naphthylamine by reaction with nitrous acid in strong sulphuric acid followed by heating of the aqueous solution of the hydrochloride of the iminoquinone oxime :— [6]

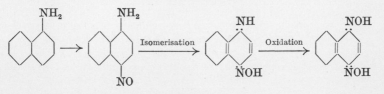

REFERENCES

[1] Schmidt, Schall, *Ber.*, 1905, **38**, 3769.
[2] Benda, *ibid.*, 1912, **45**, 54.
[3] Nijk, *Rec. trav. chim.*, 1922, **41**, 461.
[4] Täuber, Walder, *Ber.*, 1900, **33**, 2116.
[5] I.G., D.R.P. 561,425 (Fr., **19**, 695).
[6] I.G., E.P. 355,970; D.R.P. 519,729.

SALTS OF THE DIAZO-COMPOUNDS

By virtue of their capacity to function as strong bases, the diazo-compounds form salts with all strong inorganic acids, as well as a number of organic acids, particularly arylsulphonic acids (see p. 39). They have also a marked capacity to form double salts, and since many of these find technical application, they are discussed in the chapter on stabilised diazo-compounds.

In view of the fact that the diazo-compounds must appear as the salt of the acid used in the diazotisation reaction (unless some form of internal salt formation occurs), and since at least two molecules of the acid are required, the choice of this acid is usually determined by cost and convenience in handling. The acids which commonly come into use are therefore sulphuric, hydrochloric, and nitric acids, less commonly hydrobromic acid. As the sulphates and nitrates are less soluble than the halides, the former are indicated where isolation of the diazo-compound is desired.

When the nature of the acid radical is a matter of concern, the required radical may be introduced either by the above direct method or by double decomposition, which is the common practice. Examples of the first method, except for the common salts mentioned above, are few, though Hantzsch and Vock made benzenediazofluoride by this means,[1] and Vorländer the perchlorates.[2]

The chief point to remark concerning salt formation by double decomposition is that the new salt is naturally of a less degree of solubility in water, in which solvent the reaction is usually carried out, than the one from which it was made, and thus a means is afforded of precipitating and collecting many diazo-compounds in the solid state. The stability of the solid salts thus obtained varies widely, and while some are stable, most chromates and perchlorates are extremely unstable. Further, all diazo-salts, if soluble in water, are highly dissociated, and therefore, as might be expected, change in the anion does not affect the

TABLE II

Salts of Diazo-Compounds with Various Acid Radicals

Anion.	Amines affording Diazo-Cation.		Refs.
Carbonate.	p-Aminobenz-anilide.		7
Chromate.	General reaction.	Coloured : explosive and suggested for use as such : most diazochromates easily isolated : some of considerable solubility.	1, 4, 6, 11
Hydroferrocyanide.			4
Molybdate.	General reaction.		9
Nitrite.	p-Aminobenz-anilide.		
	1-Nitro-2-naph-thylamine.	Formed by interchange. (See p. 55.)	7
Perchlorate.	General reaction.		9
Phosphomolybdate.	,, ,,	Usually of very sparing solubility.	9
Thiocyanate.	Aniline. p-Chloroaniline.	Explosive. (See p. 57.)	13
Thiosulphate.	General reaction.		3, 4
Tungstate.	,,		4, 9
Acetate.	p-Aminobenz-anilide.	Rarely possible to isolate acetates : always unstable.	9
Hydrazoate.			5
Picrate.	Aniline. Aminomethyl indole Aminophenyl indole.	Would probably function as precipitant in many cases besides those cited.	2, 8
Sulphinate.	o-Nitroaniline.	Only case of isolation : all other sulphinates pass at once to diazosulphones. (See p. 50.)	10
Thioacetate.	General reaction.		12

[1] Griess, Caro, *Bull. Soc. chim.*, 1867, ii, **7**, 270.
[2] Baeyer, Jäger, *Ber.*, 1875, **8**, 894.
[3] Becker, D.R.P. 80,652. (Fr., **4**, 676.)
[4] Grant Hepburn, *J.S.D.C.*, 1901, **17**, 279.
[5] Hantzsch, *Ber.*, 1903, **36**, 2056.
[6] Meldola, Eynon, *J.C.S.*, 1905, **87**, 1.
[7] Morgan, Micklethwait, *ibid.*, p. 921.
[8] Castellana, d'Angelo, *R.A.L.*, 1905, [v], **14**, ii, 145.
[9] Morgan, Alcock, *J.C.S.*, 1909, **95**, 1319.
[10] Claasz, *Ber.*, 1911, **44**, 1415.   [11] Gray, *J.C.S.*, 1926, 3174.
[12] Friedländer, Chwala, *Monatsh.*, 1907, **28**, 247.
[13] Hantzsch, Hirsch, *Ber.*, 1896, **29**, 948.

behaviour of the cation. To this rule there are two exceptions—namely, the diazocyanides and diazosulphonates obtained by double decomposition with cyanides and sulphites, respectively. These compounds have great theoretical significance, and are described under separate headings (see pp. 188, 190).

REFERENCES

[1] Hantzsch, Vock, *Ber.*, 1903, **36**, 2059.
[2] Vörlander, *ibid.*, 1906, **39**, 2713. See also Hofmann, Arnoldi, *ibid.*, p. 3146; Herz, E.P. 27,198/12; F.P. 450,897.

Details concerning some of the salts made by double decomposition are presented in the table on p. 24.—" General reaction " means that a sufficient number of cases have been observed to assume generality. Where the amine affording the diazo-cation is mentioned by name, either the occurrence is exceptional or the data are insufficient to assume generality.

DIAZO-COMPOUNDS FROM SOURCES OTHER THAN THE ACTION OF NITROUS ACID ON AMINES

From time to time reactions have been discovered which afford diazo-compounds by means entirely different from any variants of the

TABLE III

Oxidation Reactions Leading to Diazo-Compounds

Aromatic Compound.	Oxidising Agent.	Reaction.	Refs.
Arylhydrazines.	Mercuric oxide.	$(PhN_2H_4)_2SO_4 + 2O_2 = (PhN_2)_2SO_4 + 4H_2O$	1
	Mercuric acetate.		2
	Bromine.	$PhNH \cdot NH_2 + 2Br_2 \rightarrow PhNBr \cdot NBr_2H \longrightarrow PhN_2Br$	3, 4, 8
	Nitrous acid.	$PhNH \cdot NH_2 \cdot HCl \longrightarrow PhN_2Cl$	5
Nitrosophenyl-hydrazine.	Nitrogen trioxide.	$\underset{\overset{|}{NH_2}}{PhN \cdot NO} \longrightarrow PhN_2 \cdot NO_3$	6
Anthraquinone.	Nitrous acid with mercury catalyst.	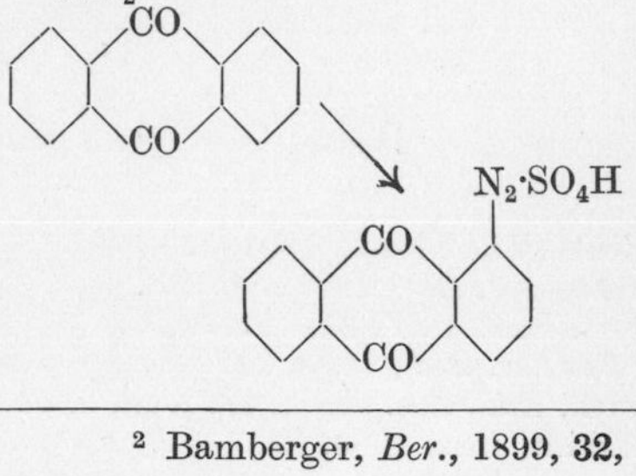	7

[1] Fischer, *Ann.*, 1877, **190**, 99.   [2] Bamberger, *Ber.*, 1899, **32**, 1890.
[3] Michaelis, *ibid.*, 1894, **26**, 2190.
[4] Chattaway, *J.C.S.*, 1908, **93**, 852. See also p. 100.
[5] Altschul, *J. pr. Chem.*, 1896, ii, **54**, 496.
[6] Rugheimer, *Ber.*, 1900, **33**, 1718.
[7] Bayer, E.P. 27,373/04; D.R.P. 161,954 (Fr., **8**, 252).
[8] Vaubel, *J. pr. Chem.*, 1896, ii, **54**, 496.

TABLE IV

Reduction or Condensation Reactions Leading to Diazo-Compounds

Aromatic Compound.	Reducing Agent.	Reaction.	Refs.
Nitrosophenol.	Nitrous acid.	$HO \cdot C_6H_4 \cdot NO + 3HNO_2 =$ $HO \cdot C_6H_4N_2NO_3 + HNO_3 + H_2O$	1
p-Nitrosodiphenylamine.	Nitrous acid.	$PhNH \cdot C_6H_4 \cdot NO + 3HNO_2 =$ $PhNHC_6H_4 \cdot N_2 \cdot NO_3 + HNO_3 + H_2O$	2, 3
Nitrosobenzene.	Hydroxylamine.	$PhNO + H_2NOH = Ph \cdot N{:}N \cdot OH + H_2O$	4
Nitrosobenzene.	Nitrous acid.	Course of reaction in question.	5
Thionylphenyl-hydrazine.	Acetyl chloride.	$Ph \cdot N{:}N \cdot S(OH) + MeCOCl = PhN_2Cl +$ $S + AcOH$	6

1 Jäger, *Ber.*, 1875, **8**, 894.
2 Ikuta, *Ann.*, 1888, **243**, 283.
3 Hantzsch, *Ber.*, 1902, **35**, 893.
4 Bamberger, *ibid.*, 1895, **28**, 1218.   See also p. 198.
5 Bamberger, *ibid.*, 1918, **51**, 634.
6 Michaelis, Ruhl, *Ann.*, 1892, **270**, 117.

TABLE V

Scission Reactions Leading to Diazo-Compounds

Aromatic Compound.	Reagent.	Reaction.	Refs.
Diazoamino-compounds.	Bromine.	$PhN{:}N \cdot NHPh + 2Br_2 \longrightarrow PhN_2Br +$ $C_6H_2Br_3NH_2$	1
Mercury-diphenyl, -ditolyl, -dinaphthyl.	Nitrogen trioxide.	$HgAr_2 + 2N_2O_3 \longrightarrow HgPhNO_3 +$ $PhN_2 \cdot NO_3$	2, 3
Nitrosophenyl-glycine.	Alcoholic HCl.	$PhN{<}^{NO}_{CH_2CO_2H} \longrightarrow$ p-diazophenylhydroxylamine.	4
Azo-compounds.	Lead peroxide.	$PhN_2C_{10}H_6 \cdot OH + 3H_2SO_4 + 2PbO =$ $PhN_2SO_3H + C_{10}H_6O_2 + 2PbSO_4 + 3H_2O$	5
	Nitric acid.	$NO_2C_6H_4 \cdot N_2 \cdot C_6H_4 \cdot OMe + 3HNO_3 =$ $NO_2C_6H_4N_2 \cdot NO_3 + C_6H_3(NO_3)_2OMe + 3H_2O$	6
	Water.	Not a general reaction.	7

1 Griess, *Phil. Trans.*, 1864, **154**, 668.
2 Bamberger, *Ber.*, 1897, **30**, 506.
3 Kunz, *ibid.*, 1898, **31**, 1528.
4 O. Fischer, *ibid.*, 1899, **32**, 247.
5 Lauth, *Bull. Soc. chim.*, 1891, iii, **6**, 94.
6 Schmidt, *Ber.*, 1905, **38**, 3201.   Rowe, Levin, *J.S.D.C.*, 1924, **40**, 219.
7 Rowe, Dangerfield, *ibid.*, 1936, **52**, 48.

reaction between an amine and nitrous acid.   For the most part they are of only academic interest, and may conveniently be arranged in three groups :—

1. Oxidation reactions.
2. Reduction reactions.
3. Scission reactions by which part of a more complex molecule appears as a diazo-compound.

The gist of the several groups can be most readily apprehended by a tabular arrangement (Tables III, IV and V), and the criterion of oxidation or reduction is the fate of the initial aromatic nucleus which is converted to a diazo-compound.

CHAPTER II

STABILISED DIAZO-COMPOUNDS

In 1880 Thomas and Robert Holliday were granted patents for dyeing cotton by impregnating the fibre with β-naphthol followed by treatment with a diazo-compound whereby a water-insoluble pigment was formed in the fibre. This was not a fundamentally new method in the art of dyeing, for it was a known method to colour cloth and yarn by precipitating into the fibre metallic oxides by a two-bath process, and that quite apart from its use for mordanting. Although this process utilising the coupling power of diazo-compounds with phenols and amines to dye cotton in fast and brilliant shades is elegant in its simplicity, it nevertheless only came but gradually into general use. For many years after 1880 only two amines came into consideration for commercial use, p-nitroaniline and β-naphthylamine, the former giving on a β-naphthol ground the shade known as Para Red, and the latter a bluer red known as Vacanceine Red. They competed with alizarine in the Turkey-Red trade. The supply of amines was uncertain, the price high, and the quality often poor, particularly of p-nitroaniline, which was usually contaminated with varying quantities of the *ortho*-isomer. Moreover, the best conditions for coupling were not known, while doubtless diazotisation, carried out as it was in the dyehouse in rough-and-ready fashion, was often far from satisfactory. It was from the ice used in the latter operation that the colours become known in the trade as Ice Colours. The basic idea of the process being so attractive, attention was paid to it on the Continent, and Koechlin first showed that sodium acetate could be used to obtain consistent results in coupling, while the addition of Turkey-Red oil to the β-naphthol padding bath was a revolutionary improvement. With these improvements the method was extended by the employment of diazotised α-naphthylamine for clarets, of tetrazotised benzidine for puce, and of tetrazotised dianisidine for navy blues. It was not, however, until 1894 that Friedländer in Volume IV of his *Fortschritte* devoted a section to patents on the art, and in the introduction to that section he voiced what was a commonly held opinion : that the discovery of a means of stabilising diazo-compounds was necessary to ensure the survival of this class of dyes on any large scale. What the dyer needed was a powder which by mere solution in water would provide him with the desired diazo-bath. In 1898 Friedländer noted how further spread of

28

the Ice Colours was hanging fire for want of more success in the attack on this problem, for by this time the other requirement—that of pure bases such as p-nitroaniline of first-class quality—had been overcome. The calico printers in particular wanted stabilised diazo-compounds, because they wished to expand the art of printing thickened diazo-compounds on prepared cloth in multi-colour machines.

A three-fold problem was set to the chemists—namely, (i) to find means of separating the very soluble diazo-compounds from water without causing decomposition in the process; (ii) to obtain the diazo-compound in a solid form in which it could be kept in safety; (iii) to ensure that the solid would dissolve again in water to a clear solution of useful concentration. The term " stabilised diazo-compound " has therefore come to designate a diazo-compound so treated or combined that it can be preserved in the solid state for a period measurable at least by weeks at the ordinary temperature; in which the explosive properties have been annulled, and which upon the addition of water will afford a solution in which the original diazo-compound displays its coupling power immediately or when liberated by suitable treatment.

Forty years of research have provided the dyer to-day with such substances as those of which the last generation dreamed, and which eliminate from the dyehouse and printworks the necessity for carrying out the operation of diazotisation, and put at his command not only a large range, but one that comprises diazo-compounds which he could not possibly prepare himself. In addition, they are at a standard of strength which is constant and reliable.

The driving force behind all this vast activity, which has increased of recent years, has arisen from the discovery that certain derivatives of β-naphthol—namely, the arylamides of 2 : 3-hydroxynaphthoic acid, termed Naphthol AS compounds—give with suitable diazo-compounds Ice Colours which approach the vat colours in fastness and, among the reds, surpass them in brilliancy. Thus the two series have become for some purposes complementary to one another, and of great importance in the fast-colour trade.

In England the stabilised diazo-compounds are usually known in the trade as Fast Colour Salts, the corresponding amines, even when actually handled as hydrochlorides, as Fast Colour Bases. A table is appended to this chapter in which are set out such constitutions of the Fast Colour Bases as have been made public. Without exception the amines are free from substituent groups able to form salts with alkalis and so allow soap to loosen the pigment from the fibre. It is no exaggeration to say that every diazo-compound of this kind which dyestuffs chemists have been able to prepare has been combined with a greater or smaller number of arylamides. The total number of combinations tested has run into tens of thousands and the marketed components are all chosen warriors of a host. The favourite amines in use comprise chloro-, dichloro-, nitro-, and chloronitro-anilines, toluidines and anisidines as well as various naphthylamines, aminoanthraquinones, aminodiphenylamines, and aminoazo-compounds.

As the cost of stabilised diazo-compounds per active unit must of necessity be higher than that of the base, the equilibrium between the usage of either form by the trade varies with time and place. Where hanks and warps are to be dyed in large quantities, diazotisation of the base on the spot is often preferred, as being cheaper to the use of stabilised diazo-compounds, but for information concerning the application of the Ice Colours treatises on the art of dyeing should be consulted.

No one method of stabilisation is applicable to all diazo-compounds, and moreover the different means employed permit of different forms of technical application, and the calico printers, rather than the dyers, have turned to best account in their art all those variations in the forms in which the stabilised diazo-compounds have been offered to the dyestuffs users.

The diversity of chemical types which embrace the stabilised diazo-compounds may be conveniently classified in two groups :—

Group 1. Compounds stable in neutral or acid solution and showing the reactions of diazo-ions immediately on solution in water.

The sub-divisions of this group are :—

Section i. Diazo-compounds which are stable as diazonium sulphates or chlorides.
ii. Diazo-compounds stabilised as complex salts.
iii. Diazo-compounds stabilised as salts of arylsulphonic acids.
iv. Sundry forms of mixture of amine with nitrite, acid, and coupling component.

Group 2. Compounds stable in neutral or alkaline solution and requiring an acid treatment in order to regenerate the diazo-compound.

The sub-divisions of this group are :—

Section i. Metallic salts of the acid isomeric forms of the diazo-compounds, the *iso*diazotates or nitrosamines. See p. 81.
ii. Diazoamino- and diazoimino-compounds. See p. 128.
iii. Diazosulphonates, $Ar\cdot N{=}N\cdot SO_3Na$. See p. 93.

The members of Group 1 are sometimes referred to as " Active " stabilised diazo-compounds, while those of Group 2 are called " Passive." The active group (with the exception of Section iv) consists entirely of diazonium salts and forms a compact whole which has really been removed en bloc from Chapter I and forms the entire subject-matter of Chapter II, together with Section iv, which contains products that are both active and passive.

In the passive group are substances obtained from diazonium salts by the action of various reagents, and they will be found in their appropriate place in the scheme of the reactions of the diazo-compounds, thus bringing out the points at which the pure chemistry of the diazo-compounds impinges on their industrial application.

TABLE VI

Commercial Names and Chemical Constitutions of Ice Colour Bases

Commercial Name.	Chemical Constitution.	Refs.
Fast Blue B.	Dianisidine.	4
BB.	4-Benzoylamino-2 : 5-diethoxyaniline.	8
RR.	4-Benzoylamino-2 : 5-dimethoxyaniline.	8
Variamine Blue B.	4-Amino-4'-methoxydiphenylamine.	8. Compare 6
FG.	4-Amino-3-methoxydiphenylamine.	8
RT.	4-Aminodiphenylamine.	8
Fast Bordeaux GP.	3-Nitro-*p*-anisidine.	8
Fast Garnet B.	α-Naphthylamine.	1
G.	*o*-Aminoazotoluene.	1, 3
Fast Orange G, GC.	*m*-Chloroaniline.	3
GR.	*o*-Nitroaniline.	4
R.	*m*-Nitroaniline.	1
Fast Red AL.	1-Aminoanthraquinone.	8
B.	5-Nitro-*o*-anisidine.	1
2B.	*o*-Anisidine.	1
2G.	*p*-Nitroaniline.	4
G, GL.	*m*-Nitro-*p*-toluidine.	1
3GL.	4-Chloro-*o*-nitroaniline.	1
ITR.	*o*-Anisidine-4-sulphondiethylamide.	8
KB.	4-Chloro-*o*-toluidine.	3
R, RC.	4-Chloro-*o*-anisidine.	1
RBE.	6-Benzoylamino-4-amino-α-xylene.	6
RL.	5-Nitro-*o*-toluidine.	1, 3
TR.	5-Chloro-*o*-toluidine.	5
Fast Scarlet G.	4-Nitro-*o*-toluidine.	1
2G.	2 : 5-Dichloroaniline.	2, 4
R.	4-Nitro-*o*-anisidine.	1
TR.	6-Chloro-*o*-toluidine.	5
Fast Violet B.	6-Benzoylamino-4-methoxy-3-aminotoluene.	7
Fast Yellow G.	*o*-Chloroaniline.	1, 3

REFERENCES

[1] Rowe, Levin, *J.S.D.C.*, 1924, **40**, 226.
[2] Rowe, Corbishley, *ibid.*, 1925, **41**, 278.   [3] Rowe, Levin, *ibid.*, p. 358.
[4] Rowe, *Industrial Chemist*, 1926, **2**, 208.
[5] Rowe, Levin, *J.S.D.C.*, 1926, **42**, 82.
[6] Rowe, *ibid.*, 1930, **46**, 227.
[7] Kishner, Krasova, *Anilinokras. Prom.*, 1933, 3, 179 ; A., 1933, 1045.
[8] Fierz-David, " Kunstliche Organische Farbstoffe," Supplement, 1935, 35 *et seq.* (Springer, Berlin, 1935.)

SECTION I. DIAZO-COMPOUNDS STABILISED AS DIAZONIUM SULPHATES AND CHLORIDES

Of the diazo-compounds first in use for Ice Colours p-nitrodiazobenzene was of outstanding stability, and, as was earlier remarked, stability is further enhanced by increase in acidity. The problem of marketing this diazo-compound in solid form was therefore first solved by evaporating an acid solution to small bulk under vacuum at a temperature of not over 45°, and then binding the remaining water as crystal water by adding anhydrous salts such as sodium sulphate or aluminium sulphate. The resulting solid mass was ground, standardised, and passed into commerce as Azophor Red PN (M.L.B).[1] Tetrazotised dianisidine is amenable to the same treatment.

In another means to the same end the operation of evaporating the water was avoided by diazotising the p-nitroaniline in strong sulphuric acid by passing in nitrous acid gases, and then solidifying with calcined sodium sulphate.[2] Thus the dyers were furnished with Nitrazol C (Cassella). It was further claimed that large quantities of mineral salts increase the stability of admixed diazonium salts,[3] and that oxalic acid is particularly beneficial for tetrazotised diaminoazo-compounds.[4] The era of Para Red dyeing reached its peak during the first decade of the twentieth century, when enormous quantities of p-nitrodiazobenzene stabilised as above were made and sold by various makers, and as late as 1913 the process was still further improved by effecting diazotisation of the p-nitroaniline in sulphuric acid by nitrosylsulphuric acid, partly removing the acid by magnesia, and then solidifying the whole with calcined sodium sulphate.[5] When the dry preparations of the above type had been dissolved in water by the dyer, the excess mineral acid had to be removed by addition of a reagent such as sodium acetate before the bath was ready to receive the padded yarn or cloth. Since 1920 the production of stabilised p-nitroaniline has declined, its place being taken by diazo-compounds which give shades faster to light, kier-boiling, and chlorine.

For many years p-nitrodiazobenzene and tetrazodianisyl enjoyed the distinction of being the only diazo-compounds in commerce requiring no stabiliser other than free mineral acid, but recently considerable additions to this small class have appeared. Easily isolated stable diazonium salts are naturally attractive to the makers, because the cost of stabilisers is saved and the solubility of diazonium salts in water is good.

Both the 2- and 4-aminophenol aryl ethers and their substitution products have long been valued for the production of fine red and pink shades with the 2 : 3-hydroxynaphthoic aryl amides. They are obtained generally by condensation of the chloronitrobenzenes with phenols and cresols, followed by reduction. Four typical ethers of this series are :—

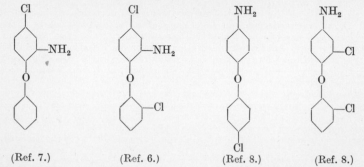

    (Ref. 7.)   (Ref. 6.)   (Ref. 8.)   (Ref. 8.)

The diazonium salts derived from these bases can be salted out of an acid solution, and are stable when dry and mixed with standardising diluents.[6, 7, 8]

Some p-phenylenediamine derivatives form a series of which the monodiazo-compounds have good stability. Thus 2 : 6-dichloro-p-phenylenediamine treated with nitrous acid yields a stable diazo-compound.[9, 10] 2 : 5-Disubstituted p-phenylenediamines in which the 4-amino-group carries the phenoxyacetyl group behave similarly :— [11]

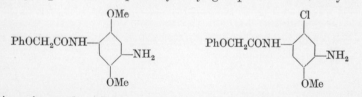

Diazonium salts of the p-aminodiphenylamines are easily isolated, and it is claimed that they can be preserved against the injurious effects of alkalis if freed from oxidation products and excess nitrous acid and mixed with a buffer.[12]

Aminoazobenzene is the parent member of a third group of amino-compounds yielding stable diazonium salts which can be precipitated by excess sulphuric acid. An ether group *ortho* to the amino-group particularly enhances stability in aminoazobenzene derivatives such as :— [13]

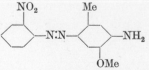

The diazo-compounds of such bases are especially useful for Ice Colours of deep shade.

Both *o*- and *m*-aminoazotoluene yield diazo-compounds of the same type, and indeed it has been shown that such salts are more stable

D

than the previously known double compounds with zinc and cadmium chlorides.[14]

As an example of the method of preparation : 225 parts of o-aminoazotoluene are introduced with stirring into 4500 parts of water and 345 parts of 32·0% hydrochloric acid are added.   The whole is cooled to 10°, and then there are run in 360 parts of 20% sodium nitrite solution.   After diazotisation is complete the solution is filtered, and 250 parts of 78% sulphuric acid are added drop by drop. The acid diazonium sulphate is precipitated in part, and completed by adding 500 parts of anhydrous sodium sulphate.   The mixture is cooled to 5°, stirred for an hour, and the acid diazonium sulphate collected and freed from mother-liquor by pressing.   The press-cake is diluted with its own weight of anhydrous sodium sulphate and dried at 40—50° with repeated turning.   The acid diazonium sulphate thus obtained forms a reddish-brown powder.
After 30 days storage at 40° a 20% mixture loses only 10% of its strength.

Lastly the wheel has come full circle, and it has been shown that many substituted benzenediazonium sulphates, which in earlier years might have been suspected of being dangerously unstable, can be isolated by diazotising the amines in strong sulphuric acid of specified composition, about 85%, with nitrosylsulphuric acid, and then precipitating with organic liquids miscible with the acid, such as the lower aliphatic alcohols, at temperatures well below 0°.   The precipitated diazonium sulphate is collected and the free sulphuric acid in the cake determined, and there is then mixed into it sufficient mild alkali to neutralise the acid and provide a stabilising diluent.   Among the amines claimed as being suitable for this process are the nitroanilines, the mono-, di-, and poly-halogen anilines, certain chloroanilines and nitro- and di-halogen aminophenol ethers.[15]

REFERENCES

[1] M.L.B., E.P. 21,227/94; D.R.P. 85,387 (Fr., **4**, 673).
[2] Cassella, E.P. 15,353/98; D.R.P. 97,933 (Fr., **5**, 482); F.P. 268,261.
[3] Cassella, D.R.P. Anm., C. 11,066 (Fr., **7**, 359).
[4] Kinzelberger, D.R.P. 93,109 (Fr., **4**, 686).
[5] Cassella, E.P. 23,945/13; D.R.P. 281,098 (Fr., **12**, 310).
[6] I.G., D.R.P. 607,536; U.S.P. 2,018,095; F.P. 771,798.
[7] S.C.I., E.P. 363,950; D.R.P. 545,852 (Fr., **18**, 1073); U.S.P. 1,875,243; F.P. 787,194; Sw.P. 150,001.
[8] I.G., E.P. 440,964; D.R.P. 609,476; U.S.P. 2,027,066; F.P. 775,463.
[9] Morgan, Cleague, J.C.S., 1918, **113**, 590.
[10] I.G., E.P. 403,013; D.R.P. Anm., I. 44,494; F.P. 755,889.
[11] S.C.I., E.P. 434,158; D.R.P. 607,870; F.P. 778,602; Sw.P. 174,081.
[12] I.G., D.R.P. 515,205 (Fr., **17**, 1057). See also Anm., I. 51,375.
[13] I.G., E.P. 305,498.
[14] I.G., E.P. 399,753.
[15] I.G., E.P. 441,085; Anm., I. 47,579; F.P. 776,009; Sw. P. 177,263. See also D.R.P. 622,306; F.P. 775,963.

SECTION II.   COMPLEX SALTS OF THE DIAZO-COMPOUNDS AND THEIR USE AS STABILISED DIAZO-COMPOUNDS

Griess, appreciating the basic nature of the diazo-compounds, naturally prepared aurichlorides and platinichlorides,[1] but some time elapsed before it was realised that the diazonium salts, particularly the halides, are characterised by a notable capacity to form double salts with metallic halides. So strong is this tendency to co-ordinate that Hantzsch prepared dry double diazonium chlorides with hydrochloric acid, *e.g.* salts such as $3(PhN_2Cl)HCl$.[2] For a long time he held the acid to be structurally combined in the molecule of the diazo-compound, but eventually altered his view.[3] A double hydrofluoride has also been prepared from tribromobenzenediazonium fluoride, $Br_3C_6H_2N_2F \cdot HF \cdot 2H_2O$.[4]

Griess also recorded the preparation of the first double salt of diazobenzene and a base metal chloride—namely, the one formed from stannic chloride—and he found it to have the formula $(PhN_2Cl)_2SnCl_4$.[5] Double salts with mercuric chloride are well known; Hantzsch obtained one having the constitution $PhN_2Cl \cdot HgCl_2 \cdot H_2O$,[6] while Nesmejanov has prepared a number having the general formula $ArN_2Cl \cdot HgCl_2$.[7] From the *p*-dialkylaminobenzenediazonium chlorides Schmidt and Maier have prepared double salts with mercurous, ferric, zinc, and cadmium chlorides.[7a]

The chlorides of the arsenic group of metalloids all form double salts with diazonium chloride.[8] Antimony trichloride affords the salt $PhN_2Cl \cdot SbCl_3$,[9] and also combines with benzene-*p*-tetrazo-chloride.[10] The double salt of bismuth chloride is an explosive white powder.[11]

When diazonium chlorides are added to a hydrochloric acid solution of lead tetrachloride a yellow crystalline precipitate is formed to which Chattaway and his co-workers ascribe the constitution :—

$$(ArN_2)_2 \begin{bmatrix} Cl & Cl \\ Cl & Pb & Cl \\ Cl & Cl \end{bmatrix} \text{ analogous to the chloroplatinates : } (ArN_2)_2 \begin{bmatrix} Cl & Cl \\ Cl & Pt & Cl \\ Cl & Cl \end{bmatrix}$$

The plumbichlorides are slightly abnormal, in that when heated with alcohol they replace the diazo-group by chlorine.[12] It is doubtless a co-ordinated structure akin to the above which accounts for the stability in the solid state of the double salts already mentioned.

Cuprous salts form double salts which are quite different from those above. Whereas the former are white or pale-coloured and stable, the cuprous salts are coloured and unstable. Lellmann and Remy prepared a reddish-yellow, crystalline double salt from β-diazonaphthalene and cuprous bromide, $C_{10}H_7N_2Br \cdot Cu_2Br_2$,[13] and Hantzsch explained their colour as being due to conversion of an unstable diazonium salt to a *syn*-diazo double salt :—

$$\begin{array}{c} Ar \cdot N \cdot Cl \cdot Cu_2Cl_2 \\ \vdots \\ N \end{array} \longrightarrow \begin{array}{c} Ar \cdot N \\ \| \\ Cl \cdot N \end{array} Cu_2Cl_2 \quad (14)$$

When chemists on the Continent attempted to apply Holliday's process to the printing of cloth prepared with β-naphthol, they came

on many difficulties, one of which was due to the decomposition of the
thickened diazo-solution, whereby a froth of nitrogen formed on the
rollers and ruined the prints.   Feer experimented with metallic salts in
the hope of finding one which would stabilise the diazo-compound so
that the trouble would be eliminated.   He found that zinc chloride as
well as stannic chloride yield a sparingly soluble double salt, and also
that a diazosulphocyanide can be made which will keep for weeks.[15]
He must have made comparative tests in practice, for later he said that
the double diazo-salts of tin, mercury, and zinc are more stable than
the sulphocyanides, but are too insoluble for technical use, with the
exception of the double salts of zinc chloride, which behave as desired,
though the metal affects the print.[16]

Zinc chloride has remained the most-used reagent for stabilising
diazo-compounds because it combines in most cases sufficient solubility
in use with isolation in good yield in the process of manufacture.   When
the question of stabilising a new diazo-compound arises, zinc chloride
is the first reagent tried, and recourse is only had to other stabilisers
when this one fails.   In those cases where the double salt formation
occurs it is only necessary to add zinc chloride solution to the diazo-
chloride solution, when the double salt frequently commences to separate
in crystalline condition :—

510 parts of dianisidine are dissolved in 4100 parts of 10% hydrochloric acid
and diazotised with 870 parts of 40% sodium nitrite solution.   After filtering,
375 parts of zinc chloride are added and then 1000 parts of salt, by which means
the separation of the double salt is completed.   The crystalline diazo-compound
is collected, pressed, and dried, either by mixing with partially dehydrated
aluminium sulphate or sodium naphthalene tetrasulphonate and dried carefully
at 40—50°.   The dried substance is mixed with standardising agents and dyeing
assistants such as chromium and copper salts.[17]
The double salt has the formula :—

$$C_6H_3 \cdot OMe \cdot N = N \cdot Cl$$
$$\mid \qquad\qquad\qquad\qquad ZnCl_2$$
$$C_6H_3 \cdot OMe \cdot N = N \cdot Cl$$

The diazo- and tetrazo-derivatives of the aminoazo- and diaminoazo-
benzenes are readily stabilised in this way, and were the first to be the
subject of a patent,[18] while the class is of some importance because
certain of its members yield deep shades approaching black with
2 : 3-hydroxynaphthoic arylides.[19, 20]   In the anthraquinone series zinc
chloride has been applied to isolate the diazo-compound derived from
1-alkyl- or dialkyl-4-p-anilino-anthraquinone :— [21]

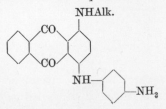

It has already been noted in the chapter on diazotisation that the aminodiphenylamines can be diazotised in zinc chloride solution, and so be isolated directly as the zinc chloride double salt. Variamine Blue Salt is a compound of this type.

No information has been published as to the extent to which double salts exist in solution, but it is certain that some measure of dissociation occurs, so that a proportion of the diazo-ions are left unprotected and will decompose if the solution is not handled carefully. Drying of the crystal pastes obtained in manufacture is therefore a matter of difficulty, as decomposition may occur in the adhering film of liquid, and unwanted insoluble substances appear on redissolving the dry powder. Drying may therefore be performed advantageously with anhydrous salts, which not only dry, but can also serve as buffers in the dye-bath.[22] Salts of arylsulphonic acids are likewise useful for this purpose, and also for their solubilising effect.[23]

Diligent search has been made to find an equivalent of zinc chloride or to extend its use in difficult cases. For instance, it has been proposed to precipitate p-nitrodiazobenzene by adding first stannic chloride (less than 0·5 mol.), followed by zinc carbonate (up to 1·0 mol.),[24] while cadmium salts have also been claimed. In the case of diazotised p-aminoazobenzene the cadmium chloride double salt is stated to be definitely superior in stability to the zinc chloride double salt.[25]

Bart discovered that borofluoric acid added to a solution of a diazonium chloride produces a plentiful precipitate of the sparingly soluble crystalline borofluoride. Diazobenzene borofluoride can be obtained by diazotising aniline in borofluoric acid, and it is the double salt of diazobenzene fluoride and boron trifluoride.[26] Funk and Binder obtained the same substance by adding borofluoric acid to the diazo-hydroxide, and they considered it to be a general reaction of the alkali salts of borofluoric acid to attach themselves to hydrazine and diazonium salts.[27] Wilke-Dörfurt and Balz have also made these substances, and describe benzenediazonium borofluoride as colourless, doubly-refracting needles, sparingly soluble in water, practically insoluble in alcohol and ether.[28] Its analysis agrees with the formula $PhN_2 \cdot BF_4$. 5-Nitro-2-diazotoluene can be stabilised as borofluoride,[29] while both m- and p-phenylenediamine can be tetrazotised by carrying out the reaction in borofluoric acid and the tetrazo-compounds isolated as borofluorides.[30] The sparing solubility of the borofluorides has been a bar to their general use, though the solubility can be improved by adding neutral ammonium salts or neutral salts of metals of the first or third groups of the periodic table.[31] Stability in solution is improved by increasing the acidity.[32]

Diazofluorosulphonates are obtained by adding fluorosulphonic acid to solutions of diazonium salts.[33] The complex metallic fluoric acids such as $[TiF_6]H$, $[AlF_6]H_3$, $[ZnF_4]H_2$ and others also form diazonium salts which are stable and soluble in water.[34]

Sieber in a recent paper gives directions for stabilising diazo-solutions for use in printing with both boric acid and tungstic acid,[35] while nearly forty years ago Hepburn sought to turn to account the great insolubility of the diazo-tungstates for use in printing. He printed cloth with tungstates, dried and passed the cloth through a diazo-solution, when an insoluble diazotungstate was formed in the cloth, which, after washing, was passed through alkaline β-naphthol solution, whereupon the insoluble azo-colour was formed in the printed areas.[36]

Lastly, it has been proposed to separate diazo-compounds from their solutions as complex cyanides, which salts have the advantage that they can be safely dried at temperatures up to 50°.[37]

REFERENCES

[1] Griess, *Ann.*, 1866, **137**, 52.   [2] Hantzsch, *Ber.*, 1897, **30**, 1151.
[3] Hantzsch, *ibid.*, 1930, **63**, 1786.   [4] Hantzsch, Vock, *ibid.*, 1903, **36**, 2063.
[5] Griess, *ibid.*, 1885, **18**, 965.   [6] Hantzsch, *ibid.*, 1895, **28**, 1743.
[7] Nesmejanov, *ibid.*, 1929, **62**, 1018.
[7a] Schmidt, Maier, *J. pr. Chem.*, 1931, ii, **133**, 153.
[8] Földi, *Ber.*, 1923, **56**, 2489.   [9] May, *J.C.S.*, 1912, **101**, 1037.
[10] Gray, *ibid.*, **1926**, 3174.
[11] Supniewsky, *Rocz. Chem.*, 1925, **5**, 298.
[12] Chattaway, Garton, Parkes, *J.C.S.*, 1924, **125**, 1981. Compare Algerino, *Gazz.*, 1932, **62**, 1145.
[13] Lellmann, Remy, *Ber.*, 1886, **19**, 810.
[14] Hantzsch, *ibid.*, 1895, **28**, 1752; Hantzsch, Blagdon, *ibid.*, 1900, **33**, 2544.
[15] Feer, *Bull. Soc. Mulhouse*, 1891, **61**, 220. Sealed Communication No. 575 of 9.3.89.
[16] Feer, *Farber Zeitung*, 1890–91, 348.
[17] Badische, E.P. 238,676; D.R.P. 454,894; U.S.P. 1,572,715; F.P. 600,311; Sw.P. 118,614.
[18] M.L.B., E.P. 1645/96.
[19] I.G., E.P. 305,498; D.R.P. 569,205 (Fr., **18**, 1066); U.S.P. 1,846,150—1, 1,889,298; F.P. 644,563.
[20] Sandoz, E.P. 365,759; D.R.P. 573,180 (Fr., **18**, 1064); Sw.P. 151,677, 155,331—33.
[21] I.C.I., E.P. 376,307.
[22] I.G., E.P. 246,870. See diazoarylsulphonates Ref. 19 for equivalents (p. 48).
[23] I.G., E.P. 273,352. See diazoarylsulphonates Ref. 18 for equivalents (p. 48).
[24] M.L.B., D.R.P. 94,495 (Fr., **4**, 676).
[25] Kalle, E.P. 294,258; D.R.P. 491,318 (Fr., **16**, 1064); F.P. 657,852; Sw.P. 135,596.
[26] Bart, D.R.P. 281,055 (Fr., **12**, 311).
[27] Funk, Binder, *Zeit. anorg. Chem.*, 1926, **159**, 123.
[28] Wilke-Dörfurt, Balz, *Ber.*, 1927, **60**, 115.   [29] I.G., E.P. 316,691.
[30] I.G., E.P. 397,034; D.R.P. Anm., I. 43,838; F.P. 751,306; Sw.P. 165,828.
[31] I.G., E.P. 332,630; D.R.P. 557,658 (Fr., **19**, 1810); U.S.P. 1,799,068.
[32] I.G., E.P. 317,355; D.R.P. 495,631 (Fr., **16**, 1062); F.P. 657,041; Sw.P. 136,915.
[33] I.G., E.P. 303,527; D.R.P. Anm., I. 33,150 (Fr., **18**, 1060); U.S.P. 1,847,513; Sw.P. 140.098, 142,648.
[34] I.G., E.P. 332,227.
[35] Sieber, *Textilber.*. 1927, **8**, 609.
[36] Hepburn, D.R.P. 108,231, 109,699 (Fr., **5**, 489, 491).
[37] I.G., D.R.P. 532,402 (Fr., **18**, 1059).

SECTION III. DIAZOARYLSULPHONATES : THEIR REACTIONS AND THEIR USE AS STABILISED DIAZO-COMPOUNDS. DIAZOARYLSULPHINATES AND DIAZO-SULPHONES

Diazoarylsulphonates

Becker first discovered that on addition of naphthalene-α- or -β-sulphonic acid to a solution of tetrazodiphenyl a precipitate is formed which can be collected, dried, and stored without change.[1] When redissolved in water, in which it is sparingly soluble, evidence of tetrazodiphenyl is at once shown by the familiar coupling reaction with β-naphthol. Becker proceeded to widen the scope of his invention by using crude naphthalenesulphonic acids and applied the reaction to p-nitrodiazobenzene.[2, 3] Feer also found that nitrobenzenesulphonic acid precipitates diazo-compounds in the same way as the naphthalenesulphonic acids,[4] and in an English patent, to which were appended only two examples, he claimed the manufacture of salts of diazo-compounds with sulphonic-, carboxysulphonic-, and polysulphonic acids of the benzene, naphthalene, and anthracene series, and likewise with methyl- and phenyl-sulphuric acids.[5] He appears therefore to have recognised the generality of the reaction. The Fabrique de Thann et de Mulhouse acquired both Becker's and Feer's patents, and manufactured stabilised p-nitrodiazobenzene salts with naphthalenemonosulphonic acids, with naphthalenedisulphonic acids, particularly naphthalene-1 : 5-disulphonic acid, and with nitrobenzenesulphonic acid.[6, 7] Schroeter, while experimenting on the coupling of various diazo-compounds with acetylated arylaminesulphonic acids, found that in a few cases he could obtain a true azo-compound, but with 1-acetaminonaphthalene-4- and -5-sulphonic acids he obtained unstable substances which could be crystallised from warm water, but evolved their nitrogen quantitatively on heating their solutions to the boil.[8] He was uncertain whether they were diazonium salts or diazoamino-compounds, and on the basis of his analysis assigned them the alternative structures :—[9]

$$NO_2 \cdot C_6H_4 \cdot \overset{\text{N}}{\underset{\text{N}}{\|}} \cdot OSO_2 \cdot C_{10}H_6 \cdot NHCOMe \quad \text{or} \quad NO_2 \cdot C_6H_4 \cdot N = N \cdot N(COMe)C_{10}H_6 \cdot SO_3H$$

The latter form is improbable. Schroeter did not detect the coupling power of the aqueous solution. At this time the Berlin Aniline Company patented the stabilisation of diazo-compounds by combination with p-toluenesulphonyl-sulphanilic and -metanilic acids, describing them in the patent as diazoimino-compounds, though the reactions given clearly indicate membership of the class of the diazoarylsulphonates.[10] Further evidence that the above might indeed all be examples of a general reaction of arylsulphonic acids with diazo-compounds was supplied by the firm of Bayer, who early took patents for condensing tetrazodiphenyl with β-naphtholtrisulphonic acid and oxy Tobias acid, in which cases coupling is prevented by the sulphonic acid group in the 1-position of the naphthalene ring.[11]   In 1913 Witt published a paper in which he briefly discussed the position in this field and described a condensation product he had recently patented formed from one mole-cule of p-nitrodiazobenzene and two molecules of naphthalene-β-sul-phonic acid.[12, 13]   He assigned to it the structure :—

$$NO_2 \cdot C_6H_4 \cdot N \equiv\!\!=\!\!= N \cdot SO_3 \cdot C_{10}H_7$$
$$NaSO_3 \cdot C_{10}H_7 \cdot H_2O$$

No analytical figures were quoted.   This substance was marketed as Paranil-A.

The basis of preparation of diazoarylsulphonates is a double decom-position :—

$$ArN_2X + ArSO_3H \rightleftharpoons ArN_2OSO_2Ar + HX$$

If the diazoarylsulphonate is sparingly soluble or can be salted out, then the equilibrium moves to the right, and the solid diazo-salt can be collected, but the strength of the diazo-compounds as bases and of the arylsulphonic acids as acids varies so much that each pair of compounds requires separate study to find the best conditions for isolation.

A typical preparation is carried out as follows : 4-chloro-o-toluidine (142·5 g.) is diazotised in weak hydrochloric acid with sodium nitrite (69 g.). Into this solution is brought, at a temperature of less than 20°, somewhat more than the calculated quantity of the sodium salt of acetylsulphanilic acid (m. p. 237°).   After a short time the separation of yellow crystals commences, and these are collected and dried at under 50°.   The dry diazonium salt of acetylsulphanilic acid is of good solubility in water, and in the solid state, either alone or mixed with diluents, is of outstanding stability, being of low inflammability and neither explosive nor sensitive to friction.[14]

The arylsulphonates of most diazo-compounds are white, yellow, or brown solids charring on heating without definite melting point.   They deflagrate, but are rarely explosive.   They are often sensitive to light and may darken quickly on exposure.   They can usually be crystallised, and when pure their aqueous solutions are neutral, provided no acid groups are present as in the acid salts of polysulphonic acids.   Although they are referred to in the literature both as salts and esters, they are in fact true ionisable salts of a strong acid with a strong base, and for this reason Schroeter's first representation of them as diazonium salts with the linkage through oxygen must be correct.   Witt mentions a very soluble, explosive substance prepared by him from one molecule of p-nitrodiazobenzene and one molecule of β-naphthalenesulphonic acid, though he does not disclose either the method of preparation or analysis, and this may have been a salt with the nitrogen linked to sulphur.

The stability of the diazoarylsulphonates in the solid state is doubt-less due primarily to their being non-ionised, and secondarily to their high molecular weight. As soon as dissolved in water they form the system :—

$$ArN_2OSO_2Ar + H_2O \rightleftharpoons ArN_2OH + ArSO_3H$$

In dilute solution equilibrium travels far to the right, and the diazo-ions (which are themselves a system of equilibrium between diazonium and diazo-hydroxides and their ions) revert to the same order of stability which they show with any other acid radical under the same conditions of acidity. It is therefore plain that addition of another arylsulphonic acid, particularly a polysulphonic acid, to a diazoarylsulphonate solution will tend to improve the keeping qualities, driving the equilibrium back to the left, and reducing the number of fragile diazo-ions by combining them with arylsulphonic acid ions. This is the principle underlying the use of the substance known as Azo Guard (I.G.), but the idea is by no means new, as a patent for stabilising diazo-solutions by adding small quantities of arylsulphonic acids was taken as long ago as 1912.[15] Viktoreff also has stated that the addition of arylpolysulphonic acids increases the stability of diazo-solutions, but he has published no figures.[16]

The results of a careful quantitative study of this matter have been recently published by Marriott,[17] who used for his experiments the carefully purified sodium salts of anisol-p-sulphonic acid and naphthalene-1 : 5-disulphonic acid. The diazo-solution under investigation was brought to the required p_H value by the addition of alkali, buffered at that value and brought to N/40 strength, and then the solid stabiliser added in varying molecular proportions to aliquot portions of solution. The amount of decomposition after various times was determined by titrating the remaining diazo-compound. The experiments were made with 5-chloro- and 4-chloro-o-toluidine, p-nitraniline, m-nitro-p-toluidine and m-toluidine. The results for the first three compounds are reproduced in extenso in the tables overleaf, and several points are brought out clearly.

It is immediately apparent from the figures that a statement as to stabilising effect of any particular substance on diazo-compounds is without meaning unless accompanied by a statement of the p_H value and temperature at which the stabilising effect is exerted, as change in acid concentration and temperature can easily overwhelm the effect due to even high concentrations of stabiliser. Further, it will be noted that the aryl radical to which the sulphonic acid group is attached is not without effect, and that naphthalene-1 : 5-disulphonic acid is more effective than anisol-p-sulphonic acid. The stabilising effect is only just apparent in the case of the very unstable m-diazotoluene at p_H 5·5 and 16·0—17·0°, decomposition having reached no less than 48% in two hours with 5 molecular proportions of naphthalene-1 : 5-disulphonic acid. A continuance of this investigation with several more mono-, di-, and poly-sulphonic acids would be interesting.

TABLE VII

$M/40$ *Solution of 5-Chlorotoluene-2-diazonium Chloride,*

	p_H 5·2. 16—17°.			p_H 6·5. 16—17°.				p_H 7·5. 16—17°.			
	Initial p_H.	Percentage Decomposed after 240 hrs.	Final p_H.	Initial p_H.	Percentage Decomposed after		Final p_H.	Initial p_H.	Percentage Decomposed after		Final p_H.
					16 hrs.	66 hrs.	240 hrs.		7 hrs.	48 hrs.	127 hrs.	
No buffer.	5·10	4·9	2·65	6·4	—	—	5·5	2·9	1·0	8·4	12·7	3·6
Buffer : no stabiliser	5·17	39·9	5·04	6·55	14·1	45·4	85·0	6·16	12·6	61·5	96·2	7·00
1 mol. anisolsul- phonate.	5·10	39·2	5·06	6·5	14·1	42·7	81·0	6·18	11·6	56·3	88·2	7·00
2 mols. do.	5·00	37·4	5·05	6·5	12·1	38·8	77·2	6·17	11·6	54·8	86·0	6·97
3 mols. do.	5·15	38·0	4·95	6·5	10·7	34·0	74·5	6·16	11·6	49·0	81·6	7·00
1 mol. 1 : 5-N-disul- phonate.	5·10	40·2	4·95	6·55	11·3	34·9	75·7	6·20	10·0	49·0	83·6	7·00
2 mols. do.	5·10	38·0	4·95	6·55	9·9	32·0	72·0	6·18	8·4	43·2	76·8	7·02
3 mols. do.	5·05	35·3	4·90	6·5	4·5	20·8	56·5	6·16	7·4	31·6	63·8	7·02

TABLE VIII

$M/40$ *Solution of* p-*Nitrobenzenediazonium Chloride,*

	Initial p_H 5·5. 19—20°.					Initial p_H 6·5. 19—20°.					
	Percentage Decomposed after			p_H Values.		Percentage Decomposed after			p_H Values.		
	6 hrs.	22 hrs.	47 hrs.	0·5. hrs.	106. hrs.	4·5 hrs.	12 hrs.	30 hrs.	0. hrs.	12. hrs.	32. hrs.
No buffer.	1·6	3·80	4·3	3·2	3·0	—	—	—			
Buffer : no stabiliser.	11·9	38·1	80·5	5·62	5·20	12·0	31·5	64·1	6·5	6·38	6·15
1 mol. anisolsulphonate.	16·8	42·2	74·1	5·62	5·20	15·2	40·8	71·2	6·5	6·38	6·05
2 mols. do.	19·5	47·6	78·4	5·60	5·20	19·6	48·4	78·3	6·5	6·38	6·04
3 mols. do.	30·8	54·5	86·0	5·6	5·20	28·3	52·1	87·5	6·5	6·32	6·15
1 mol. 1 : 5-N-disul- phonate.	8·6	24·3	45·4	5·57	5·25	8·2	24·2	42·1	6·5	6·32	6·15
2 mols. do.	7·0	17·8	34·6	5·57	5·25	6·5	21·2	35·9	6·5	6·32	6·15
3 mols. do.	6·5	16·8	28·6	5·55	5·25	4·9	19·6	30·5	6·45	6·31	6·15

Addition of an arylsulphonic acid will also improve the solubility of sparingly soluble diazosulphonates by taking the diazo-ions into solution partnered by the ions of the more soluble sulphonic acid, and this solubilising action is to be seen not only with diazoarylsulphonates, but also when the diazo-compound is present as a sparingly soluble metallic double salt.[18]

TABLE IX

M/40 Solution of 4-Chlorotoluene-2-diazonium Chloride,

Me — C_6H_3 — N_2Cl — Cl (benzene ring bearing Me, N_2Cl and Cl substituents)

	Initial pH 8.3. 15°.							Initial pH 7.25. 15°.						Initial pH 6.0. 15—16°.						
	Percentage Decomposed after				pH Values.			Percentage Decomposed after			pH Values.			Percentage Decomposed after				pH Values.		
	3·20 hrs.	6·70 hrs.	10·20 hrs.	21·20 hrs.	0·0 hrs.	10·3 hrs.	21·6 hrs.	3·2 hrs.	7·1 hrs.	23·3 hrs.	0·25 hrs.	7·25 hrs.	23·4 hrs.	8·75 hrs.	19·0 hrs.	27·5 hrs.	43·0 hrs.	0·16 hrs.	19·5 hrs.	43·0 hrs.
No buffer.	—	—	—	—	—	—	—	—	—	—	—	—	—	13·8	24·7	35·7	43·7	7·7	2·70	2·00
Buffer : no stabiliser.	19·6	33·3	44·3	62·1	8·32	7·65	7·32	16·6	29·9	62·1	7·25	6·9	6·64	12·6	32·2	49·4	63·8	6·6	5·53	5·32
1 mol. anisolsulphonate.	19·6	33·3	44·9	60·9	8·32	7·65	7·32	15·5	29·9	63·2	7·25	6·9	6·62	12·1	31·6	47·7	63·8	6·6	5·53	5·37
2 mols. do.	19·6	33·9	44·9	58·7	8·32	7·65	7·32	16·7	30·4	62·1	7·25	6·9	6·61	14·3	31·6	47·2	62·6	6·0	5·54	5·37
1 mol. 1 : 5-N-disulphonate.	17·2	31·6	39·7	57·5	8·32	7·65	7·34	13·2	28·2	59·2	7·25	6·9	6·62	12·1	28·8	46·6	60·9	6·0	5·54	5·37
2 mols. do.	15·5	28·7	38·0	55·2	8·30	7·68	7·36	12·6	27·0	56·3	7·25	6·93	6·60	12·1	28·2	43·1	57·5	6·0	5·54	5·36
5 mols. do.	13·2	23·6	29·9	47·7	8·30	7·70	7·37	10·3	21·3	50·0	7·25	6·96	6·60	9·2	23·6	38·5	50·6	6·0	5·54	5·40

The dyer expects the stabilised diazo-compound to dissolve to a clear solution in water, and in the process of manufacture of such compounds special care is necessary at the drying stage, because the diazo-compound contained in the film of mother-liquor on the crystals tends to decompose unless suitable drying methods are adopted. In addition to the desiccating salts, such as the sulphates of sodium and magnesium, which have been used from the early days, aluminium sulphate and alum only partially dehydrated (to prevent formation of basic salts) have been introduced into the technique, and they also possess the additional valuable property of buffering the dye-bath against alkali brought in with the naphthol on the yarn.[19] Removal of water by distillation at low temperatures with immiscible liquids [20] or by improved methods of salting out [21] has also been described.

The diazoarylsulphonates are of importance, because a number of the more valuable diazo-compounds fail to give suitable double salts with metallic salts, and so must needs be stabilised in this way. The art of manufacture consists in choosing for any given diazo-compound that arylsulphonic acid which will allow the salt to be isolated in good yield while at the same time being sufficiently soluble, either with or without the addition of another sulphonic acid, to satisfy the needs of the dyer. As one way of overcoming the difficulty of steering between the extremes of poor solubility and poor yield it has been proposed to evaporate to dryness under vacuum at low temperatures the mixed solution of the diazo-compound with naphthalenetri- and tetra-sulphonic acids.[22] Besides the sulphonic acids of aromatic hydrocarbons, their substituted derivatives incapable of coupling with diazo-compounds also form salts, as shown in the example quoted above, and considerable activity has been displayed in trying various sulphonic acids of the benzene and naphthalene series so weighted by substituents that the desired degree of solubility may be attained. Among the acids of the benzene series which have been recently mentioned are the chlorobenzene mono-, di-, and poly-sulphonic acids, as well as the acylaminobenzenesulphonic acids.[23, 24, 25, 26] Aussig has also claimed that sulphobenzoic and chlorosulphobenzoic acids are specially suitable for stabilising 4-chloro- and 4-nitro-2-diazotoluene.[27]

The naphthalenedisulphonic acids have been much used from the earliest times on account of their cheapness and accessibility, and both neutral and acid salts are known and have been patented both for use and manufacture.[28] In certain cases the acid salts are said to be strikingly different from the neutral. Thus 3-nitro-4-diazotoluene and naphthalene 1 : 5 disulphonic acid yield a greenish crystalline salt of the structure :—

$$C_{10}H_6-SO_3N{=}N{\cdot}C_6H_3{\cdot}Me \begin{smallmatrix} {}^{SO_3H} \\ {} \\ {}^{NO_2} \end{smallmatrix}$$

whereas the colour of the normal salt is white to buff.[29]   As might be expected, the mono-salts of a disulphonic acid have the advantage of more ready solubility, but the neutral salt may tend to precipitate from the solution, a condition which can be corrected by the addition of more sulphonic acid.

The salts as brought into commerce are standardised at 20% of active diazo-component.   As the molecular weight of the arylsulphonic acid is nearly always greater, and often much greater, than that of the diazo-compound, the amount of the latter available in the pure salts usually lies between 30% and 40%, the addition of drying salts and buffers bringing it down to the standard value.

There is one series of diazoarylsulphonates some members of which undergo an interesting succession of reactions if their solution is allowed to become alkaline.   Mention has been made that β-naphthol sulphonated in the 1-position forms the normal diazosulphonate, coupling being prevented.   But it has further long been known that under appropriate conditions the 1-sulphonic acid group can be ejected by the diazogroup with formation of the corresponding azo-derivative of β-naphthol (see p. 115).   Unsulphonated diazo-compounds yield salts with β-naphthol-1-sulphonic acid which have poor solubility in water, but which Grant Hepburn found to be readily soluble in mild alkalis without decomposition.   Provided not more than one equivalent of alkali has been used, reacidification of the solution causes precipitation of the expected azo-compound, an acid alkali sulphate being eliminated.   This formed the basis of a convenient means of printing calico,[30] for the alkaline solution containing the diazo-β-naphthol-1-sulphonate is perfectly stable, and can be thickened and printed on calico.   Exposure of the dried prints to air for a few hours or passage of the cloth through a weakly acid bath brings about development of the insoluble colour in the fibre.   In later years attempts have been made to extend the process to cover the diazosulphonates of the 2 : 3-hydroxynaphthoic arylamide-1-sulphonic acids, but so far there has been no commercial development.[31]

Grant Hepburn also observed the very curious fact that if more than one equivalent of alkali is added to the diazoarylsulphonate solution derived from p-nitrodiazobenzene and β-naphthol-1-sulphonic acid a yellow compound is produced from which no insoluble azo-colour results on acidification.   This transformation cannot be due to decomposition, for no nitrogen appears.   The soluble substance intermediate between the diazoarylsulphonate and the azo-compound whose properties Grant Hepburn utilised had been investigated some years earlier by Bucherer,[32] who explained its formation as due to the migration of the p-nitrobenzenediazo-radical from the sulphonic group to the oxygen atom of the naphthol, thus :—

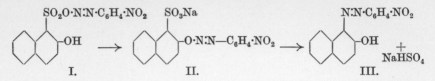

Wahl and Lantz also concurred in this opinion.[33] But this view hardly explains the profound changes brought about if the single molecular proportion of alkali is exceeded, and the course of these complex reactions has now been elucidated by Rowe and his co-workers in a series of papers published since 1926.

The soluble product to which Bucherer assigned the formula II above must be produced by intramolecular rearrangement of the diazo-arylsulphonate, because the latter does not decompose, no nitrogen being evolved, nor are diazo-ions to be found in the solution. Moreover, a free sulphonic acid group has probably resulted from the rearrangement to confer the observed solubility, and accordingly Rowe assigned to the product the hemi-quinonoid structure :— [34]

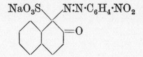

Bucherer and his co-workers have adhered to explanations of the chemistry of these substances based on the existence of the O-azo-compound as an essential intermediate step.[35, 36] Rowe and Peters pointed out that such substances are in fact known, being stable if the β-naphthol is substituted in the 1-position by halogen, and that when acted on by alkali they either decompose or give Para Red with ejection of the substituent (see p. 114). But as the derivative of p-nitrodiazobenzene with β-naphthol-1-sulphonic acid behaves in an entirely different way, the hemi-quinonoid structure is the alternative which fits the facts.[37] All aryldiazo-2-naphthol-1-sulphonates afford the hemi-quinonoid compounds, and all of these can undergo acid hydrolysis to give the corresponding azo-derivative of β-naphthol :—

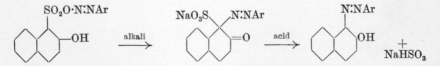

The transformation of the hemi-quinonoid compounds by caustic alkali, first observed by Grant Hepburn, is, however, peculiar (with some few exceptions) to that class in which the aryldiazo-radical contains nitro-groups and takes place with diazo-compounds derived from the following amines :—

o-, *m*-, and *p*-nitroaniline, 2 : 4-dinitroaniline, 4-chloro-2-nitro-aniline, 4-nitroaniline-2-sulphonic acid, 2 : 6-dibromo-4-nitroanil-ine, 3-nitro-4-toluidine, *p*-aminoazobenzene.

The reaction fails with the diazo-compounds derived from :—

Aniline, toluidines, tribromoaniline, sulphanilic acid, dichloro-aniline, *p*-aminoacetanilide, anthranilic acid and α- and β-naphthyl-amine.

On adding caustic soda to a solution of the hemi-quinonoid salt which contains the *p*-nitrodiazoaryl radical an intense crimson colour appears, fading soon to yellow, and the first product of the reaction which can be isolated is disodium 4′-nitrophenyl-3 : 4-dihydrophthal-azine-1-sulphonate-4-acetate. The naphthalene ring has been opened and closed again thus :— [38]

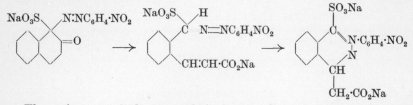

The existence of the open-chain intermediate compound remained unproved until the investigation was extended to the case where the nitro-group is *ortho* to the azo-link. If cold caustic soda is allowed to act for a minute on the hemi-quinonoid substance acidification gives sodium benzaldehyde-2′-nitrophenylhydrazone-ω-sulphonate-2-β-acrylic acid (I below), while if reaction is allowed to continue for two days the 3 : 4-dihydrophthalazine (II below) is the product :— [39]

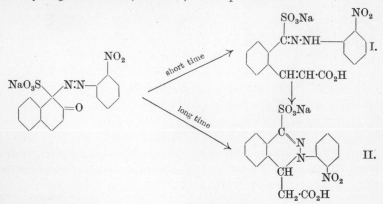

The subsequent reactions of the phthalazines which have been worked out by Rowe and his school are complicated, but as at this stage the identity of the diazo-compounds has been entirely lost, the subject passes from the purview of this book.

REFERENCES

[1] Becker, D.R.P. 81,039 (Fr., **4**, 678).   [2] Becker, D.R.P. 86,367 (Fr., **4**, 367).
[3] Becker, D.R.P. 89,998 (Fr., **4**, 681).   [4] Feer, D.R.P. 88,949 (Fr., **4**, 682).
[5] Feer, E.P. 18,429/94.
[6] Thann, Mulhouse, D.R.P. 92,237 (Fr., **4**, 679).
[7] Thann, Mulhouse, D.R.P. 94,280 (Fr., **4**, 680).
[8] Schroeter, *Ber.*, 1906, **39**, 1567. See also Hinsberg, *ibid.*, 1894, **27**, 598.
[9] Beilstein, 4th Ed., Vol. **16**, 491.
[10] Agfa, D.R.P. 229,247 (Fr., **10**, 786). See also S.C.I., F.P. 735,865.
[11] Bayer, E.P. 11,757/95; D.R.P. 93,305 (Fr., **4**, 685); F.P. 251,403; E.P.
     8995/95; D.R.P. 92,169 (Fr., **4**, 684); F.P. 251,403.
[12] Witt, *Färber Zeitung*, 1913, **24**, 273.
[13] Witt, E.P. 11,290/13; D.R.P. 264,268 (Fr., **11**, 370); U.S.P. 1,093,567;
     F.P. 458,493.
[14] I.G., Sw.P. 166,218.   [15] Bayer, E.P. 2037/12.
[16] Viktoreff, *Textilber.*, 1932, **13**, 435.
[17] Marriott, *J.S.D.C.*, 1936, **52**, 172.
[18] I.G., E.P. 273,352; D.R.P. 553,787 (Fr., **18**, 1067); U.S.P. 1,758,912; F.P.
     610,261; Sw.P. 121,312, 123,627—37.
[19] I.G., E.P. 246,870; D.R.P. 448,728 (Fr., **15**, 577); U.S.P. 1,607,462; F.P.
     609,746; Sw.P. 121,311.
[20] S.C.I., E.P. 393,830; F.P. 744,157.
[21] S.C.I., E.P. 359,339; D.R.P. 572,269 (Fr., **18**, 1062); U.S.P. 1,846,113;
     F.P. 697,425; Sw.P. 145,444.
[22] S.C.I., E.P. 280,945.
[23] I.G., E.P. 265,985; F.P. 628,973.
[24] S.C.I., E.P. 364,490.
[25] I.G., E.P. 415,768; F.P. 750,619; Sw.P. 168,924.
[26] Veinberg, *Anilinokras. Prom.*, 1934, **4**, 281; B., **1934**, 793.
[27] Aussig, D.R.P. 559,421 (Fr., **19**, 1815).
[28] I.G., E.P. 246,181.
[29] I.G., E.P. 269,212; D.R.P. 499,294 (Fr., **16**, 1651); U.S.P. 1,744,903.
[30] Grant Hepburn, E.P. 116,360.
[31] Scottish Dyes, E.P. 385,307.
[32] Bucherer, *Ber.*, 1909, **42**, 47.
[33] Wahl, Lantz, *Bull. Soc. chim.*, 1923, iv, **33**, 97.
[34] Rowe, Levin, Burns, Davies, Tepper, *J.C.S.*, **1926**, 690; *J.S.D.C.*, 1926, **42**,
     242.
[35] Bucherer, Tama, *J. pr. Chem.*, 1930, ii, **127**, 39.
[36] Bucherer, Frohlich, *ibid.*, 1931, ii, **133**, 72.
[37] Rowe, Peters, *J.C.S.*, **1931**, 1965.
[38] Rowe Peters, *ibid.*, **1933**, 1067.
[39] Rowe, Dovey, Garforth, Levin, Pask and Peters, *ibid.*, **1935**, 1796.

Diazoarylsulphinates and Diazosulphones

The close relationship of the arylsulphinic acids to the arylsulphonic acids might lead to the expectation that they would form similar salts with diazo-compounds. That they do so is almost certainly true, but only one case is on record in which the diazonium sulphinate has been isolated, as in general a rearrangement at once occurs and a diazo-sulphone is the substance isolated :—

$$\underset{\ddot{N}}{ArNX} + Ar'SO_2H \longrightarrow \left[\underset{\ddot{N}}{ArN\cdot SO_2Ar'}\right] \longrightarrow ArN{:}N\cdot SO_2Ar'$$

Königs,[1] who discovered the diazosulphones, assigned the above constitution to them, and demonstrated that they are sulphones, and not the expected sulphinates, both because of their stability and because the same substance is produced when benzenesulphonchloride acts on phenylhydrazine as when diphenyldiazosulphone is reduced :—

$$PhN_2X + PhSO_2H \longrightarrow PhN\text{:}N\cdot SO_2Ph \longrightarrow$$
$$PhNH\cdot NH\cdot SO_2Ph \longleftarrow PhNH\cdot NH_2 + PhSO_2Cl$$

The same reaction also occurs with ethylsulphinic acid.

p-Nitrobenzenediazo-p'-nitrobenzene sulphone, $NO_2\cdot C_6H_4\cdot N_2\cdot SO_2\cdot C_6H_4\cdot NO_2$, has been made by the action of dry sulphur dioxide on p-nitrodiazobenzene hydroxide dissolved in absolute alcohol.[2]

v. Pechmann [3] made a number of diazosulphones in the hope of finding evidence among them for Hantzsch's stereochemical theory of the constitution of the diazo-compounds. v. Pechmann found that formation from diazo-salt and sulphinic acid does not occur in the presence of caustic alkali, but in strong mineral acid or alkali carbonate, while with bromine in cold chloroform the diazosulphone is split and the diazo-perbromide is formed. Hantzsch and Singer [4] extended v. Pechmann's work, but came to the same conclusion—namely, that no stereoisomers exist in this series, while they confirmed the sulphone constitution by showing that the diazosulphone will not couple with phenols. Later Hantzsch found that some, particularly those containing positive substituents, will couple quite quickly if alkali is present. Hantzsch and Glogauer [5] attempted to bring normal and isodiazotates into reaction with sulphinic acids, but found that it is only diazonium compounds which afford the sulphones, which latter are decomposed by alkalis giving isodiazotate and sulphinate. When normal or isodiazo-cyanides are brought into reaction with sulphinic acids they may give a sulphone, as in the case of $pseudo$-cumene, but the normal cyanides often give an addition product which splits off the sulphinic acid, again leaving the isodiazo-cyanide.[6] There are some incongruities in this series of papers which probably arose because it was not recognised that in solution an equilibrium exists between the diazonium sulphinate and the diazosulphone, while the sluggishness of reaction in aqueous solution is due to the sparing solubility of the sulphone, so that the active mass is small.

The diazonium sulphinates were first prepared by Claasz,[7] who discovered that the condition which prevents rearrangement to the diazosulphone is the presence of a negative group so placed as to increase the acidity of the sulphinic acid group. Thus o-nitrodiazobenzene and o-nitrobenzenesulphinic acid yield $o : o'$-dinitrobenzenediazonium sulphinate :—

yellow, decomp. 100°

It can be rearranged to the sulphone :—

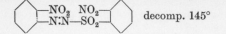

$$\text{decomp. } 145°$$

According to Claasz, the diazonium sulphinates are differentiated from the stable and inert diazosulphones in being explosive, losing nitrogen in boiling water to give $o : o'$-dinitrodiphenylsulphone, coupling instantly with β-naphthol in alcoholic solution, while their specific conductivity in alcohol is that to be expected of a diazonium salt.

Diazoarylthiosulphonates are also known, and an extensive series was investigated by Troeger and Ewers,[8] who also gave to them the structure $Ar \cdot N = N \cdot SO_2S \cdot Ar'$, where Ar' is benzene, o-toluene, and α- and β-naphthalene.

Dybowski and Hantzsch[9] also examined these substances for evidence of stereoisomerism and found none. The product they obtained from benzenethiosulphonic acid and β-diazonaphthalene consisted of some orange crystals dissolving to a clear solution in water and coupling at once with β-naphthol. They therefore considered it to be a diazonium salt. When it is dissolved in water, sulphur is rapidly eliminated with formation of the diazosulphone.

REFERENCES

[1] Königs, *Ber.*, 1877, **19**, 1531.
[2] Ekbom, *ibid.*, 1902, **35**, 656.
[3] v. Pechmann, *ibid.*, 1895, **28**, 861.
[4] Hantzsch, Singer, *ibid.*, 1897, **30**, 1897.
[5] Hantzsch, Glogauer, *ibid.*, p. 2558.
[6] Hantzsch, *ibid.*, 1898, **31**, 638.
[7] Claasz, *ibid.*, 1911, **44**, 1911.
[8] Troeger, Ewers, *J. pr. Chem.*, 1900, ii, **63**, 369.
[9] Dybowski, Hantzsch, *Ber.*, 1902, **35**, 268.

SECTION IV. MIXTURES SERVING THE PURPOSE OF STABILISED DIAZO-COMPOUNDS

Since a solution containing a primary aromatic amine, nitrite, and an acid has the only components necessary for the formation of a diazo-compound, it is not surprising that attempts have been made to manufacture stable mixtures of such components in powder form by such devices as complete desiccation, or by protecting the amino-group from diazotisation until the desired moment by easily-removed substituents. On dissolving the powder in water the acid liberates nitrous acid, the amine is forthwith diazotised, and the mixture therefore behaves as an active stabilised diazo-compound.

A decade ago the I.G. described various ways of practising the art according to the device of desiccation. Dry amine salts, such as the sulphate, oxalate, or naphthalene disulphonate, are mixed with dry acid salts and the correct quantity of sodium nitrite; the diazo-compound results on solution in water.[1] An obvious technical disadvantage of such mixtures is that absolute dryness is essential to secure keeping qualities, and exposure to damp air is likely to induce rapid deterioration.

The first attempt to employ mixtures for the preparation of printing pastes goes back to the earliest days of the Ice Colours, the requisite acid being then generated by steaming an ammonium salt.[2] Present-day attempts to make mixtures which behave as passive stabilised diazo-compounds are based on temporarily solubilised amines which are mixed with nitrite and a coupling component. The mixture is stable under alkaline or neutral conditions, and when dissolved can be thickened and printed. On treating with acid the solubilising group is split away, the nitrous acid diazotises the amine, and coupling ensues. On this principle passive mixtures have been made of salts of aryl-sulphamic acids with nitrite and a naphthol. These give clear solutions in weak alkali, and after printing are developed by acid ageing.[3] The methyl-ω-sulphonate, $Ar \cdot NH \cdot CH_2 \cdot SO_3Na$, obtained by treating aryl-amines with formaldehyde-bisulphite, can be used in the same way, as acetic acid suffices to split away the ω-sulphonate group and bring about diazotisation.[4] The arylnitroamines, $ArNH \cdot NO_2$, which give stable salts in alkaline solution and lose the nitro-group very easily in an acid medium, have also been claimed,[5] as have also the arylnitrosohydroxylamines, $Ar, N \cdot OH \cdot NO$.[6]

Protection of the coupling position in the 2 : 3-hydroxynaphthoic arylides from nitrous acid during the time the amine is being diazotised also appears necessary. Such protection can be afforded by using the formaldehyde condensation products which are split when the diazo-compound couples.[7]

Many difficulties are likely to crop up in attempting to meet the stringent demands of technical usage with such mixtures—difficulties of solubility, of uneven rate of development, and difficulty of manu-facture, which probably explains why this group has not reached the importance of those previously described.

REFERENCES

[1] I.G., E.P. 260,682; D.R.P. 425,033, 430,621, 438,743, 443,284, 447,069 (Fr., 15, 572—4); D.R.P. 453,985.
[2] Grässler, D.R.P. 14,950 (Fr., 1, 547).
[3] I.G., E.P. 262,987. See also I.G., F.P. 801,094.
[4] I.C.I., E.P. 374,497; U.S.P. 1,947,433.
[5] Bader, E.P. 430,167, 430,222, 430,236; F.P. 761,811.
[6] Bader, E.P. 437,824; F.P. 43,788.
[7] S.C.I., E.P. 449,267, 452,177.

CHAPTER III

ELIMINATION AND INTERCHANGE OF GROUPS IN DIAZO-COMPOUNDS

WHEN the amino-group in an aromatic amine is converted to the diazo-group a considerable effect is exerted on other groups occupying certain definite positions in the same benzene ring. With the exception of the alkoxy-group, the substituents affected are the negative substituents which induce high stability in the diazo-salts as long as the anions of a strong acid are present, but when the latter are withdrawn by adding alkalis or the alkali salts of weak acids the stability falls very rapidly (see p. 71). Destruction of the diazo-group does not, however, necessarily ensue from this loss of stability, but instead one of the substituents may be lost, being replaced by an hydroxyl group with which the diazo-group immediately forms a stable internal anhydride, thus arresting further change. For example, 2 : 4-dinitro-diazobenzene salts when treated with weak aqueous alkalis lose the *ortho*-nitro-group, and the 4-nitro-1 : 2-benzenediazo-oxide thus formed is identical with the substance obtained by diazotising 2-hydroxy-4-nitroaniline :—

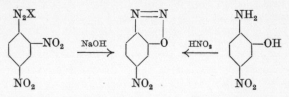

(For the reason for the adoption of the diazo-oxide structure rather than one of the isomeric forms, see p. 180.)

From the above the expectation naturally arises that the attempt to diazotise many negatively substituted amines in the presence of weak acids will lead to failure to obtain the diazo-salt, the diazo-oxide being obtained instead. This is precisely what occurs, and it was through the unexpected appearance of examples of the elimination of substituents that it has become recognised as a reaction to which an extensive class of diazo-compounds is susceptible.

For more than a decade Meldola and his school carried on research as to the conditions under which substituents are eliminated from the polynitroanisidines. If these compounds are diazotised in sulphuric acid or nitric acid, the diazo-sulphate or nitrate results quite in the usual way. If diazotised in hydrochloric acid a nitro-group *ortho* to the amino-group may be exchanged for chlorine,[1] but if diazotised in glacial acetic acid, either a nitro- or a methoxy-group can be eliminated, according to the arrangement of the substituents. Among the compounds the configurations of which are given below the removable groups are marked by an asterisk :— [2]

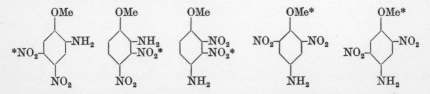

In summing up these results Meldola and Hay[3] reached and confirmed the conclusion that in this series a group only becomes sufficiently mobile to be eliminated during the act of diazotisation if two conditions are fulfilled. These conditions are that the mobile group shall be *ortho* or *para* to the diazo-group, and in addition have a nitro-group in its other *ortho* position to act as " activator." Such activating groups will be found in each of the five compounds above, but are lacking in 4 : 6-dinitro-3-anisidine,

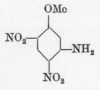

hence in the latter neither a nitro- nor a methoxy-group can be eliminated during diazotisation. If conditions are such that either a nitro- or a methoxy-group can be eliminated, then it is the nitro-group which goes. This point was settled by Meldola and Reverdin,[4] who prepared the two trinitroanisidines :—

In each case above the *ortho*-nitro-group exchanges for hydroxyl, but it must be noted that no elimination occurs if the molecule already contains a free hydroxyl group *ortho* or *para* to the diazo-group, as the demands of stability are immediately satisfied by oxide formation without elimination of any group. Thus when 2 : 3-dinitro-4-amino-phenol is diazotised in strong sulphuric acid, the yellow diazo-oxide is precipitated immediately on dilution.[5]

There is a further point of interest in those nitroanisidines in which the nitro-group is labile, in that they are self-diazotising once the diazotisation reaction has commenced. Thus Meldola and Eyre [6] started off diazotisation of 4 : 5-dinitro-*o*-anisidine with one quarter the theoretical amount of nitrous acid, but found that nevertheless the formation of the diazo-oxide continued by utilising the nitrous acid generated as the labile nitro-group was split off the benzene ring.

The rule given above to determine which group shall be eliminated is peculiar to the polynitro-anisidines where the methoxy-group, a positive group, stands either *ortho* or *para* to the amino-group. In the *meta* position it has no effect. If both the *ortho* and the *para* positions to the diazo-group are occupied by negative groups, then almost invariably the *ortho*-group will be found to be labile in some degree, and sometimes so labile that it is eliminated in acid solution. For instance, the nitro-groups in the nitrodiazonaphthalenes are much more labile than in the corresponding configurations of the benzene series, so much so that the nitro-group in the 2-position in 1-diazo-2 : 4-dinitro-naphthalene is eliminated with the greatest ease.[7] If negative groups occupy both positions *ortho* to the diazo-group, then one may be eliminated, though not with great ease, as is shown by the case of 2 : 6-dibromoaniline below.

Like the nitro-group, the halogens often behave like negative substituents in the benzene ring, and many cases of their elimination are known and have been studied. Silberstein early noticed the reaction with salts of tribromodiazobenzene.[8] Meldola and Streatfeild diazotised 1 : 4-dibromo-2-naphthylamine sulphate in glacial acetic acid, and after diluting with water warmed the solution. No nitrogen was given off, but hydrobromic acid was found in the liquid from which the insoluble 4-bromo-2 : 1-naphthalene diazo-oxide had been collected.[9] Orton studied the elimination of halogen atoms very extensively, and as a result was able to construct the table of relative rates of elimination given below.[10]

TABLE X

Diazo-compound from :	Percentage of 1 mol. of halogen set free at room temperature in 24 hrs.
2 : 4-Dibromo-1-naphthylamine.	97
2 : 4 : 6-Tribromo-3-nitroaniline.	93
2 : 4-Dibromo-5-nitroaniline.	80
1-Chloro-2-naphthylamine.	76
2 : 3 : 4 : 6-Tetrabromoaniline.	74
2 : 4 : 6-Tribromoaniline.	64
2 : 4 : 6-Trichloroaniline.	63
2 : 6-Dibromoaniline.	24
2 : 4-Dichloroaniline.	trace

Orton was further interested in the mechanism of the reaction, and was concerned to know whether transformation proceeds directly from the diazonium ion or through a diazotate. He showed that both tribromobenzenediazonium sulphate and normal sodium tribromo-benzene diazotate are stable, and that the elimination occurs at inter-mediate values of the acidity in the region where both diazonium and hydroxyl ions are present.[11]   On these grounds the mechanism which he suggested postulated an interchange of the diazonium hydroxyl ion with the more negative group attached to the ring, a quinonoid form being the intermediary :—

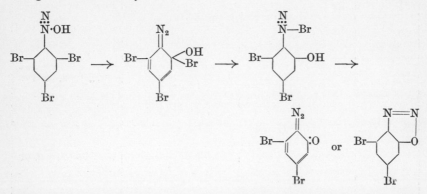

While it is difficult to see how this mechanism accounts for the expul-sion of an alkoxy-group, a further fact which can be brought forward in its support is that an interchange of the ion attached to the diazonium group and the substituent in the *ortho* or *para* position of the ring can occur without, however, the subsequent replacement by hydroxyl.   A further resemblance of this interchange to the elimination reaction is also found in the fact that, in those cases where it can be controlled, the interchange does not take place in the strongly acid diazotisation medium, but in a weak acid or organic solvent.   Thus diazotisation of 1-nitro-2-naphthylamine in hydrochloric acid affords 1-chloro-2-diazonaphthalene nitrite,[12] while Schremann and Ley were unable to obtain 1-nitro-2-fluoronaphthalene by the borofluoride process (see p. 156) from 1-nitro-2-naphthylamine because the nitro-group is eliminated on diazotisation in hydrochloric acid, and hence their product was 1-chloro-2-fluoro-naphthalene.[13]   The case mentioned above, where in diazotising a dinitroanisidine one nitro-group is exchanged for chlorine, is an example of the same change which cannot be separated into stages.

The bromodiazobenzene chlorides have a strong tendency to inter-change to chlorodiazo-bromides, and Hantzsch and his co-workers investigated the reaction from the kinetic view-point and found the reaction to be unimolecular.[14]   As in the elimination reaction it is only bromine atoms in the positions *ortho* or *para* to the diazo-chloride

TABLE XI

Amines Eliminating a Substituent from their Diazo-Derivatives by Alkaline Treatment.

Substituent Eliminated.	Amine.	Product.	References.
Halogen.			B.A.S.F., D.R.P. 139,327 (Fr., **6**, 896).
			Noelting, Battegay, *Ber.*, 1906, **39**, 79.
			Witt, *Ber.*, 1909, **42**, 2957.
			B.A.S.F., E.P. 12,584/'02; D.R.P. 141,750 (Fr., **7**, 99).
			B.A.S.F., E.P. 6615/ '02; D.R.P. 145,906 (Fr., **7**, 400); U.S.P. 710,059; F.P. 319,868.
			B.A.S.F., E.P. 16,995/'03.
			B.A.S.F., E.P. 16,811/'01.

TABLE XI—*continued*

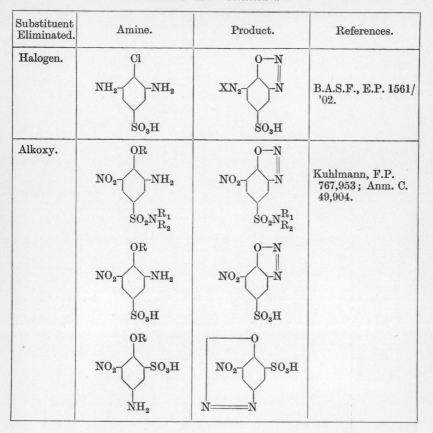

Substituent Eliminated.	Amine.	Product.	References.
Halogen.			B.A.S.F., E.P. 1561/ '02.
Alkoxy.			Kuhlmann, F.P. 767,953; Anm. C. 49,904.

group which can effect interchange, and the ease of interchange increases as the bromine atoms increase in number. Hence interchange cannot be prevented even in the dry state in the case of tribromodiazobenzene chloride, and though the dibromo-salts are stable when dry, interchange takes place rapidly on solution in alcohol.

Curiously enough, no interchange can be brought about with tri-iodobenzenediazo-chloride or tribromodiazobenzene fluoride.[15] On the other hand, *p*-chlorodiazobenzene thiocyanate on solution in alcohol at once interchanges and affords *p*-thiocyanodiazobenzene chloride, a neat way of attaching the thiocyanate group direct to the benzene ring :— [16]

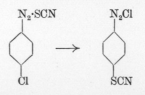

TABLE XII

Amines Eliminating a Substituent from their Diazo-Derivatives by Alkaline Treatment.

Substituent Eliminated.	Amine.	Product.	References.
Nitro group.	NH_2 / NO_2 / NO_2 (benzene ring)	$N{=}N$ / O / NO_2 (benzene ring)	B.A.S.F., D.R.P 144,640 (Fr., **7**, 380).
	NH_2 / NO_2 / SO_3H (benzene ring)	$N{=}N$ / O / SO_3H (benzene ring)	M.L.B., D.R.P. 138,268 (Fr., **6**, 894); F.P. 315,932.
	NH_2 / NO_2 / AsO_3H_2 (benzene ring)	$N{=}N$ / O / AsO_3H_2 (benzene ring)	M.L.B., E.P. 15,438/'11; D.R.P. 243,648 (Fr., **10**, 1245).
	NH_2 / NO_2 / Cl (benzene ring)	$N{=}N$ / O / Cl (benzene ring)	Kuhlmann, E.P. 288,572; F.P. 643,560.
	NH_2 / HO_3S—NO_2 / Cl (benzene ring)	$N{=}N$ / HO_3S—O / Cl (benzene ring)	Kuhlmann, E.P. 295,050.
Sulphonic acid group.	SO_3H / HO_3S—NH_2 / SO_3H (naphthalene ring)	$O{-}N$ / HO_3S—N / SO_3H (naphthalene ring)	M.L.B., E.P. 23,993/'02; Anm. F. 16,863 (Fr., **7**, 405); U.S.P. 737,967; F.P. 328,137.
	NH_2 / SO_3H / SO_3H (naphthalene ring)	$N{=}N$ / O / SO_3H (naphthalene ring)	B.A.S.F., E.P. 27,372/'03; D.R.P. 156,440, 157,325 (Fr., **8**, 656—7); F.P. 338,819.

TABLE XII—*continued*

Substituent Eliminated.	Amine.	Product.	References.
Sulphonic acid group.	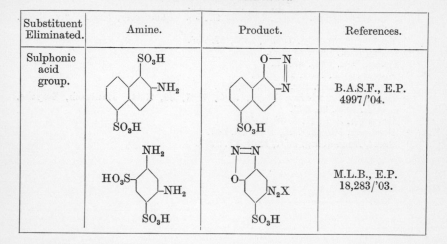		B.A.S.F., E.P. 4997/'04.
			M.L.B., E.P. 18,283/'03.

While a group must be " activated " by other substituents as described above before it can be eliminated during diazotisation, negative groups *ortho* or *para* to the diazo-group can often be eliminated by subsequent treatment of the diazonium salt. This removal may take place so easily as to suppress the normal reactions of the diazo-group. Thus, when Gaess and Ammelburg [17] attempted to remove the diazo-group from diazotised 1 : 6-dinitro-2-naphthylamine by the usual method of boiling with alcohol, they found that the nitro-group in the 1-position was replaced by hydroxyl, and the diazo-group remained intact.

The usual way of removing the negative group and replacing it by hydroxyl is to treat the diazonium salt with alkali, whereupon the elimination proceeds at a high speed. This reaction is of great technical importance because the replacement of the substituent *ortho* to the diazo-group by hydroxyl means that *ortho*-oxyazo-compounds are formed on coupling, and as such compounds have the power to combine with metallic mordants, this is an easy way to the synthesis of many valuable mordant azo-dyestuffs. There are therefore to be found in the patent literature a number of patents for the manufacture of *ortho*-hydroxydiazo-compounds by this means, and these have been grouped together in tables, pp. 56–59, according to the group eliminated.

REFERENCES

[1] Meldola, Eyre, *J.C.S.*, 1902, **81**, 988.
[2] Meldola, Wechsler, *ibid.*, 1900, **77**, 1172. Meldola, Stephens, *ibid.*, 1905, **87**, 1199.
[3] Meldola, Hay, *ibid.*, 1907, **91**, 1474.
[4] Meldola, Reverdin, *ibid.*, 1910, **97**, 1204.
[5] Meldola, Hay, *ibid.*, 1909, **95**, 1378.
[6] Meldola, Eyre, *ibid.*, 1901, **79**, 1076.

[7] Gaess, *J. pr. Chem.*, 1891, ii, **43**, 32.   Friedländer, *Ber.*, 1895, **28**, 1951. Morgan, Evens, *J.C.S.*, 1919, **116**, 1126.

[8] Silberstein, *J. pr. Chem.*, 1883, ii, **27**, 98.   Bamberger, Kraus, *Ber.*, 1906, **39**, 4248.

[9] Meldola, Streatfeild, *J.C.S.*, 1895, **67**, 908.

[10] Orton, *ibid.*, 1903, **83**, 796.

[11] Orton, *ibid.*, 1905, **87**, 99.

[12] Morgan, *ibid.*, 1902, **81**, 1376.

[13] Schremann, Ley, *Ber.*, 1936, **69**, 960.

[14] Hantzsch, Schleissing, Jäger, *ibid.*, 1897, **30**, 2334.   Hantzsch, Smythe, *ibid.*, 1900, **33**, 505.

[15] Hantzsch, *ibid.*, 1903, **36**, 2069.

[16] Hantzsch, Hirsch, *ibid.*, 1896, **29**, 947.

[17] Gaess, Ammelburg, *ibid.*, 1894, **27**, 2211.

CHAPTER IV

THEORY OF THE DIAZOTISATION REACTION: HETERO-CYCLIC DIAZO-COMPOUNDS: STABILITY: ANALYSIS: THERMOCHEMISTRY OF DIAZO-COMPOUNDS

THEORY OF THE DIAZOTISATION REACTION

THE manifold reactivity of the diazo-compounds so invited study of their chemical transformations that many years elapsed after their discovery before any inquiry was made as to the mechanism by which the diazotisation reaction occurs. Bamberger ventured the opinion that diazotisation is analogous to the rearrangement of the aryl-nitramines to nitroarylamines, diazo-compounds arising by rearrangement of unstable primary arylnitrosamines which are the first product of the action of nitrous acid on arylamines :— [1]

$$Ar \cdot NH_2 \xrightarrow{N_2O_5} Ar \cdot NH \cdot NO_2 \quad > \quad NO_2 \cdot Ar \cdot NH_2$$

$$Ar \cdot NH_2 \xrightarrow{N_2O_3} Ar \cdot NH \cdot NO$$

However, a survey of the discussion of the first chapter brings out clearly the fact that the *sine qua non* for the occurrence of diazotisation is that the amine must be present as a salt before attack by nitrous acid can commence. Hantzsch and Schümann based the now accepted view of the mechanism of the reaction on this fact, the general equation being :— [2]

$$(Ar \cdot NH_3)X + HNO_2 = (Ar \cdot N_2)X + 2H_2O$$

The implications of this view are that the nitrous acid reacts in its undissociated form with the cation of the ammonium salt. A criterion by which the idea can be judged is the speed of diazotisation of different amines, though the technique of measuring so fast a reaction is by no means easy. The method adopted by Hantzsch and Schümann consisted in diazotisation by the direct method, and in order to slow down the reaction sufficiently they worked with solutions at $N/1000$. They measured the consumption of nitrous acid as time went on by zinc-iodide–starch (Tromsdorff's method), though later Schümann showed that the conductivity of the solution also gives a measure of the rate, provided certain assumptions are made.[3] With one molecule of free acid and at 0° the velocity constants found were: Aniline, 0·036; p-toluidine, 0·038; m-xylidine, 0·041; p-bromoaniline, 0·045. p-Nitroaniline, being less basic, gave lower values. The figures were found to satisfy the equation for a reaction of the second order. It can hence be concluded that all arylammonium cations probably react with nitrous acid at the same high speed, provided the base is so strong that salt formation is complete with acid at the concentration of the experiment. Naturally rise in temperature increases the speed of the reaction.

Another technique the use of which in one form or another has displaced the method of Hantzsch and Schümann is the spectrophotometric method of Tassily. Here again $N/1000$ solutions must be used, and the extent of diazotisation measured by the depth of colour produced on coupling the diazo-compound to a naphtholsulphonic acid.[4] Among others the observation was made that the speed of diazotisation of sulphanilic acid increases with the concentration.

A further corollary of the above state of affairs must be that if a base is weakened by substitution, hydrolytic dissociation of the salts must occur, and so the speed of diazotisation will fall, only to be equalised when sufficient acid has been added to overcome the hydrolytic effect. Reilly and Drumm confirmed this deduction by measuring the speed of diazotisation of a series of three amines in which the basicity was progressively reduced by the influence of a quaternary ammonium group :— [5]

$$\text{NH}_2\text{—C}_6\text{H}_4\text{—NMe}_3{}^+\text{Cl}^- \qquad \text{NH}_2\text{—C}_6\text{H}_4\text{—CH}_2\text{NMe}_3{}^+\text{Cl}^- \qquad \text{NH}_2\text{—C}_6\text{H}_4\text{—CH}_2\text{CH}_2\text{NMe}_3{}^+\text{Cl}^-$$

I.   II.   III.

Using the colorimetric technique, they found that the amine III, in which the amino-group is the most strongly basic because most completely shielded from the quaternary ammonium group, diazotises faster than either II or I with one equivalent of acid, but that all react at the same speed with excess acid. The stability of the diazo-compounds when formed is in the reverse order.

The foregoing, where variation is induced in one substituent, is not quite parallel to the case where different substituents are attached to different positions in the benzene ring. Boeseken and Schoutissen [6] have pointed out that such substituents have two influences on diazotisation, each opposing the other. Thus velocity diminishes with increasingly negative substituents in the order m-, p-, o-, on account of decreased basicity, but this effect is counteracted by increase in velocity of conversion of the amino-group to the quaternary salt, substituents acting in the reverse order to the above.

Ueno and Suzuki [7] examined a series of no less than forty-seven amines, establishing the following points concerning the diazotisation reaction :—

1. The velocity of diazotisation increases when the concentration of hydrochloric acid rises from $0 \cdot 05N$ to $4N$.

2. The speed of diazotisation is 3 to 4 times greater at $10°$ than at $0°$.

3. Substituents affect speed in the order $Cl < CO_2H < SO_3H < NO_2$.

4. Substituents in the *ortho* position have most effect, while those *para* or *meta* have less. Alkyl and alkoxy-groups have no effect.

5. The speed of diazotisation is much greater with hydrobromic acid than with hydrochloric acid, while with nitric acid, sulphuric acid, and naphthalene-1 : 5-disulphonic acid the speed is yet slower.

Rostovtseva has based a method for the determination of the content of either constituent of a binary mixture of aromatic amines on the speeds of diazotisation measured relatively to that of benzidine as a standard.[8]

The question inevitably arises as to what part the aromatic nucleus plays in the diazotisation reaction, for it cannot be without influence, else there is no reason why the reaction should be unknown in the aliphatic series. Cain, in constructing his theory of the diazo-compounds, called on the possibility of quinonoid tautomerism in the aromatic nucleus to account for the reaction (see p. 203). However, all schools of the present-day electronic theory of organic chemistry are agreed that the unsaturation of the aromatic nucleus is alone sufficient explanation. The negative field arising from the unshared electrons in the unsaturated aromatic nucleus stabilises the charge on the pentavalent nitrogen atom, permitting it to form a cation of greater or less stability. The properties of the diazo-compounds, which vary so widely as to make it difficult to enunciate any unqualified general statement concerning them, arise from the drift imparted to these unshared electrons by substituents, and to this movement of charges can in part be traced the equilibrium between diazonium and diazo-isomers mentioned on p. 178. Negative groups in the *ortho* or *para* positions intensify the electron drift away from the nitrogen atom, and so increase the stability of the diazonium salt up to a point, after which the inductive effect may become so strong that the positive pole is transferred to the second nitrogen atom and the diazo-isomer becomes stable, as is shown by the capacity of trinitrodiazobenzene to couple in strongly acid solution (see p. 104). Positive substituents by balancing or reversing the inductive effect lower the stability until, with a mono-alkylamino-group in the *para* position, the stability is virtually nil, and the molecule breaks up just as does a primary aliphatic amine when treated with nitrous acid. The following diagrams represent these intramolecular forces in terms of the electron theory of valency :—

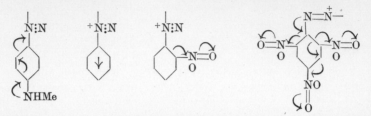

No doubt if unsaturated aliphatic amines could be made in which the carbon chain could exert an inductive effect on the amino-group such amines would afford diazo-compounds, but such amines are extremely unstable, and it has so far proved impossible to bring them to the test of reaction with nitrous acid.

REFERENCES

[1] Bamberger, *Ber.*, 1894, **27**, 547, 1948.
[2] Hantzsch, Schümann, *ibid.*, 1899, **32**, 1691.
[3] Schümann, *ibid.*, 1900, **33**, 572.
[4] Tassily, *Compt. rend.*, 1913, **157**, 1148; 1914, **158**, 335, 489; *Bull. Soc. chim.*, 1920, iv, **27**, 19.
[5] Reilly, Drumm, *J.C.S.*, **1935**, 871. See also Schoutissen, *J.Am.C.S.*, **1936**, **58**, 259.
[6] Boeseken, Schoutissen, *Rec. trav. chim.*, 1935, **54**, 956.
[7] Ueno, Suzuki, *J. Soc. Chem. Ind. Japan*, 1933, **36**, 615B; A., **1934**, 36.
[8] Rostovtseva, *Anilinokras. Prom.*, 1935, **5**, 199; *Z. anal. Chem.*, 1936, **105**, 32.

HETEROCYCLIC DIAZO-COMPOUNDS

Other unsaturated rings beside the aromatic ring can, however, exert the same effect on the amino-group, and as a result a number of non-aromatic diazotisable amines are known, though they have never attained to any industrial importance, and work on their application has been chiefly in the field of pharmaceutical chemicals.

As among the aromatic amines, the ease of diazotisation and stability of the diazo-compounds varies greatly in the heterocyclic group. Thus β-aminopyridine is easily diazotised, but a considerable time elapsed before it was discovered that α-aminopyridine is best diazotised with amyl nitrite and γ-aminopyridine by the method of Witt. Some examples of diazotisable heterocyclic amines are included in the following table, and it will be observed, as was pointed out by Morgan and Burgess, that such amines invariably contain the grouping $\gg$C·NH$_2$ and one other centre of unsaturation, usually another double bond,

$$=\!\!\!\overset{|}{\text{C}}-\overset{\|}{\text{C}}\cdot\text{NH}_2 \quad \text{or} \quad =\!\!\!\overset{|}{\text{C}}-\text{N}\!=\!\!\overset{|}{\text{C}}\cdot\text{NH}_2$$

TABLE XIII

Diazotisable Heterocyclic Amino-Compounds

Series.	Amino-Compound.	Constitution.	Ref.
Pyridine.	α-Aminopyridine.	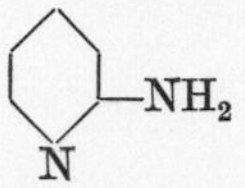	18
	β-Aminopyridine.	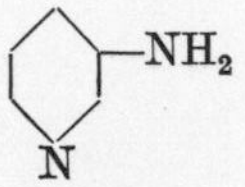	3
	γ-Aminopyridine.	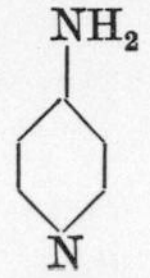	20, 26
	2-Alkoxy-5-aminopyridines (alkyl=Me, Et, Bu).	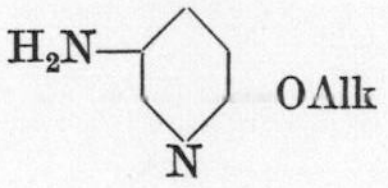	27
	α-Amino-α-picoline.	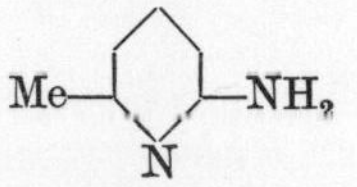	18
	α-Amino-γ-picoline.	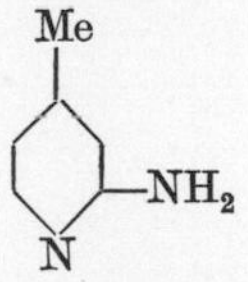	21
Pyrrole.	3-Amino-2 : 5-diphenyl-pyrrole.	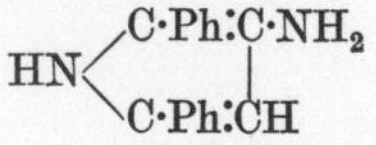 HN⟨ C·Ph:C·NH₂ / C·Ph:CH	6
	4-Amino-2 : 3 : 5-tri-phenylpyrrole.	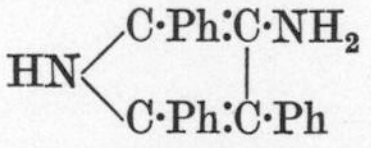 HN⟨ C·Ph:C·NH₂ / C·Ph:C·Ph	6
Pyrazole.	4-Amino-3 : 5-dimethyl-pyrazole.	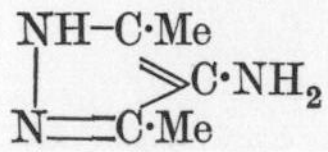 NH–C·Me, N═C·Me, >C·NH₂	11, 22
	4-Amino-1-phenyl-3-methylpyrazole.	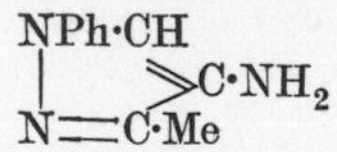 NPh·CH, N─C·Me, >C·NH₂	14
	5-Chloro-4-amino-1-phenyl-3-methylpyr-azole.	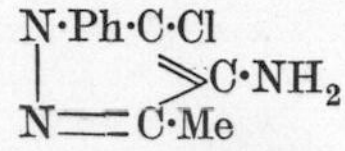 N·Ph·C·Cl, N═C·Me, >C·NH₂	15
	4-Amino-5-methylanilido-1-phenyl-3-methylpyr-azole.	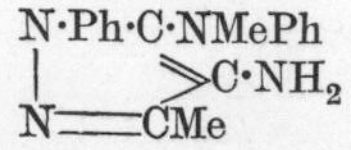 N·Ph·C·NMePh, N═CMe, >C·NH₂	9

F

TABLE XIII—*continued*

Series.	Amino-Compound.	Constitution.	Ref.
Pyrazole.	4-Aminoantipyrine.	$\begin{array}{c} N\cdot Me\text{---}C\cdot Me \\ \quad\quad\quad \gg C\cdot NH_2 \\ NPh\text{---}CO \end{array}$	2, 8, 10
	4-Amino-1-phenyl-5-methyl-3-pyrazolone.	$\begin{array}{c} N\cdot Ph\text{---}C\cdot Me \\ \quad\quad\quad \gg C\cdot NH_2 \\ NH\text{---}CO \end{array}$	7
	5-Amino-1-phenyl-3-methyl-4-alkylpyrazoles (Alk.=Me, Et, Pr, Bz).	$\begin{array}{c} N\cdot Ph\text{---}C\text{---}NH_2 \\ \quad\quad\quad \gg C\cdot Alk \\ N\text{====}CMe \end{array}$	12
Triazole.	5-Amino-1 : 2 : 4-triazole.	$\begin{array}{c} N\text{---}NH \\ \quad\quad \gg C\cdot NH_2 \\ CH\text{---}N \end{array}$	4, 24
	5-Amino-3-methyl-1 : 2 : 4-triazole.	$\begin{array}{c} N\text{------}NH \\ \quad\quad\quad \gg C\cdot NH_2 \\ C\cdot Me\text{---}N \end{array}$	
*iso*Oxazole.	4-Amino-3 : 5-dimethyl-*iso*oxazole.	$\begin{array}{c} O\text{---}C\cdot Me \\ \quad\quad \gg C\cdot NH_2 \\ N\text{====}C\cdot Me \end{array}$	19
	5-Amino*iso*oxazole.	$\begin{array}{c} O\text{---}CH \\ \quad\quad \gg CH \\ N\text{====}C\cdot NH_2 \end{array}$	25
Thiazole.	2-Aminothiazole.	$\begin{array}{c} CH\text{---}N \\ \quad\quad \gg C\cdot NH_2 \\ CH\text{---}S \end{array}$	1, 13
	2-Aminobenzthiazole.	$\gg C\cdot NH_2$ (benzthiazole ring)	23
Indole.	3-Amino-2-phenylindole.	$\begin{array}{c} C\text{---}NH_2 \\ \quad\quad C\cdot Ph \\ NH \end{array}$ (indole ring)	5

REFERENCES

[1] Hantzsch, Popp, *Ann.*, 1889, **250**, 257.
[2] Knorr, Stolz, *ibid.*, 1896, **293**, 58.
[3] Mohr, *Ber.*, 1898, **31**, 2495.
[4] Thiele, Manchot, *Ann.*, 1898, **303**, 33.
[5] Angeli, d'Angelo, *R.A.L.*, 1904, (v), **13**, i, 258.
[6] Angelico, *ibid.*, 1905, (v), **14**, ii, 167.
[7] Michaelis, *Ann.*, 1906, **350**, 288.
[8] Stolz, *Ber.*, 1908, **41**, 3849.
[9] Michaelis, Abraham, *Ann.*, 1911, **385**, 1.
[10] Morgan, Reilly, *J.C.S.*, 1913, **103**, 808, 1494.
[11] Morgan, Reilly, *ibid.*, 1914, **105**, 436.
[12] Mohr, *J. pr. Chem.*, 1914, ii, **90**, 509.
[13] Morgan, Morrow, *J.C.S.*, 1915, **107**, 1291.

[14] Michaelis, Schäffer, *Ann.*, 1915, **407**, 274.
[15] Michaelis, Bressel, *ibid.*, p. 274.
[16] Tschitschibabin, Rjasanzew, *J. Russ. Phys. Chem.*, 1915, **47**, 1571.
[17] Morgan, Reilly, *J.C.S.*, 1916, **109**, 155.
[18] Seide, *J. Russ. Phys. Chem.*, 1918, **50**, 534.
[19] Morgan, Burgess, *J.C.S.*, 1921, **120**, 697, 1546.
[20] Koenigs, Kime, Weisz, *Ber.*, 1924, **57**, 1172.
[21] Seide, *ibid.*, p. 791.
[22] Reilly, Madden, *J.C.S.*, 1925, **127**, 2936.
[23] Hunter, *ibid.*, 1926, 1388.
[24] Reilly, Madden, *ibid.*, **1929**, 815.
[25] Quilico, *Gazz.*, 1931, **61**, 970.
[26] Koenigs, Greiner, *Ber.*, 1931, **64**, 1051.
[27] Schering-Kahlbaum, D.R.P. 543,288.

THE STABILITY OF DIAZO-COMPOUNDS

Diazo-salts in the Solid State. All diazo-salts which have been isolated in the solid state should be treated with the greatest care, even when damp, and still more so if dry or if they have been in storage for any length of time, unless prolonged experience has shown certain individuals to be quite safe. Some such individuals are now coming into commerce (see p. 33), and for that purpose the diluents added for standardising purposes further decrease the likelihood of danger. References to damage caused by severe explosions are to be found in the literature from the time of Griess onwards. As will have been gathered, the anion has a great effect in determining the explosibility of a given diazo-salt. Usually the chloride and sulphate are less dangerous than the nitrate, while the introduction of nitro-groups in the nucleus further increases explosiveness.[1] The insoluble and apparently stable *p*-diazobenzenesulphonic acid obtained from sulphanilic acid is notorious in respect of its fickleness, Wichelhaus and Cain both having left warning of its treachery.[2]

It has long been sought to turn to account the instability of diazo-compounds by using them as explosives. Griess and Caro patented the diazo-chromates for this purpose,[3] and Seidler the diazosulphonic acids,[4] but the greatest measure of success has been obtained by 4 : 6-dinitrobenzene-2 : 1-diazo-oxide, the substance produced by diazotising picramic acid. A number of patents have been taken for its use.[5] A complete account of its properties as a detonating explosive has been published by Clark.[6] This substance detonates when struck, but is less sensitive to friction than mercury fulminate or lead azide, though in strength as an explosive it is twice as strong as lead azide and its equal as an initiator. The whole of this explosive effect is not due to the diazo-group, for dinitrophenol is itself an effective high explosive, but the diazo-group augments its effectiveness.

Diazo-salts in Aqueous Solution. The want of a solvent in which reaction can proceed prevents smooth and continuous decomposition of diazo-salts in the solid state, hence when the molecule is excited to the rupturing point explosion ensues. When in solution decomposition can proceed steadily at all temperatures until the process has reached completion. Much study has been given to this process when taking place in aqueous solution, in order to obtain knowledge as to the nature of the process itself, the effect of substituents and to compare the stability of various diazo-compounds with one another.

A considerable number of workers have taken part in the researches which have brought our knowledge of the subject to its present level, and although there is some disagreement between them on certain points, the main body of knowledge is firmly established. Though earlier work had been carried out by Oddo [7] and by Hirsch,[8] the foundations of exact quantitative measurements were laid by Hantzsch,[9] Hausser and Muller,[10] Euler,[11] and Cain and Nichol.[12] These showed that in acid solution the decomposition of a diazo-compound which is in complete solution follows the ordinary law for a unimolecular reaction, namely :—

$$K = \frac{1}{t} \log \frac{A}{A - x}.$$

The products of the decomposition do not interfere with the reaction except in the naphthalene series, where the naphthols which are formed remove the diazo-compound by coupling when they have reached a certain concentration. The tetrazo-compounds of the diphenyl series do not strictly obey the unimolecular law.

Knowledge of the relation between K, the velocity constant, and temperature is due to Cain and Nichol,[13] who found the relation to follow the Arrhenius expression for an irreversible reaction

$$K_{t_1} = K_{t_0} e^{A \cdot \frac{T_1 - T_0}{T_1 T_0}}$$

where A is a constant and T_1 and T_0 are the absolute temperatures corresponding to K_{t_1} and K_{t_0}. Euler checked experimentally the calculated values of Cain and Nichol, finding good agreement. The work which has been done in recent years by the Japanese school has further confirmed all the above findings.[14]

The diazo-salts are highly ionised in solution, and the diazo-ions steadily break down according to the unimolecular law at any particular temperature irrespective of the anion, so long as it be that of a strong mineral acid such as hydrochloric, hydrobromic, sulphuric, or nitric acids.[15] The main equation for the decomposition is therefore :—

$$[Ar \cdot N_2]^+ X^- + H_2O = Ar \cdot OH + H^+ X^- + N_2$$

from which it follows that the acid concentration increases during the progress of the reaction, and measurement of this acid was actually attempted by Euler as a means of following the process, but the results were manifestly unreliable. The reaction is not affected by the amount of free mineral acid present, except that Cain found that it falls when much sulphuric acid is present.[16] Nor does it matter whether the solution is agitated or allowed to remain still, the rate of decomposition is unaltered.[17]

Blumberger showed why both Euler's and Cain's results are to be expected. He pointed out that the equation given above is not the only one possible and that other reactions may proceed :— [18]

1. $Ar \cdot N_2 \cdot Cl \longrightarrow Ar \cdot Cl + N_2$
2. $Ph \cdot N_2^+ + HCl \longrightarrow Ph \cdot Cl + N_2 + H^+$

No acid is produced in these reactions, and hence Euler's failure to use the acid produced in the decomposition as a measure of the total decomposition. Further, a solution of a diazo-sulphate may contain ions of $[Ar \cdot N_2 \cdot SO_4]^-$ which may well decompose more slowly than the ion $[Ar \cdot N_2]^+$. Blumberger found support for this view in that by adding chlorides to weakly acid solutions of diazobenzene chloride he was able to increase the yield of monochlorobenzene.

Both Hantzsch and Cain showed experimentally that concentration does not affect the rate of decomposition, and though Hantzsch supposed Schwalbe, who held the opposite view, to be in error, fresh evidence has recently been brought forward by Snow to show that in concentrated solutions the rate of decomposition does fall somewhat.

Substituents in the benzene ring have a marked effect on the stability of diazo-compounds, so that there is an enormous difference between the most stable and the least stable compounds known. It is, however, impossible to foretell what stability any given diazo-compound will possess beyond the general rules already mentioned on p. 63. Agreement has also been lacking as to the exact order of stability in which the various diazo-compounds fall, and Cain in his book gives a table of comparison of five sets of results.[19] A more complete list which combines the individuals given in the various columns of Cain's table has been published by Snow, who measured the rate of decomposition of the diazo-chlorides at 20°. In the following list the amines are arranged in descending order of the stability of the diazo-chlorides :— [20]

p-Chloroaniline.
m-Nitroaniline.
m-4-Nitroxylidine.
o-Nitroaniline.
o-Anisidine.
p-Nitroaniline.
p-Bromoaniline.
o-Phenetidine.
p-Iodoaniline.

5-Aminosalicylic acid.
p-Toluidine.
Aminoazobenzene.
p-Aminophenol.
p-Phenylenediamine (diazotised).
Picramic acid.
Sulphanilic acid.
p-Aminobenzoic acid.
α-Naphthylamine.

p-Anisidine.

β-Naphthylamine.

m-4-Xylidine.

Anthranilic acid.

Aminoazotoluene.

m-Aminobenzoic acid.

o-4-Xylidine.

o-3-Xylidine.

Aniline.

o-Toluidine.

m-Toluidine.

m-Anisidine.

p-Xylidine.

p-Phenylenediamine (tetrazotised).

While variation of the acid radical has but little effect on the stability of solutions of diazo-compounds, other substances can be added which have a considerable effect. Certain metallic salts which form double salts with diazo-compounds and also sulphonic acids have the effect of slowing up decomposition, and these two groups, being of technical importance, are treated under the heading of stabilised diazo-compounds (see pp. 34 and 39). Neutral metallic salts can in some cases cause slowing down of decomposition, while in other cases the effect is nil.[21] Schwalbe found the rate of decomposition of p-nitro-diazobenzene to be halved by the addition of salt at the rate of 90 g. per litre, and Hantzsch and Thompson found a 40% decrease in the rate for the same diazo-compound by increasing salt from 6 to 12 g. per litre. Viktoreff has stated that for salts having the same anion as the p-nitrodiazobenzene, decomposition is speediest for the most basic cation.[22] Knecht and Platt found evidence that the traces of nitrate with which all technical sodium nitrite is contaminated has a deleterious effect on diazo-compounds, and they added small quantities of reducing agents such as metabisulphite to diazo-solutions in order to remove nitrate,[23] and Viktoreff has confirmed that metabisulphite and bisulphite, but not hydrosulphite, retard decomposition during the first few hours.

That excess of nitrous acid is harmful to the stability of diazo-solutions was discovered by both Schwalbe and Hantzsch. The latter showed that the decomposition is at first accelerated, but returns to the normal rate when the nitrous acid has been used up. When ferrous ions are present—as, for instance, in technical diazotisation where iron may come in contact with the acid diazo-solution—excess nitrous acid has the opposite effect, being used to oxidise the ferrous to ferric ions, for whereas the former cause rapid decomposition, the latter are harmless. The following table shows how great this effect is with o-chlorodiazobenzene :— [24]

Original content of base in solution, 0·925 g. per litre.

	1 Hr.	Loss.	2 Hrs.	Loss.	3 Hrs.	Loss.
Without HNO_2.	0·508	45%	0·214	77%	0·0	100%
With HNO_2.	0·853	8%	0·877	13%	0·71	23%

Colloidal metals bring about very rapid destruction of diazo-compounds in solution. Euler found that 0·0002 g. of colloidal platinum per litre raises the speed of decomposition of diazobenzene six-fold. Colloidal organic substances, provided they do not react with nitrous acid or diazo-compounds, have no effect. In experiments, also with diazobenzene chloride, Pray added gelatin, dextrin, starch, agar, and egg-albumin, and found no change in either the velocity of decomposition or the rate of evolution of nitrogen.[25] Copper acts catalytically in bringing about the decomposition and condensation of diazo-compounds (see p. 147), especially in the cuprous form, but the action of cupric salts in forming complexes, and so accelerating the decomposition of diazobenzene as well as the action of copper sulphide, has been recorded by Blumberger.[26]

It must be emphasised that all the preceding remarks apply to solutions of diazo-compounds sufficiently acid at the start to give a positive reaction on Congo paper, i.e. a p_H value of 3·5 or less, while acidity increases as the decomposition proceeds. Moreover, the measurements were nearly all made before the technique of employing buffers had reached its present-day level of accuracy, and the determination of the p_H value by the simple and speedy glass electrode was unknown. Both Cain[27] and Hantzsch found that adding the salt of an organic acid to the diazo-solution did not alter the rate of decomposition until all acidity to Congo paper had disappeared, but on adding excess sodium acetate changes occur. Thus diazobenzene acetate retains the same rate of decomposition as diazobenzene chloride, but p-nitrodiazobenzene chloride undergoes a ten-fold increase in the velocity constant. If bicarbonate is used instead of acetate, a rapid initial decomposition eventually gives place to a state where the unimolecular reaction sets in.[28] The following figures for the amount of decomposition against acidity are taken from the tables in the paper by Marriott on the stabilising effect of arylsulphonic acids (see p. 42), and show clearly how important is the matter of accurate control of acidity if comparable results are to be obtained.

TABLE XIV

Relation of Acidity to Decomposition of Diazo-Compounds

5-Chloro-o-toluidine.			4-Chloro-o-toluidine.			p-Nitroaniline.			m-Nitro-p-toluidine.		
p_H.	Percentage Decomposition.		p_H.	Percentage Decomposition.		p_H.	Percentage Decomposition.		p_H.	Percentage Decomposition.	
	127 hrs.	240 hrs.		21 hrs.	43 hrs.		30 hrs.	47 hrs.		18 hrs.	21 hrs.
7·5	96	—	8·3	62	—	6·5	64	—	5·8	74	—
6·5	—	85	7·2	62	—	5·6	—	80·5	5·1	—	34
5·1	—	40	6·0	—	64	3·0	—	4·0	3·5	—	0·0
3·6	13	—	2·0	—	44	—	—	—	—	—	—
2·6	—	5	—	—	—	—	—	—	—	—	—

Of recent years some investigations have been carried out to the fully alkaline side of the neutral point. Although a consideration of this area properly belongs to the metallic diazotates, yet dismemberment of the problem of stability would make so much useless repetition that it will be dealt with here in its entirety.

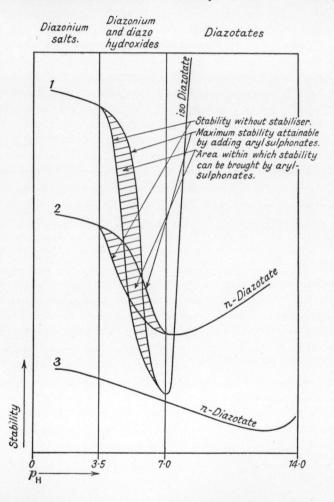

The tautomeric forms into which diazo-compounds pass when treated with alkali complicate the problem of examining stability, because of the uncertainty as to what are actually the active substances under any given conditions. Obscurity is also caused because the diazo-compounds may couple with the phenols produced, and because condensation reactions occur in alkaline solution.[29] Sufficient data have, however, been published to obtain an outline of the facts, though their presentation in diverse forms makes comparison difficult. In the case of α-diazonaphthalene chloride, Yamamoto has shown that treatment with acetate increases the decomposition velocity 3·5 times, sodium carbonate 800 times, and caustic soda still further.[30]   Jolles and Camiglieri examined the normal diazotates derived from aniline, o-, m-, and p-toluidine, p-anisidine, o- and p-phenetidine, and α-naphthylamine, and concluded that for diazotates the rules for the effects of substituents are the reverse of those which apply to diazo-salts and that alkoxygroups in the o- and p-positions increase the rate of decomposition of the diazotates.[31]   Without doubt the degree of alkalinity affects the rate of decomposition, while nearly all workers report decomposition as initially rapid and later slowing down to a more steady state.[32]   Blumberger actually showed by plotting alkalinity against decomposition rate that there is a maximum speed of decomposition for diazobenzene at p_H 12·7, and suggested that at greater concentrations of alkali the more stable isodiazotate ions are in the majority.[33]

There is, indeed, only one all-embracing way of reducing to order all that has been said of the stability of diazo-compounds, and that is graphic representation as a function of stability versus p_H value. Stability may be measured by arbitrary units such as rate of evolution of nitrogen or time of half-life period of the diazo-compound at any selected temperature. If this is done the result will be a diagram having the general outlines shown on p. 72, though it must not be surprising if, when more information is available, some diazo-compounds show curves of different shape from these curves, which are necessarily speculative to some degree.

The first point to be noted on the above diagram is that the classical determinations of stability were made in the area between the stability ordinate and p_H 3·5. Possibly some curves cross in this area, and so account for the discrepancies in the order of stability assigned by different experimenters.

To sum up, diazo-compounds can be roughly divided into three types as far as stability is concerned. There is the negatively substituted type in which formation of the isodiazotate is so facile that the normal metallic diazotate is unknown. p-Nitroaniline is the representative of this type which follows curve 1, and in which stability falls sharply to a low value as neutrality is approached, but high stability is regained once the alkaline side is reached. Secondly, there is the type of curve 2, of good stability both acid and near the neutral point, but not greatly increasing in stability on the alkaline side, since cold alkali produces the normal metallic diazotate only. 5-Chloro-o-toluidine is a representative of this type. Lastly, there is the type of diazobenzene itself following curve 3, having at all times low stability little reduced either by conversion to the salt of a weak acid or on the alkaline side, but gradually improving somewhat as the highest concentrations of alkali are reached. The flatness of curve 3 shows why the stabilising effect of arylsulphonates is virtually undetectable in diazo-compounds of low initial stability.

In spite of all that has been done, much yet remains to be learned of the stability of the diazo-compounds. The task awaits some investigator of determining the exact boundaries of the area of stabilisation in some particular cases, and no curve of stability for *iso*diazotates can be drawn except at a guess, because data on the subject are completely lacking.

REFERENCES

[1] Knoevenagel, *Ber.*, 1890, **23**, 2994. Bamberger, *ibid.*, 1895, **28**, 538. Hantzsch, *ibid.*, 1897, **30**, 2342 footnote.
[2] Wichelhaus, *ibid.*, 1901, **34**, 11. Cain, p. 34.
[3] Griess, Caro, E.P. 1956/66; F.P. 73,286.
[4] Seidler, D.R.P. 46,205 (Fr., **2**, 556).
[5] Burns, U.S.P. 1,862,295. Kaiser, U.S.P. 1,852,054. Dehn, U.S.P. 1,428,011. Howles, E.P. 125,600. Herz, D.R.P. 373,426.
[6] Clark, *Ind. Eng. Chem.*, 1933, **25**, 663.
[7] Oddo, *Gazz.*, 1895, **25**, i, 327; 1896, **26**, ii, 541.
[8] Hirsch, *Ber.*, 1891, **24**, 324.
[9] Hantzsch, *ibid.*, 1900, **33**, 2517. Hantzsch, Thompson, *ibid.*, 1908, **41**, 3519.
[10] Hausser, Muller, *Bull. Soc. chim.*, 1892, iii, **7**, 721; 1893, iii, **9**, 353; *Compt. rend.*, 1892, **114**, 549, 669, 760, 1438.
[11] Euler, *Ann.*, 1902, **325**, 292.
[12] Cain, Nichol, *J.C.S.*, 1902, **81**, 1412; 1903, **83**, 206.
[13] Cain, Nichol, *ibid.*, 1903, **83**, 470.
[14] Yamamoto, *J. Soc. Chem. Ind. Japan*, 1929, **32**, 308 (A., **1930**, 333); 1930, **33**, 231 (A., **1930**, 1128); 1930, **33**, 358 (A., **1930**, 1529); 1932, **35**, 11 (A., **1932**, 345); 1932, **35**, 564 (A., **1933**, 233); 1932, **35**, 59 (A., **1933**, 470). Yamamoto, Hashima, Goshima, *ibid.*, 1932, **35**, 490 (A., **1933**, 1250).
[15] Hantzsch, Thompson, *Ber.*, 1908, **41**, 3510. See also Schwalbe, *ibid.*, 1905, **38**, 2196, 3071.
[16] Cain, *ibid.*, 1905, **38**, 2511.
[17] Euler, *Ann.*, 1902, **325**, 292. See also Cain, Nichol, *Proc.*, **1908**, 282; Lamplough, *ibid.*, **1906**, 280; **1909**, 23.
[18] Blumberger, *Rec. trav. chim.*, 1930, **49**, 259.
[19] Cain, p. 44.
[20] Snow, *Ind. Eng. Chem.*, 1932, **24**, 1420.
[21] Euler, *Ann.*, 1902, **325**, 292. Schwalbe, *Ber.*, 1905, **38**, 2196. Hantzsch, Thompson, *ibid.*, 1908, **41**, 3510.
[22] Viktoreff, *J. appl. Chem., Russ.*, 1931, **4**, 777; A., **1932**, 841.
[23] Knecht, Platt, *J.S.D.C.*, 1925, **44**, 275.
[24] I.G., E.P. 326,866; D.R.P. 496,823 (Fr., **17**, 1066); F.P. 666,140.
[25] Pray, *J. Physical Chem.*, 1926, **30**, 1417.
[26] Blumberger, *Rec. trav. chim.*, 1930, **49**, 257, 267.
[27] Cain, *Ber.*, 1905, **38**, 2511.
[28] Yamamoto, *J. Soc. Chem. Ind. Japan*, 1929, **32**, 352; A., **1930**, 426.
[29] Jolles, Camiglieri, *Atti Cong. Naz. Chim.*, 1933, **4**, 491.
[30] Yamamoto, *J. Soc. Chem. Ind. Japan*, 1934, **37**, 687B; A., **1935**, 173.
[31] Jolles, Camiglieri, *Gazz.*, 1932, **62**, 720.
[32] Oddo, Indovina, *ibid.*, p. 1119.
[33] Blumberger, *Rec. trav. chim.*, 1930, **49**, 276.

THE ANALYTICAL DETERMINATION OF DIAZO-COMPOUNDS

Quantitative Determination.—The methods available for the quantitative determination of diazo-compounds are as follows :—

1. By the nitrometer.
2. By titration with reducing agents.
3. By titration with coupling components.

1. *The Nitrometer Method.*—This is the method which all investigators except Hirsch and Schwalbe used for the determination of the speed of decomposition of diazo-compounds in acid solution. Wherever conditions permit, treatment of the diazo-compound by heat so that it gives off all its nitrogen is the first method to consider, for its ease of manipulation and directness make it very convenient. It is, of course, useless where side-reactions prevent complete evolution of nitrogen as, for example, under alkaline conditions when coupling and resinification occur. It is sometimes useful when the problem is to determine a monamine which is a constituent of a mixture of substances.

Diazo-compounds which are slow couplers, and therefore not susceptible to determination by titration, can sometimes be rapidly determined by the nitrometer if means of accelerating their decomposition can be found. Thus the industrially important 1-diazo-2-hydroxynaphthalene-4-sulphonic acid is accurately and quickly determined by treating with sodium arsenite when its nitrogen is immediately evolved quantitatively.[1] The nitrometer has also been used to determine the rate of decomposition of diazo-compounds under the action of light.[2]

2. *Titration with Reducing Agents.*—This method is due to Knecht, and is an application of his researches with titanous chloride as a reducing agent in volumetric analysis.[3] Titration is carried out in cold acid solution using H-acid as an external indicator to show the end-point of the complete reduction of the diazo-compound. Only two equivalents of reducing agent are necessary, because the diazo-compound reacts with the hydrazine produced :—

$$2PhN_2Cl + 4TiCl_3 + 2HCl = Ph \cdot N{:}N \cdot NPh \cdot NH_2 + 4TiCl_4$$

Sodium hydrosulphite can also be used as the reducing agent with Acid Green as an internal indicator, and here the reduction goes completely to the hydrazine :—

$$PhN_2Cl + 2Na_2S_2O_4 + 4H_2O = Ph \cdot NHNH_2 \cdot HCl + 4NaHSO_3$$

The reduction method cannot be used indiscriminately with diazo-compounds containing other reducible groups beside the diazo-group— for example, the large class of nitro-diazo-compounds. Knecht, however, showed that sodium *p*-nitrobenzene *iso*diazotate (" Nitrosamine

Red," see p. 87) could be accurately titrated with alkaline hydro-sulphite using Safranine or Rosinduline as internal indicator. The diazo-group is reduced before the indicator and the indicator before the nitro-group :—

$$NO_2 \cdot C_6H_4 \cdot N_2ONa + 2Na_2S_2O_4 + 3NaOH = NO_2 \cdot C_6H_4 \cdot NHNH_2 + 4Na_2SO_3$$

Titanous chloride brings about complete reduction of " Nitrosamine Red " to p-phenylenediamine and ammonia :—

$$NO_2 \cdot C_6H_4 \cdot N_2ONa + 2H_2 \longrightarrow NO_2 \cdot C_6H_4 \cdot NHNH_2 + 4H_2 \longrightarrow C_6H_4(NH_2)_2 + NH_3$$

3. *Titration with Coupling Components.*—Titration with coupling components may be regarded as a supplement to the nitrometer method for use in cases where the reaction solution is alkaline or acid with organic acids. In such solutions diazo-compounds couple quickly and completely. To obtain accurate and consistent results requires some practice, which may be the reason why it has been alleged that the method is not accurate. In skilled hands it is quite as accurate as the nitrometer, and for industrial purposes is largely used.

The method was used by Hirsch and by Schwalbe in their work on the stability of diazo-compounds when they applied the method to titrate the residual diazo-compound after decomposition had proceeded for a determined period. The accuracy obtainable depends on a number of factors, including a standardised end-point against fresh H-acid solution and the choice of the correct coupling component. Hirsch used Schäffer acid to combine with the diazo-compound; Schwalbe used β-naphthol. The disadvantage of β-naphthol is that it yields insoluble azo-compounds with diazo-compounds not containing solubilising groups, and inaccurate results may be obtained because uncombined naphthol is occluded in the grains of precipitated azo-compound. Rostovtseva has given full details for preventing this by the use of protective colloids, particularly gum arabic or gelatin, which prevents the precipitation of the insoluble azo-compound.[4] To-day phenylmethyl-pyrazolonesulphonic acid is much used, the coupling being carried out in acetic acid solution. Unlike β-naphthol, the sparingly soluble azo-compound does not occlude the unused coupling component, while it is more convenient than R-salt and gives a sharper end-point.[5] The determination is carried out by adding an aliquot portion of the diazo-solution to excess of a standard solution of the coupling component mixed with sodium acetate solution. Coupling at once proceeds to completion, after which the precipitation of the azo-compound is completed by salt and the excess of coupling component back-titrated with a standard diazo-solution, usually $N/20$ p-nitrodiazobenzene.

Lastly, in some cases the coupling method can be used differentially to determine the proportion either of two different primary amines in a mixture or of primary amines in admixture with other amines. Thus, if aniline is mixed with the nitroanilines its amount can be determined by diazotising the mixture, making alkaline with caustic soda and titrating with $N/20$ β-naphthol when only the diazobenzene couples.[6] Naturally if concordant results are to be obtained, standardised conditions must be observed, particularly in the matter of alkalinity, as too little alkali will not entirely inhibit the coupling of the nitro-diazobenzenes, while too much will commence destruction of the diazobenzene.

If mixed with monomethylaniline, aniline can be diazotised and its amount determined by titration,[7] but each case where it is proposed to use this method requires examination on its own merits.

Equally useful is the converse of the above method—namely, the use of standardised diazo-solutions to determine the purity of substances which will couple, such as m-diamines, naphthols, amino-naphthols, and their sulphonic acids.[8]

Qualitative Determination.—The coupling reaction is probably the readiest means of showing the presence of a diazo-compound, and many can be identified in this way because the melting points of their azo-compounds with β-naphthol have been recorded.

Occasionally, however, it is necessary to ascertain which of the tautomeric forms is in hand, and the following specific tests have been published. Diazonium salts are present in an acid solution when the fluorescence developed on adding resorufin dissolved in sodium carbonate does not persist on making the entire solution alkaline.[9]

Nitrohydroxylamine is a reagent which will distinguish between normal and *iso*diazotate. With the latter it does not react, but with the former it gives a temporary violet-blue colour.[10] The sodium stannite reagent of Hantzsch and Vock (see p. 146) depends on the fact that it at once reduces normal diazotate with evolution of nitrogen, whereas the *iso*diazotate remains unattacked. Bigiavi has also applied the coupling reaction which *iso*diazotates undergo when exposed to the air to their detection in small amount. Acetic acid followed by R-salt or β-naphthol is added to the solution to be tested, in which filter-paper is then dipped. If *iso*diazotate is present, a red stain develops on exposure to air.[11]

REFERENCES

[1] Ostroshinskaja, *Anilinokras. Prom.*, 1934, **4**, 368.
[2] Schmidt, Maier, *Ber.*, 1931, **64**, 778.
[3] Knecht, Thompson, *J.S.D.C.*, 1920, **36**, 215.
[4] Rostovtseva, *Anilinokras. Prom.*, 1933, **3**, 308; A., **1934**, 199.
[5] Compare Vaubel, *Chem. Zeit.*, 1893, **17**, 465.
[6] Terentiev, Schschetinina, *Anilinokras. Prom.*, 1934, **4**, 359; B., **1934**, 1002.
    See also Skvirskaya, *Org. Chem. Ind.*, *U.S.S.R.*, **1936**, 163; *Chem. Abs.*,
    1936, **30**, 5150. Determination of *o*- and *p*-isomers in *m*-nitroaniline.
[7] Reverdin, de la Harpe, *Ber.*, 1889, **22**, 1004.

[8] Bucherer, *Zeit. angew. Chem.*, 1907, **20**, 877. Schwalbe, *ibid.*, 1098. Ueno, Sekiguchi, *J. Soc. Chem. Ind. Japan*, 1935, **33**, 142B.
[9] Eichler, *Z. anal. Chem.*, 1934, **99**, 348; *Analyst*, 1935, **60**, 190.
[10] Bigiavi, *Ber.*, 1929, **62**, 2101.
[11] Bigiavi, Albanesi, *Gazz.*, 1935, **65**, 773.

THERMOCHEMISTRY OF THE DIAZO-COMPOUNDS

Berthelot and Vieille [1] first studied the thermochemistry of the diazo-compounds and showed that they are endothermic. The heat of formation of solid diazobenzene nitrate from its elements was found to be -47.4 kg.-cal., and though no similar determinations have been made for other diazo-compounds it is probable that nearly all diazo-compounds of the benzene series are endothermic. It will be recalled that aniline itself has a negative heat of formation of -17.4 kg.-cal. at constant pressure (Thomsen).

Vignon [2] commenced the study of the thermochemistry of the diazo-compounds in aqueous solution, and pointed out that although heat is given out on diazotisation by the direct method, the heat arises from the formation of water and sodium chloride, the heat of formation of the diazo-compound itself being negative. The determination of the heat effects in the various transformations of the diazo-compounds is a subject which has been studied for many years by Swientoslawski and the Polish school of physical chemists.[3]

No laws have been discovered which permit calculation of the heat effects in specific instances when basic values of certain changes are

TABLE XV

Heat Changes in the Transformations of p-*Chlorodiazobenzene*

	Reaction (Ar = (p)Cl·C_6H_4-).	Heat Change (kg.-cal./mol.).
1.	$ArNH_2+HCl=ArNH_2 \cdot HCl$.	6·49
2.	$ArN \cdot OH + HCl = ArNCl + H_2O$.	11·39
3.	$n\text{-}ArN_2OH + NaOH = ArN_2ONa + H_2O$.	3·95
4.	$iso\text{-}ArN_2OH + NaOH = iso\text{-}ArN_2ONa + H_2O$.	9·44
5.	$ArNH_2 \cdot HCl + NaOH = ArNH_2 + NaCl + H_2O$.	6·71
6.	$ArN \cdot Cl + NaOH = ArNOH + NaCl$.	2·31
7.	$n\text{-}ArN_2ONa + HCl = n\text{-}ArN_2OH + NaCl$.	9·50
8.	$iso\text{-}ArN_2ONa + HCl = iso\text{-}ArN_2OH + NaCl$.	4·26
9.	$ArN \cdot OH = n\text{-}ArN \colon N \cdot OH$.	0·50
10.	$ArN \cdot OH = iso\text{-}ArN \colon N \cdot OH$.	$- 2·39$
11.	$ArNH_2 + HNO_2 = ArN \cdot OH + H_2O$.	16·74
12.	$n\text{-}ArN_2OH + C_{10}H_7OH$ (β) solid $= ArN_2C_{10}H_7 \cdot OH + H_2O$.	31·04

known, in the same way that heats of formation can be calculated from the number of atoms in a molecule and their linkages. As it would be impossible here to compress into sufficiently small space the immense mass of figures which has been published, the reader must be referred to the original papers for detailed information. Wojeiechowski has, however, recently published the figures, as determined by the method of Swientoslawski, for twelve transformation of p-chloroaniline commencing with its diazotisation. These are reproduced in the table on p. 78, because they give an idea of the magnitude of heat changes pertaining to each reaction.[4]

REFERENCES

[1] Berthelot, Vieille, *Compt. rend.*, 1881, **92**, 1076.
[2] Vignon, *ibid.*, 1888, **106**, 1162; *Bull. Soc. chim.*, 1888, ii, **49**, 906.
[3] Swientoslawski, *Ber.*, 1910, **43**, 1479, 1488, 1767; *ibid.*, 1911, **44**, 2429, 2437; *J. Russ. Phys. Chem. Soc.*, 1913, **45**, 1739; A., **1914**, ii, 105. Swientoslawski, Manoszan, *ibid.*, 1913, **45**, 1765. Swientoslawski, *Rocz. Chem.*, 1925, **5**, 214; A., **1925**, ii, 1044. Swientoslawski, Blaszkovska, *Rocz. Chem.*, 1925, **5**, 233. Swientoslawski, *Ber.*, 1929, **62**, 2035.
[4] Wojeiechowski, *Bull. int. Acad. polon. Sci. lettres.*, Ser. A, 1934, 280; *Cent.*, 1935, **106**, ii, 1686. See also Wojeiechowski, *Rocz. Chem.*, 1934, **14**, 739.

CHAPTER V

REACTIONS OF THE DIAZO-COMPOUNDS. CLASS A. DERIVATIVES IN WHICH THE DIAZO-GROUP REMAINS FUNCTIONALLY INTACT

THE reactions of the diazo-compounds fall into three classes according to the nature of the substances produced, and to each class is allotted a chapter in this book. Into the scheme below fit, in their proper places, the various diazo-derivatives which have already been mentioned as passive stabilised diazo-compounds (see p. 30), while at the head of Class B stand the azo-compounds, a group so numerous and important that they require for their treatment a separate and additional chapter.

CLASS A.   Derivatives in which the Diazo-group Remains Functionally Intact

Group 1.   Metallic diazotates.
     2.   Diazo-ethers.
     3.   Diazo-cyanides.
     4.   Diazo-sulphonates.
     5.   Nitrosoacylarylamines.
     6.   Nitration, halogenation, and sulphonation products.
     7.   Diazo-*per*halides.

CLASS B.   Derivatives in which the Diazo-function Disappears, but the Diazo-nitrogen Atoms Remain in the New Molecule.

Group 1.   Azo-compounds.
     2.   Oxidation products.
     3.   Reduction products.
     4.   Diazoamino-compounds or Triazenes.
     5.   Azoimides.
     6.   Azothiophenols and azomercaptans.

CLASS C.   Derivatives Formed by Replacement of the Diazo-group by :—

Group 1.   Hydrogen.
     2.   Aryl radicals.
     3.   Hydroxyl.
     4.   Halogens.

Group 5. Nitrogen-containing radicals : Cyano-, nitro-, and amino-
groups.

6. Sulphur- and selenium-containing radicals.

7. Arsenic and antimony.

8. Metals.

GROUP 1. METALLIC SALTS OF THE DIAZOHYDR-OXIDES ; THE USE OF THE *ISO*DIAZOTATES OR NITROSAMINES AS STABILISED DIAZO-COMPOUNDS

The free base of a diazonium salt cannot be obtained by the action of alkalis, for as soon as it is liberated a tautomeric change occurs, the tautomer being an acidic substance, the diazohydroxide, which forms metallic salts. Griess [1] described the isolation of potassium benzene diazotate, obtained by acting on benzenediazonium salts with an excess of strong caustic potash solution, which salts out the very soluble potassium salt (see p. 83). From the potassium salt he obtained a number of others of smaller solubility by double decomposition. Griess's observation seems to have entirely escaped the attention of other chemists for many years except that Curtius,[2] from the action of heat on the diazotate, concluded that the structure proposed by Griess, $PhN:N \cdot OK$, must be wrong, though the reactions of Griess's diazotate show it at once to be a diazo-compound.

Schraube and Schmidt, chemists on the staff of the B.A.S.F., first showed that when cold caustic alkali acts on *p*-nitrodiazobenzene chloride a similar change to that observed by Griess takes place, except that the diazo-compound passes without any evolution of nitrogen into a stable substance which no longer immediately shows any of the typical reactions of a diazo-compound in alkaline solution.[3, 4] The sodium salt was isolated by them in crystalline form as a reddish-brown powder, and on treatment with methyl iodide afforded a substance identical with the nitrosamine of *N*-monomethyl-*p*-nitroaniline, made by acting on that body with nitrous acid. The series of changes were therefore supposed to be :—

$$NO_2 \cdot C_6H_4 \cdot N_2 \cdot Cl \xrightarrow{NaOH} (NO_2 \cdot C_6H_4 \cdot N{=}N \cdot ONa) \longrightarrow$$
$$NO_2 \cdot C_6H_4 \cdot NNa \cdot NO \xrightarrow{MeI} NO_2 \cdot C_6H_4 \cdot N {<}^{Me}_{NO}$$

The nitrosamine melts at $100°$. The compound in brackets above represents a labile form supposedly first produced by the action of the alkali, but which has never been isolated.

v. Pechmann and Bamberger had both already independently realised that the diazo-compounds are tautomeric, and the idea was current that one tautomer had the constitution of a nitrosamine because coupling products had been obtained which were undoubtedly hydrazones.

G

The intense exploration of the diazo-field was just reaching its height, and further facts bearing on the subject were soon forthcoming. Bamberger had been studying the alkaline oxidation of the α- and β-diazonaphthalenes, and had observed among the products derived from β-diazonaphthalene a nitrogen-containing substance unable to couple with naphthols but able to do so after treatment with acid. β-Diazonaphthalene afforded a similar substance after treatment with caustic alkali alone.[5] Bamberger called these substances " isodiazo "-compounds, although recognising the possible nitrosamine structure.

v. Pechmann and Frobenius also had Schraube and Schmidt's nitrosamine in hand, but had converted it into the silver salt. This salt, however, when treated with methyl iodide, did not give the nitrosamine of N-methyl-p-nitroaniline, but the ether of p-nitrodiazobenzene :—

$$NO_2 \cdot C_6H_4 \cdot N{=}N \cdot OMe, \text{ nearly colourless needles, m. p. } 83°.[6]$$

The ether shows the reactions of a diazo-compound, being decomposed by boiling with weak acid, giving a diazoamino-compound with aniline and coupling with phenol. v. Pechmann and Frobenius pointed out that the difference in behaviour of the alkali metal salt and the silver salt is typical of tautomeric substances in general, such as hydrocyanic acid, pyridone, and carbostyril. In this case the tautomers which give rise to the silver and sodium salts respectively are :—

$$NO_2 \cdot C_6H_4 \cdot N{=}N \cdot OH \rightleftharpoons NO_2 \cdot C_6H_4 \cdot NH \cdot NO$$

The chemists of the B.A.S.F. made a thorough study of the reaction by which the substances which they called nitrosamines could be made, and showed it to be widespread among benzenoid compounds, including those derived from diamines.[7, 8] Where strong negative groups are present in the nucleus, particularly ortho- or para- to the diazo-group, the nitrosamine is formed easily by comparatively weak alkali in the cold, even by mild alkali in the case of 2 : 5-dichlorodiazobenzene.[9] When negative groups are not present or have been replaced by alkoxygroups, then more and more drastic treatment is required to form the nitrosamine, and to attain complete conversion even 60% caustic potash at temperatures up to 140° may become necessary. In one patented variation of the process solid caustic alkali was added to the diazo-solution, which was then heated.[10]

Schraube and Schmidt found an important difference between those diazo-compounds which are easily converted to nitrosamines without any isolable intermediary and those which require strong alkali with heating; in the latter case two distinct series of salts can be isolated. The less stable salt is obtained by the action of alkali in the cold, shows the reactions of a diazo-compound and is evidently the substance which

was handled by Griess and Curtius. The more stable salt is the nitrosamine discovered by themselves, and therefore shows the diazo-reactions
imperfectly or not at all. Evidently where negative substituents are
present in the aromatic nucleus the less stable salt cannot exist, but at
once passes over to the stable salt or nitrosamine with which it is
isomeric. Positive substituents, on the other hand, increase the stability
of the unstable salt, so that its conversion to the stable isomer becomes
increasingly difficult. Bamberger considered that heat alone brings
about the conversion, and that the function of the high concentration
of caustic alkali is to raise the boiling point of the solution to the
necessary temperature and protect the diazo-compound from damage
by oxidation.[11] As it will be shown that the reactions of the nitrosamines are influenced to a considerable degree by alkali concentration,
Bamberger's view probably represents only a part of the truth. The
upshot of the matter is therefore that the diazo-compounds in general
are able to form two series of isomeric metallic salts, the one stable, the
other unstable. The question of the constitution of these two series is
discussed in the last chapter of this book, and the concern at this point
is to describe their preparation and behaviour.

A word must be said here about nomenclature, as more than one
name is in use for either series.

The unstable salts prepared by the action of cold alkali have been
called the " labile," " normal," or " *syn* "-series, the latter name con-
noting the theoretical view of Hantzsch.

The stable salts have been called " stable," " *iso-*," or " *anti-*," the
latter again being due to Hantzsch, while among chemists engaged in
industry, who have for the most part remained loyal to the original
views of Schraube and Schmidt, they are still called " nitrosamines."

In this book the terms " normal " and " *iso-* " will be used as far
as possible, because such terminology is both in accordance with sound
chemical usage, and likewise non-committal in respect of any particular
theoretical view as to their structure.

That some well-marked difference exists between the normal and
*iso*diazotates can be appreciated by comparing the processes used to
prepare the two type-isomers—the benzene normal diazotate and
benzene *iso*diazotate.

Normal Potassium Benzene Diazotate.

10 c.c. of a 15% solution of diazobenzene chloride is allowed to drop with
stirring into a mixture of 150 g. of caustic potash and 60 g. of water at − 5°.
The temperature is then allowed to rise to 15—20°, so that all the potash dissolves,
and the crystals which separate are collected. The crude salt so obtained can be
converted to snow-white silky needles when 1 g. of the substance is dissolved in
3 c.c. of absolute alcohol at − 5° and precipitated with eight to ten volumes of
ether. The salt is hygroscopic and soon becomes coloured pink. The same
procedure can be followed with other normal diazotates.[12]

Potassium Benzene iso*Diazotate.*

A 15% diazobenzene chloride solution is run at 0° into 1·5 times its volume of 75% caustic potash. The undissolved alkali dissolves, and the whole is heated in a silver vessel as quickly as possible to 140°, which for a 60—70 g. charge should take three minutes. At this temperature boiling suddenly stops and the solution thickens, heating being continued at 140°. On cooling to 100° the melt is diluted with one half to an equal volume of boiling water, and on cooling further the salt crystallises in yellowish leaflets. It is collected, freed from mother-liquor by pressing, dissolved in alcohol at 40—50°, filtered, and precipitated in silvery leaflets by adding double the volume of ether. Treated with methyl iodide it affords the nitrosamine of monomethylaniline, which itself yields methylaniline on removal of the nitroso-group.[13]

Wojciechowski has recently described in detail the preparation of potassium *p*-chlorobenzene-*iso*diazotate by the above method. He was unable to obtain the salt entirely free from caustic alkali.[14]

A recent patent states that yields of *iso*diazotates are improved if the diazo-solution is first made weakly alkaline while cold and then run in a thin stream into a sufficiency of strong caustic alkali at or above the temperature of conversion. For each diazo-compound the conversion temperature is sharply marked, and this procedure avoids losses due to decomposition while heating up the bulk of the cold liquid. The preparation of the *iso*diazotate of 5-chloro-*o*-toluidine is described as follows :—

75 parts of 5-chloro-*o*-toluidine are diazotised in concentrated solution, made alkaline, and then allowed to run with stirring into a solution of 400 parts of caustic potash in 200 parts of water at 115°. The potassium salt of the nitrosamine is obtained as small light-reddish prisms in excellent yield and having the formula :— [15]

While treatment of diazonium salts with concentrated alkali is the only means which comes into consideration for the technical manufacture of diazotates, they can be obtained by other reactions.

Normal diazotates are produced by the hydrolysis of nitrosoacetanilide with caustic potash;[16] by the union of nitrosobenzene and hydroxylamine :— [17]

$$Ph \cdot NO + H_2NOH \longrightarrow Ph \cdot N{:}N \cdot OH + H_2O$$

Diazotates are also formed from arylhydroxylamines and benzene sulphhydroxamic acid and similar substances in alkaline solution, a reaction discovered by Angeli and considered by him to be due initially to the formation of "nitroxyl," NOH, which can act in either of two ways :— [18]

$$\text{(i) } Ar \cdot NHOH + HNO \longrightarrow Ar \cdot N{:}N \cdot OH + H_2O$$

$$\text{(ii) } Ar \cdot NH \atop \overset{\cdot\cdot}{O}H + ONH \longrightarrow {Ar \cdot N{:}NH \atop \overset{\cdot\cdot}{O}} + H_2O$$

and from nitro-compounds and alkali amides, in very small yield :— [19]

$$Ar \cdot NO_2 + H_2N \cdot Na \longrightarrow Ar \cdot N{:}N \cdot ONa + H_2O$$

Bamberger obtained *iso*diazotates by the reduction of nitroso-hydroxylamine :—

$$Ar \cdot N \!\!\begin{array}{l} \diagup NO \\ \diagdown OH \end{array} \longrightarrow Ar \cdot N{:}N \cdot OH + H_2O \ [20]$$

while Thiele has described a laboratory method for making sodium benzene*iso*diazotate based on the action of two molecules of alkyl nitrite on phenylhydrazine in the presence of sodium ethoxide.   He assumed that the compound $\begin{array}{l}PhN{-\!\!-\!\!-}N \cdot NO\\ \ \ NO \ \ H\end{array}$ is formed as an intermediate, and in one of its tautomeric forms liberates a molecule of nitrous acid and gives the *iso*diazotate.   The reaction is carried out as follows :—

Phenylhydrazine (5 c.c.) is dissolved in 4N-sodium methoxide (12·5 c.c.) and ether (50 c.c.).   The solution is cooled externally by ice, and ethyl nitrite (8·5 c.c.) added.   Nitrous oxide is then given off, and the desired sodium salt crystallises out of the solution, is collected, and washed with ether.   It is completely white and pure.   Thiele characterised it as the *iso*diazotate, because this salt gives a brown precipitate with ferric chloride, a blackish-violet one with copper sulphate, and a white one with mercuric nitrate.[21]

Bamberger obtained the potassium salt of a diazo-compound by dropping N-methylphenylnitrosamine on fused potash, though he believed the process to be more complex than the mere replacement of the N-methyl group by potassium.[22]

Metallic diazotates cannot be obtained from diazo-compounds having an hydroxyl group *ortho* to the diazo-group or a group which can be displaced for hydroxyl under the influence of alkali.   In place of the expected *iso*diazotates the compounds formed are the stable internal diazo-oxides, also known as quinone diazides on the supposition that they possess a quinonoid structure (see p. 181).

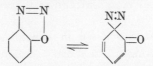

Methyl groups *ortho* to the diazo-group may also prevent formation of *iso*diazotates, as ring-closure to indazoles results from the action of alkali :—

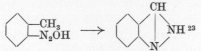

There are but few specific reactions by which the normal or *iso*-diazotates may be differentiated, and they usually behave in the same way, but reaction proceeds at markedly different rates.   When isolated, the normal diazotates usually have water of crystallisation, whereas the corresponding *iso*diazotates crystallise with less water or none. Probably the most-used means of distinguishing between the normal and *iso*diazotates is by their reaction with β-naphthol or one of its congeners in alkaline solution. The normal diazotates couple at once, and if the azo-compound is filtered off, the filtrate remains clear. The *iso*diazo-salts, on the other hand, do not give a precipitate immediately, but the azo-compound is formed slowly, and if after an hour or two the solution is filtered, the formation of the azo-compound will continue in the filtrate. Twenty-four hours or more may elapse before coupling is complete at room temperature. The greater the concentration of the caustic alkali the longer does the coupling take, but if a drop of the original solution of the *iso*diazotate and naphthol is spotted on filter-paper and exposed to the air or steamed, the colour will form to completion of the reaction in a short time. Their sensitiveness to the concentration of caustic alkali is always an important point to bear in mind when dealing with *iso*diazotates, and moreover the solvent used is not without effect, for Orton found that in alcoholic solution Schraube and Schmidt's nitrosamine salt coupled at once with β-naphthol.

Hantzsch and Vock distinguished between normal and *iso*diazotates by the action of sodium stannite, which reduces the normal diazotate to the hydrocarbon, but does not attack the *iso*diazotate.[24]

Naturally many attempts have been made to isolate the free acidic substances from which the metallic salts are derived. Liberation, with the exact equivalent of mineral acid, of organic acid or by carbon dioxide in inert solvents have all been tried, but the products are without exception exceedingly unstable, and it is doubtful if any have ever been obtained analytically pure. The work done by Hantzsch and his school aimed at elucidation of the constitution of the *iso*diazotates, and is discussed in the last chapter, but Bamberger discovered a new group of substances in his attempts to prepare the free normal hydroxides.

When the *iso*diazotates are acted on by acids the expected hydroxide is liberated, and though its life is short—amounting only to minutes—yet during this time the *iso*diazotate can be reformed by the action of alkali. Such as have been examined have been found to be colourless solids with the exception of *o*- and *p*-nitro*iso*diazobenzene hydroxides, which are yellow, and *iso*diazobenzene hydroxide, which is a colourless, very unstable oil.

The action of acids on the normal diazotates does not lead to the liberation of an hydroxide, but to substances which Bamberger called diazo-anhydrides and Hantzsch diazo-oxides.[25] These substances bear, in fact, the same relationship to the diazo-hydroxides that the ethers bear to the alcohols. In place of the expected reaction :—

$$Ar\cdot N{=\!=}N\cdot OM + AcOH = Ar\cdot N{=\!=}N\cdot OH + AcOM$$

which Bamberger had sought to bring about, the reaction actually took place according to the equation :—

$$2(\text{Ar·N}{=}\text{N·OM}) + 2\text{AcOH} = (\text{ArN}{=}\text{N})_2\text{O} + 2\text{AcOM} + \text{H}_2\text{O}$$

Bamberger had some controversy with Hantzsch concerning the constitution of these substances, for they can also be formed from a diazonium salt and a diazotate,[26] but Hantzsch's view that they are oxides is undoubtedly correct, and he wrote their structural formula in accordance with his theory, thus [27] :—

These diazo-anhydrides (which must not be confused with the substances generally known as diazo-oxides) are yellow, extremely explosive substances the reactions of which are those of a normal diazotate, in that they couple with phenols, yield diazoamino-compounds with amines, bisdiazoamino-compounds with ammonia, and diazo-ethers with alcohols. Alkalis convert them back to two molecules of the normal metallic diazotate, and mineral acids to two molecules of the diazonium salt. With cyanides and sulphites they afford the normal cyanides and sulphonates. They exhibit a singular reaction, in that with aromatic hydrocarbons they react violently to give diaryls; for example, with benzene :—

$$(\text{Ph·N}{=}\text{N})_2\text{O} + 2\text{C}_6\text{H}_6 = 2\text{PhPh} + 2\text{H}_2\text{O} + 2\text{N}_2$$

The technical value of the discovery made by Schraube and Schmidt was at once appreciated, for here was a method of isolating *p*-nitro-diazobenzene far superior to the ticklish process of evaporating an acid solution to dryness *in vacuo*. The B.A.S.F. put the sodium salt on the market as Nitrosamine Red, and the term nitrosamine has since remained fixed in the vocabulary of the dye-making and dye-using chemists.

When an *iso*diazotate in solution is acidified, the process of formation is reversed, and the normal reactions of the diazo-compounds again appear.[28] This was the manner in which the dyers treated the stable Nitrosamine Red in order to prepare developing baths for Para Red or developed cotton colours. In this direction, however, the " nitrosamines " were not able to compete with the more convenient acid-stabilised diazo-compounds which also began to come into commerce about the same time. The main value of the " nitrosamines " lies in their use for calico printing.

As has been shown above, the *iso*diazotates behave as if they are tautomeric with the normal diazotates, the former being the stable form in the presence of caustic alkali, so that the higher the concentration of the latter the more completely is the normal form suppressed. Hence in strongly alkaline solutions coupling is so much retarded that there is time for the mixed solution of *iso*diazotate and naphthol to be thickened and printed on cloth. When the prints are subsequently exposed to the air, so that the alkalinity is reduced by absorption of carbon dioxide, or if they are treated with hot weak organic acids or steamed in an ager, then coupling occurs, the insoluble azo-compound being generated in the fibre, and the shade is said to be developed. The *iso*diazotates can be printed on cloth grounded with β-naphthol, but it is usually more economical to print the mixture, and so avoid any difficulty in clearing the whites. The B.A.S.F. patented these processes, but they did not become of technical value at the time, because with the components then available the results were too erratic.[29, 30] Twenty years later the Griesheim concern found Naphthol AS ideal for preparing ready-made mixtures of *iso*diazotate and naphthol, and at once began to introduce such patented pastes and powders to the printing trade.[30, 31, 32] The reliability of the prints was also improved by using small amounts of chromate in the paste.[33] It was at the time believed that the improvement was due to lake-formation, but Bucherer and Möhlau, in the course of a careful study of the conditions under which *iso*diazotates are best used in printing technique, have pointed out that the pigments formed are incapable of lake-formation, and the true action of the chromate still remains unknown.[34]

With the growth of available coupling components through the expansion of the Naphthol AS series, the use of acetoacetarylamides for yellow shades,[35] and of the hydroxycarbazole carboxylamides for browns, there has been built up gradually the extensive range of the Rapid Fast colours of the I.G. Company. Patents for improvements still continue to emerge. Various patents have been taken for refinements in the manufacture of the powders for the market.[36, 37, 38, 39] Lastly, Bucherer, as a result of his studies, has proposed to add calcium chloride to the printing paste immediately before use, or to pad the cloth with a similar substance so as to reduce the alkalinity at the time of printing, and so favour rapid development.[40]

Some of the standard commercial Rapid Fast powders have been examined from time to time by Rowe and his co-workers and shown to possess the following compositions :— [41, 42, 43]

Rapid Fast Red GL	*iso*Diazotate of	4-amino-3-nitrotoluene	+ Naphthol AS
,, ,, Red B	,,	5-nitro-2-amino-anisol	+ Naphthol AS
,, ,, Red 2B	,,	5-nitro-2-amino-anisol	+ Naphthol ASBS
,, ,, Red 2G	,,	*p*-nitroaniline	+ Naphthol AS
,, ,, Red 3GL	,,	2-nitro-4-chloroaniline	+ Naphthol AS
,, ,, Red GZ	,,	2 : 4-dichloroaniline	+ Naphthol AS
,, ,, Orange RG	,,	*o*-nitroaniline	+ Naphthol AS

REFERENCES

[1] Griess, *Ann.*, 1866, **137**, 39.
[2] Curtius, *Ber.*, 1890, **23**, 3035.
[3] B.A.S.F., E.P. 20,605/93; D.R.P. 78,874 (Fr., **4**, 658).
[4] Schraube, Schmidt, *Ber.*, 1894, **27**, 514.
[5] Bamberger, *ibid.*, p. 679.
[6] v. Pechmann, Frobenius, *ibid.*, p. 672.
[7] B.A.S.F., D.R.P. 81,202 (Fr., **4**, 661).
[8] B.A.S.F., D.R.P. 81,206 (Fr., **4**, 665).
[9] B.A.S.F., D.R.P. 81,134 (Fr., **4**, 659); U.S.P. 531,973, 531,975; F.P. 234,029.
[10] B.A.S.F., E.P. 13,460/95; D.R.P. 84,609 (Fr., **4**, 667).
[11] Bamberger, *Ber.*, 1896, **29**, 455.
[12] Bamberger, *ibid.*, p. 461.
[13] Schraube, Schmidt, *ibid.*, 1894, **27**, 522.
[14] Wojciechowski, *Rocz. Chem.*, 1934, **14**, 739.
[15] I.G., E.P. 307,965; U.S.P. 1,724,062.
[16] Bamberger, *Ber.*, 1894, **27**, 915; 1897, **30**, 266; Hantzsch, Wachter, *Ann.*, 1920, **325**, 229.
[17] Bamberger, *Ber.*, 1895, **28**, 218.
[18] Angeli, *ibid.*, 1904, **37**, 2390.
[19] Bamberger, Wetter, *ibid.*, p. 629.   Bergstrom, Fernelius, *Chem. Revs.*, 1933, **12**, 151.
[20] Bamberger, *Ber.*, 1898, **31**, 582.
[21] Thiele, *ibid.*, 1908, **41**, 2806; Stolle, *ibid.*, p. 2811.
[22] Bamberger, *ibid.*, 1894, **27**, 1179; 1900, **33**, 1957.
[23] Bamberger, *Ann.*, 1899, **305**, 289.
[24] Hantzsch, Vock, *Ber.*, 1903, **36**, 2065.
[25] Bamberger, *ibid.*, 1896, **29**, 446; *ibid.*, p. 1383.
[26] Bamberger, *ibid.*, 1898, **31**, 2636.
[27] Hantzsch, *ibid.*, 1896, **29**, 1074; 1897, **30**, 626; 1898, **31**, 636.
[28] B.A.S.F., D.R.P. 80,263 (Fr., **4**, 668).
[29] B.A.S.F., D.R.P. 81,791 (Fr., **4**, 669); D.R.P. 83,010 (Fr., **4**, 671).
[30] Griesheim, E.P. 9,102/14; D.R.P. 287,086 (Fr., **12**, 364); F.P. 471,123.
[31] Griesheim, E.P. 6663/15; D.R.P. 291,076 (Fr., **12**, 370).
[32] Griesheim, E.P. 15,884/15; D.R.P. 292, 118 (Fr., **13**, 472).
[33] Griesheim, E.P. 104,108; D.R.P. 292,118.
[34] Bucherer, Möhlau, *J. pr. Chem.*, 1931, ii, **131**, 193.
[35] Griesheim, E.P. 217,594; D.R.P. 408,505 (Fr., **14**, 1043).
[36] I.G., E.P. 303,942; D.R.P. 465,564 (Fr., **16**, 893).
[37] I.G., E.P. 305,787; D.R.P. 474,659 (Fr., **16**, 1687).
[38] I.G., E.P. 328,383; D.R.P. 524,268 (Fr., **18**, 1051); F.P. 671,164; Sw.P. 141,507.
[39] I.G., E.P. 340,534; D.R.P. 540,607 (Fr., **18**, 1952); F.P. 689,488; Sw.P. 147,411.
[40] Bucherer, E.P. 249,526; D.R.P. 448,426 (Fr., **15**, 579).
[41] Rowe, Levin, *J.S.D.C.*, 1921, **37**, 204.
[42] Rowe, Stafford, *ibid.*, 1924, **40**, 228.
[43] Rowe, Corbishley, *ibid.*, p. 230.

GROUP 2. DIAZO-ETHERS

By diazo-ethers are understood the O-ethers produced by the action of alkyl halides on metallic diazotates, under which heading they have already been mentioned (see p. 82). As there are two series of diazotates, the normal and the *iso*-, two corresponding series of ethers might be expected, but such is not the case, for v. Pechmann and Frobenius showed that the nature of the product is not determined by the series to which the salt belongs, but by the metal. The silver salt of *p*-nitro-

*iso*diazobenzene hydroxide affords the O-ether or diazo-ether, whereas the sodium salt affords *N*-nitroso-*p*-nitromethylaniline, which is certainly not a diazo-compound, though v. Pechmann and Frobenius looked on it as the true *N*- or *iso*diazo-ether.[1] Moreover, Bamberger made both potassium benzene diazotate and potassium benzene *iso*diazotate, converted both of them to their silver salts, and acted on the latter with methyl iodide. The same ether was obtained from both diazotates.

His method of carrying out the reaction was as follows :—

The silver salt (10 g.) and methyl iodide (10 g.) were stirred with ether (30 g.) at − 5° to − 10° for six hours with exclusion of light. After that time the silver iodide was filtered off and the ether removed *in vacuo*, leaving the diazo-ether as a brownish-yellow oil.

Diazobenzene methyl ether is an unstable oil which decomposes completely in an open tube in two days. It explodes on heating, couples with phenols instantly, and decomposes with water. It is, however, sufficiently stable to be distilled with steam, in which it is volatile, and care must be taken not to inhale the vapour, which produces unpleasant symptoms.[2]

The ether obtained from silver *p*-nitrodiazobenzene *iso*diazotate is more stable, being a yellow solid, m. p. 83°; but although obtained from an *iso*-salt, a comparison with the original sodium *p*-nitrodiazobenzene *iso*diazotate affords every indication that the ether belongs to the normal series.[3] The accepted structure for the diazo-ethers is therefore Ar·N=N·OAlk.

But despite their behaviour, concerning which there is no lack of agreement, there has been much controversy as to whether the diazo-ethers are to be considered as normal or *iso*diazo-compounds, though at first sight most chemists would answer, with v. Pechmann and Frobenius, that they obviously belong to the normal series. Hantzsch considered that, notwithstanding their reactions, they must, according to his stereochemical theory, be members of the *anti*-series, having the

structure $\begin{matrix} \text{Ar·N} \\ \| \\ \text{N·OAlk} \end{matrix}$.[4] Euler considered the criterion of this view to be

the nature of the metallic diazotates resulting from alkaline hydrolysis of the ether, and he sought to show that such hydrolysis products are normal diazotates.[5] Hantzsch disputed the interpretation of his observations, maintaining that the manifestations of the normal salts are secondary and that the primary product of hydrolysis is an *iso*-diazotate.[6]

The subject of the diazo-ethers is one which could well be reinvestigated making use of some of the interesting amines now available commercially as Ice Colour bases.

REFERENCES

[1] v. Pechmann, Frobenius, *Ber.*, 1894, **27**, 672.   Compare Angeli, R.A.L., 1923, v. **32**, i, 539.
[2] Bamberger, *Ber.*, 1895, **28**, 225.
[3] v. Pechmann, Frobenius, *ibid.*, p. 170.
[4] Hantzsch, *ibid.*, 1894, **27**, 1865, 2968; 1895, **28**, 741.
[5] Euler, *ibid.*, 1903, **36**, 2503, 3835.
[6] Hantzsch, *ibid.*, pp. 3097, 3835, 4361; 1904, **37**, 3030.

GROUP 3. DIAZOCYANIDES

When cyanides in aqueous solution act on diazo-salts which are free of sulphonic or carboxylic acid groups, coloured diazocyanides are precipitated. The reaction is virtually a coupling, as the diazonium salt is converted into a derivative having in its insolubility, colour, and non-ionised state attributes of an azo-compound :—

$$Ar \cdot N \cdot Cl + HCN \longrightarrow Ar \cdot N = N \cdot CN + HCl$$
$$\ddot{N}$$

The reaction differs from the normal coupling reaction, however, in that the solution should remain acid until combination is complete, while compounds having differing properties are produced, according to the conditions of reaction; for, unlike the diazo-ethers, the diazo-cyanides exist in two modifications. Whether these correspond strictly to the normal and *iso*diazohydroxides is one of the crucial questions for the theory of the constitution of the diazo-compounds (see p. 188).

Although Kunze and Hubner had brought diazo-compounds and cyanides into reaction as early as 1865,[1] and Griess made some investigations in 1876,[2] Gabriel first isolated the orange-coloured double cyanide of benzene diazocyanide, Ph·N=N·CN·HCN.[3]

The existence of the two isomeric cyanides was demonstrated by Hantzsch and Schultze, who obtained labile cyanides from *p*-chloro- and *p*-nitro-diazobenzene salts by carrying out the condensation with potassium cyanide at temperatures not above — 5°.[4] Above — 5° the stable diazo-cyanides are produced, and the differences between the two forms are shown in the table below.

TABLE XV

Comparison of Labile and Stable p-*Chlorodiazobenzene Cyanides*

	Labile Diazocyanide.	Stable Diazocyanide.
Crystal form.	Yellow needles.	Yellow needles or brown prisms.
Melting point.	29°.	105—106°.
β-Naphthol.	Couples in alcohol.	Does not couple.
Active copper.	Affords *p*-chlorobenzonitrile.	Unattacked.
Metallic cyanides.	Forms double cyanides.	Reacts with difficulty.
Alkalis.	Forms additive compound.	No reaction.

Morgan and Wootton have described the very well-defined labile and stable diazo-cyanides afforded by 1-diazo-4-benzoylaminonaphthalene.[5]

If the reaction between the diazo-compound and the alkali cyanide takes place in alkaline solution, the course is entirely different from that described above. A yellow oil is first formed when benzene-diazonium chloride is added to potassium cyanide and excess caustic potash, and this affords a colourless solution from which a sparingly soluble, unstable red salt separates. The latter can be stabilised by conversion to the free acid, to which Heller and Meyer assign the constitution $Ph \cdot N_2 \cdot \underset{NH}{C} \cdot O \cdot N_2 \cdot Ph$, benzenediazo-oxydiazobenzene carbimide, and which appears to arise by addition of the normal diazotate to the diazo-cyanide.[6]

Diazobenzenecarboxylic acid, $Ph \cdot N{=}N \cdot CO_2H$, is obtained by hydrolysis of the diazobenzene cyanide, and the reaction is a general one for the substituted derivatives. Water adds by boiling with weak acid, forming diazocarbonamides, $Ph \cdot N{=}N \cdot CONH_2$, and these easily split off ammonia with alkali to give the salt of the diazocarboxylic acid. The free acids are unstable.[7] It is important to note that both the labile and stable diazocyanides give the same diazocarboxylic acid or its amide. Similarly, while the two forms differ in their sensitivity to oxidising agents, yet the products of oxidation are identical. Bamberger and Baudisch found that only the labile p-chlorodiazobenzene cyanide is attacked by hydrogen peroxide in ethereal solution in presence of magnesium carbonate, the product being p-chloronitrosophenyl-hydroxylamine, $\underset{NO}{\overset{Cl \cdot C_6H_4 \cdot N \cdot OH}{|}}$, with some p-chlorophenylazocarbonamide, $Cl \cdot C_6H_4 \cdot N{=}N \cdot CONH_2$, as by-product. The latter is the main product if the magnesium carbonate is replaced by caustic soda.[8]

Pieroni, by treating the respective diazocyanides in moist ether with hydrochloric acid gas, also obtained p-bromo- and p-nitro-phenyldiazo-carbonamides, and further oxidised the latter with hydrogen peroxide to the azoxy-compounds, which can only be obtained in one form, though, according to Angeli, two might exist, $\underset{O}{\overset{Ar \cdot N{=}N \cdot CONH_2}{\ddot{}}}$ and $\underset{\ddot{O}}{Ar \cdot N{=}N \cdot CONH_2}$,[9] nor is it yet known to which nitrogen atom the oxygen is attached. While, as has been noticed, the stable diazocyanides will not couple with β-naphthol, yet the azoxycarbonamides will do so, because alkalis quickly degrade them back to the diazo-compounds, changes represented thus by Pieroni :—

$$\underset{\ddot{O}}{Ar \cdot N{=}N \cdot CONH_2} \longrightarrow \underset{\ddot{O}}{Ar \cdot N{=}N \cdot CO_2H} \longrightarrow \underset{\ddot{O}}{Ar \cdot N{=}NH} \longrightarrow Ar \cdot N{=}N \cdot OH$$

This is paralleled by the stable diazosulphonates which require the presence of an oxidising agent before coupling will take place (see p. 95).

REFERENCES

[1] Kunze, Hubner, *Ann.*, 1865, **137**, 106.
[2] Griess, *Ber.*, 1876, **9**, 132.
[3] Gabriel, *ibid.*, 1879, **12**, 1637.
[4] Hantzsch, Schultze, *ibid.*, 1895, **28**, 666.
[5] Morgan, Wootton, *J.C.S.*, 1907, **91**, 1311.
[6] Heller, Meyer, *Ber.*, 1919, **52**, 2287.
[7] Hantzsch, Schultze, *ibid.*, 1895, **28**, 2073.
[8] Bamberger, Baudisch, *ibid.*, 1912, **45**, 2054.
[9] Peironi, *Gazz.*, 1922, **52**, ii, 32.

GROUP 4. THE DIAZOSULPHONATES; THEIR PREPARATION AND USE AS STABILISED DIAZO-COMPOUNDS

Sulphites in neutral or alkaline solution act on diazo-compounds to give substances called diazosulphonates, and commonly represented by the structure $Ar \cdot N {=} N \cdot SO_3M$, where M is an atom of a monovalent metal or its equivalent. They thus differ from the diazo-compounds of sulphonated arylamines in which the sulphonic acid group is attached to a carbon atom of the aromatic ring. The reaction is one of the most general and reliable of the diazo-compounds; failure is rare, while crystalline, stable and easily isolated salts are nearly always obtained. α-Diazonaphthalene is one of the few exceptions, as α : α'-azonaphthalene is formed when it is treated with sulphite.[1]

The diazosulphonates were early discovered, for Schmitt and Glutz made the derivative of *p*-diazophenol,[2] Griess of *m*-diazobenzoic acid,[3] while E. Fischer made potassium diazobenzene sulphonate as an intermediate step in his classic work on the reduction of diazo-compounds to hydrazines.[4] Diazosulphonates can be made from *iso*diazotates [5] and from nitrosoacetanilide,[6] and by the oxidation of phenylhydrazine-sulphonic acid.[7] Hall and Gibbs have recently reviewed the matter, and recorded the conditions which favour the best yields when working from diazo-compound and sulphite. The point of cardinal importance is that the p_H must be carefully controlled, no sulphur dioxide should be liberated, while excess alkalinity leads to deeply coloured products. Only a slight excess of sulphite over the amount equivalent to the diazo-compound may be used, and the reaction solutions should be at a high concentration.[8] As the sulphites of sodium and potassium are the only ones coming into ordinary use, the diazosulphonates are commonly handled as salts of these metals, and in the benzene and naphthalene series are found to be rather sparingly soluble orange or red substances.

From the formula set out above it might be expected that they would couple with phenols and amines, but such is not the case, and they remain unchanged even when warmed in alkaline solution with these substances. Their yellow colour and their stability suggest that the nitrogen is held in the same way as in the azo-compounds, and that they may be looked on as a species of mixed azo-compounds. Schmidt found that, like some azo-compounds, when treated with chlorine they regenerate the diazonium halide.[9]

A curious reaction with lead and silver nitrates has also been observed—namely, generation of the diazonium nitrate :—

$$PhN_2 \cdot SO_3K + 2AgNO_3 = Ag_2SO_3 + KNO_3 + PhN_2 \cdot NO_3$$

In 1894 Hantzsch described a second form of potassium diazo-benzene sulphonate, which is made by adding diazobenzene nitrate solution to an excess of alkaline potassium sulphite. Immediately on mixing the cold solutions very unstable flat orange crystals separate, and can be collected on a tile and dried. This form of the diazosul-phonates is capable of coupling with phenols. Hantzsch found analysis difficult, on account of their instability, but the composition of the crystals as they separate from water appears to be $PhN_2 \cdot SO_3K \cdot H_2O$. Decomposition, sometimes explosive, follows loss of the crystal water, but Hantzsch was eventually able to obtain the anhydrous substances by drying over phosphorus pentoxide. Similar labile substances can be obtained from other diazo-compounds such as the halogenobenzene diazo-salts,[10] but not from the nitrodiazobenzenes, which give only the stable form.[11] In aqueous solution the labile variety of the diazo-sulphonates pass over to the well-known stable form, the colour becoming paler. At the same time their characteristic reaction, the power of coupling with phenols, is lost.

Claus in repeating Hantzsch's experiments observed that the orange salt cannot be obtained from sodium sulphite, because the unstable sodium salt is too soluble to be salted out. On adding a potassium salt to a freshly-made solution of the sodium salt the unstable orange potassium salt crystallises.[12]

Hantzsch and Schmiedel found that the labile diazo-sulphonates react with iodine :—

$$ArN_2 \cdot SO_3K + I_2 + H_2O = ArN_2 \cdot SO_4H + KI + HI$$

The stable salt does not undergo this reaction. They therefore used titration with iodine to measure the speed of conversion of the labile into the stable form and the influence of substituents on the change.[13] They found that the speed on conversion does not follow any definite law, and both labile and stable forms are equally reduced to hydrazines.[14]

In spite of Bamberger's criticism of the weakness of Hantzsch's analytical results,[15] the fact is beyond question that some diazosulphonates appear to exist in different forms, but the structure of such isomers and the value of the evidence they afford have been one of the hotly contested questions touching the theory of the diazo-compounds (see p. 190).

During the past few years diazo-compounds stabilised as diazo-sulphonates have made their appearance in commerce. The labile form is, of course, too unstable for use, but the stable form is considerably modified in the case of the diazo-derivative of *p*-aminodi-phenylamine and its congeners, which are much valued for the blue mon-azo-compounds they afford. 4-Amino-4'-methoxydiphenylamine diazo-tised and coupled on the fibre with 2 : 3-hydroxynaphthoic arylides is the well-known Variamine Blue of the I.G. Company. The diazonium salts of the aminodiphenylamines are instantly and irreversibly decomposed by alkalis, the product being the quinone diazide. Therefore stabilisa-tion as *iso*diazotates or as diazoimino-compounds is out of the question. Treatment of the diazo-compounds with neutral sulphite, however, affords the diazosulphonates, and these are of good stability under alkaline conditions, so that they can be incorporated in printing pastes with the other components. To obtain full development of the azo-colour a neutral oxidising agent is often necessary, the purpose being met by an alkali chromate, while it is undesirable that the steam in the ager should contain acid vapours. Colours working on this principle are the Rapidasols of the I.G. Company.[16] The tetrazotised 4 : 4'-aminodiphenylamines are also amenable to this treatment and give black prints.

Monoacyl derivatives of substituted *p*-phenylenediamines also give stable diazosulphonates such as :—

These couple on the fibre merely by neutral steaming, and give blue shades.[17]

Lastly, Schmidt's method of regenerating a diazonium salt from the diazosulphonate has also been applied, the dry salt being mixed with dry bromide–bromate and a dry acid salt such as acid sodium sulphate. When this mixture is dissolved in water the acid salt liberates the bromine from the bromide-bromate, and the latter converts the diazo-sulphonate to the diazonium bromide.[18] Prints of the diazosulphonate and a coupling component can also be developed by treatment with very dilute chlorine and hypochlorite solution.[19]

REFERENCES

[1] Lange, D.R.P. 78,225 (Fr., **4**, 1016).
[2] Schmitt, Glutz, *Ber.*, 1869, **2**, 51.
[3] Griess, *ibid.*, 1876, **9**, 1657.
[4] E. Fischer, *Ann.*, 1878, **190**, 73.
[5] Bamberger, Kraus, *Ber.*, 1895, **29**, 1835.
[6] Bamberger, *ibid.*, 1896, **30**, 371.
[7] Paal, Kritscher, *ibid.*, 1894, **27**, 1245.
[8] Hall, Gibbs, *J. Wash. Acad. Sci.*, 1927, **17**, 433.
[9] Schmidt, *J. pr. Chem.*, 1912, ii, **85**, 239.
[10] Hantzsch, *Ber.*, 1894, **27**, 1726; *ibid.*, p. 3527.
[11] Hantzsch, Borghaus, *ibid.*, 1897, **30**, 89.
[12] Claus, *J. pr. Chem.*, 1894, ii, **50**, 239.
[13] Hantzsch, Schmiedel, *Ber.*, 1897, **30**, 71.
[14] Hantzsch, *ibid.*, p. 342.
[15] Bamberger, *ibid.*, 1894, **27**, 2582.
[16] I.G., E.P. 377,207, 421,971; D.R.P. 560,797 (Fr., **19**, 1648); U.S.P. 1,920,542; F.P. 737,365.
[17] I.G., E.P. 379,279; U.S.P. 1,970,070; F.P. 727,665.
[18] I.C.I., E.P. 377,978, 414,681.
[19] St. Denis, E.P. app. 35,118/35; F.P. 795,558.

GROUP 5. NITROSOACYLARYLAMINES

With a view to throwing light on the structure of the metallic diazotates, v. Pechmann [1] benzoylated a cold solution of sodium *p*-toluene diazotate by the agency of benzoyl chloride. He obtained a product which crystallised from acetone in almost colourless needles, gave the Liebermann nitroso-reaction, and on reduction afforded benz-*p*-toluidide. He noted that this substance showed a close resemblance to nitrosoacetanilide, $Ph \cdot N {<}^{NO}_{COMe}$, which O. Fischer [2] made by the action of nitrous acid gases on acetanilide. v. Pechmann from his benzoylation experiment reached the conclusion that one tautomer of the diazotates must have the nitrosamine constitution, $Ar \cdot N {<}^{NO}_{K}$ (see p. 81). Almost immediately Wohl [3] described nitrosobenzanilide prepared from sodium benzene diazotate and benzoyl chloride in 30% yield, and v. Pechmann confirmed his impression as to constitution by acetylating sodium benzene diazotate with acetic anhydride when he obtained Fischer's nitrosoacetanilide. [4]

Although readily produced by O. Fischer's method, and apparently genuine nitroso-compounds, yet in their reactions the nitrosoacylarylamines behave as diazo-compounds. They couple with phenols to form azo-compounds, with arylamines to form diazoamino-compounds, and with sulphites to form hydrazine disulphonates. [5] Because of these characteristic reactions Bamberger pointed out that the nitrosoacylarylamines are tautomeric with the diazoacyl ethers. [6]

$$Ar \cdot N {<}^{NO}_{COMe} \rightleftharpoons Ar \cdot N {=\!\!=} N \cdot O \cdot COMe$$

Thus the coupling reaction follows alkaline hydrolysis to the normal diazotate,[7] while Gutmann showed that their decomposition by arsenic trioxide is also a manifestation of the diazo-structure.[8]

The nitrosoacylarylamines are unstable yellow substances, and even when dry cannot be kept for more than a few days. A damp specimen placed between watch-glasses is seen soon to be surrounded by fumes of nitrogen peroxide, and though the melting points are sharp, explosion results from sudden heating. Bamberger stated that *iso*diazotates cannot be acylated,[9] but Hantzsch [10] showed that taking equivalent quantities of normal and *iso*diazotates and benzoyl chloride, the yields of nitrosobenzanilide are 4·4% and 5·2%, respectively, rising with much alkali and excess benzoyl chloride to 26%, and eventually to 57% with ten equivalents of benzoyl chloride.

If oxidised without special control of the conditions, nitrosoacetanilide affords nitrosobenzene and acetic acid :—

$$Ph{\cdot}N{\Big<}^{NO}_{COMe} \longrightarrow Ph{\cdot}NO + MeCO_2H$$

If the conditions are carefully controlled, the temperature being kept down to below $- 15°$, and in the presence of magnesium carbonate, then nitrosophenylhydroxylamine is obtained in 94% yield :—[11]

$$Ph{\cdot}N{\Big<}^{NO}_{COMe} \longrightarrow Ph{\cdot}N{\Big<}^{NO}_{OH} + MeCO_2H$$

The most convenient way of preparing these substances is that of O. Fischer by acting on acylarylamines with nitrous acid gases. Nitrosoacetanilide is prepared as follows :—

Acetanilide (20 g.) is dissolved in glacial acetic acid (100 c.c.) and nitrous acid gases passed in at 5—10° until the colour is dark green. The whole is then poured into water and the yellow solid collected, washed, and dried on a tile. The material thus prepared should be crystalline, having m. p. 50—51° (decomp.), and can be recrystallised from ether or light petroleum, when the melting point rises to 51—52°, but the keeping quality is inferior to the less pure material, which can be kept in a desiccator for a few days without serious loss.[12]

Unfortunately the reaction fails in the case of the acetyl derivative of many common amines, like *p*-nitroaniline, *o*-chloroaniline, and α- and β-naphthylamine,which afford only tars by this process, and acet-*p*-anisidide, which is nitrated.[13]

It will be observed that the above process permits the preparation of what are in effect normal diazotates, but they are different in some important respects from the metallic diazotates. They are soluble in many non-hydroxylic solvents, and are thus able to react in ways different from those of diazo-compounds, which are usually held in aqueous solution. Nitrosoacetanilide dissolved in benzene liberates

H

nitrogen, and diphenyl is formed in high yield.[14] Bamberger considered the formation of unstable addition products of nitroso-compound and solvent to be the mechanism of this reaction,[15] but the matter has been since studied extensively by Grieve and Hey,[16] who have put forward the view that free phenyl radicals are formed in the spontaneous decomposition of nitrosoacetanilide. By analogy with known thermal decompositions, this is not at all unlikely to be the case. Grieve and Hey found this decomposition, as measured by nitrogen evolution, to be a unimolecular reaction largely independent of the solvent in which it proceeds, showing that the solvent has but a secondary influence on a process which originates in, and is confined entirely to the nitrosoacetanilide molecule itself. The fate of the free phenyl radicals could not be determined by these investigators, except when benzene or methyl alcohol was used as solvent. In the latter solvent nitrosoacetanilide reacts in the typical manner of a diazo-compound, being itself reduced to hydrocarbon, and oxidising the methyl alcohol to formaldehyde. The order of this reaction has, unfortunately, not been determined. Nitrosoacet-p-chloro- and p-bromo-anilides and nitrosoacet-p-toluidide also decompose according to the unimolecular law, while the relative speeds of the reactions are the same as those of the corresponding sodium diazotates and the inverse to those of the diazonium salts.[17]

Grieve and Hey have suggested in the work quoted that the decomposition of all diazo-compounds proceeds by the mechanism of free radicals. It must be questioned whether such a suggestion can be accepted without some modification if it is to apply to diazo-compounds at all p_H values. It may prove to be the mechanism of decomposition of the diazotates and their alkyl and acyl ethers, but the differences between the nitrosoacetanilides and the diazonium salts are deep-seated. Many examples of the latter can be cited which are quite stable when dry and can be kept for long periods without appreciable change, but commence to decompose as soon as dissolved. While on decomposition the reaction speed obeys the unimolecular law (see p. 68), yet it is rare for the fate of the aryl radical not to be clearly apparent.

REFERENCES

[1] v. Pechmann, *Ber.*, 1892, **25**, 3505.
[2] O. Fischer, *ibid.*, 1876, **9**, 463; 1877, **10**, 959.
[3] Wohl, *ibid.*, 1892, **25**, 3631.
[4] v. Pechmann, Frobenius, *ibid.*, 1894, **27**, 651.
[5] Bamberger, Meyenburg, *ibid.*, 1897, **30**, 374.
[6] Bamberger, *ibid.*, 1894, **27**, 914.
[7] Bamberger, Müller, *Ann.*, 1900, **313**, 126.
[8] Gutmann, *Ber.*, 1912, **45**, 821.
[9] Bamberger, *ibid.*, 1897, **30**, 211.
[10] Hantzsch, *ibid.*, p. 621. See also Blomstrand, *J. pr. Chem.*, 1897, ii, **55**, 496.

[11] Bamberger, Baudisch, *Ber.*, 1909, **42**, 3582.
[12] Grieve, Hey, *J.C.S.*, **1934**, 1797.
[13] Grieve, Hey, *ibid.*, **1935**, 689.
[14] Bamberger, *Ber.*, 1897, **30**, 366.
[15] Bamberger, *ibid.*, 1920, **53**, 2308.
[16] Grieve, Hey, *J.C.S.*, **1934**, 1797.
[17] Grieve, Hey, *ibid.*, **1935**, 689.

GROUP 6. NITRATION, HALOGENATION, AND SULPHONATION PRODUCTS

Chief among the diazo-compounds which can be successfully submitted to the above operations is the diazo-compound of 1 : 2-aminonaphthol-4-sulphonic acid.   This diazo-compound owes its great stability to the 1 : 2-diazo-oxide ring, which remains unaffected while reagents attack other parts of the molecule.   While sulphonation of this compound has been described,[1] it does not compare in importance with its nitration [2] and bromination,[3] which are operations carried out to-day on a large scale.   The diazo-compound can also be chlorinated.[4]   Both nitration and bromination take place at the 6-position in the naphthalene ring, as was proved by Ruggli and his co-workers, who removed first the diazo-group, then the sulphonic acid group, and so arrived at known derivatives of β-naphthol.[5]

Diazonium salts of α-aminoanthraquinone can be nitrated when the nitro-group enters the 5-position.[6]

The diazo-group is so reactive that in few instances can other atoms or groups in the molecule take part in a reaction without the diazo-group being also affected. Nevertheless some diazonium salts in which hydroxy-groups are not situated *ortho* to the diazo-group can be preferentially acetylated in the hydroxy-group,[7] while diazo-compounds derived from 4-aminodiphenylamine, *p*-aminophenol, or *p*-phenylenediamine, and which therefore contain free amino- or hydroxy-groups, can be condensed with formaldehyde.[8]

REFERENCES

[1] Kalle, D.R.P. 176,618, 176,620 (Fr., **8**, 651,652).
[2] Geigy, E.P. 15,418/94; D.R.P. 164,655 (Fr., **8**, 647); U.S.P. 790,363; F.P. 349,996.
[3] Kalle, D.R.P. 176,619 (Fr., **8**, 653).   Sandoz, E.P. 3508/11; D.R.P. 236,656 (Fr., **10**, 788); F.P. 425,837.
[4] Kalle, E.P. 20,072—3/11; D.R.P. 246,573—4 (Fr., **11**, 372—3); U.S.P. 1,023,199, 1,026,257, 1,028,006; F.P. 434,405.
[5] Ruggli, Knapp, *Helv. Chim. Acta*, 1929, **12**, 1034. Ruggli, Michael, *ibid.*, 1931, **14**, 779. See also Battegay, Silbermann, Kunzle, *Bull. Soc. chim.*, 1931, iv, **49**, 716.
[6] I.G., Anm., I 49,024.
[7] Bayer, D.R.P. 206,455.
[8] Kalle, E.P. 418,011; Anm., K 124,486; F.P. 755,908.

GROUP 7. DIAZO-*PER*HALIDES

The diazonium halides combined by addition with two atoms of halogen elements which may be the same as or different from each other. In this way there are formed stable crystalline compounds which possess the constitution $Ar{\cdot}N{:}(X_1X_2X_3)$. The *per*bromides are the most easily obtained members of the group, and were first prepared by Griess, who added a solution of bromine in hydrobromic acid to an aqueous solution of diazobenzene nitrate.[1]   The brownish-red oil which separates under these conditions crystallises on removal from the mother-liquor and removal of excess bromine by ether.   Large yellow plates crystallise from ether solution, and the *per*bromide is stable as long as dry, but is decomposed by water.   Hantzsch pointed out the close analogy of the diazo-*per*halides and the *per*halides of the alkali metals, and also prepared nine out of the ten possible combinations of chlorine, bromine, and iodine :— [2]

ArN_2I_3	ArN_2Br_3	(ArN_2Cl_3)
I_2Br	Br_2Cl	ArN_2Cl_2Br
I_2Cl	Br_2I	Cl_2I
	ClBrI	

The colour of these compounds varies from almost black for the tri-iodide to yellow for the chloroiodide.

Chattaway advanced the thesis that the *per*bromides have the constitution of N-tribromoarylhydrazines,[3] $Ar{\cdot}NBrNBr_2$, because they can be obtained by the action of bromine on arylhydrazines and are widely different from the ammonium *per*halides, but the arguments advanced by Hantzsch [4] and by Forster [5] leave no room for doubt that the *per*halides are true diazonium derivatives. Substances of the constitution proposed by Chattaway probably cannot exist, for bromine will not add to the double bond in benzene diazocyanide to form a cyano-dibromophenylhydrazine, but ejects the cyano-group, forming first the diazonium bromide and then the *per*bromide if sufficient bromine is present.

The *per*bromides give up two atoms of bromine with ease, and will saturate ethylenic double bonds, as in cinnamic acid.[6]   They differ from the diazonium salts in that when boiled with alcohol they afford the bromohydrocarbon instead of the hydrocarbon.[7]   The bromohydro-carbons are also obtained by thermal decomposition in solvents such as glacial acetic acid.

When bromine in sufficient excess acts on certain nitroamines of the naphthalene series, both the amine and the nitro-group are replaced by bromine through the intermediary of the diazo-*per*bromide.   The bromine replaces the nitro-group, the nitrous acid thus set free diazotises the amino-group, which is converted to the *per*bromide, which then replaces the diazo-group by bromine :— [8]

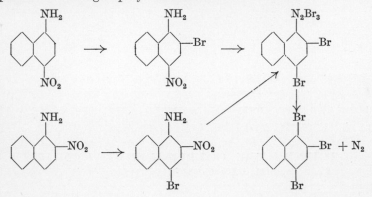

Still higher *per*halides can be formed. Chattaway showed that the brown oil which separates in the preparation of the *per*bromide contains no less than nine atoms of bromine, but they can only be retained in combination if the bromine vapour is prevented from escaping.

Very stable diazonium tetrachloroiodides are formed when diazonium chlorides are poured into a strong hydrochloric acid solution of iodine trichloride. They crystallise in bright yellow prisms, and are quite stable if kept dry. Chattaway assigns them the structure :— [9]

$$ArN_2 \begin{bmatrix} Cl & & Cl \\ & I & \\ Cl & & Cl \end{bmatrix}$$

REFERENCES

[1] Griess, *Ann.*, 1864, **137**, 50; *Phil. Trans.*, 1864, **154**, 673.
[2] Hantzsch, *Ber.*, 1895, **28**, 2754.
[3] Chattaway, *J.C.S.*, 1909, **95**, 862.
[4] Hantzsch, *Ber.*, 1915, **48**, 1344.
[5] Forster, *J.C.S.*, 1915, **107**, 260.
[6] Bülow, Schmachtenberg, *Ber.*, 1908, **41**, 2607.
[7] Saunders, *Amer. Chem. J.*, 1891, **13**, 486.
[8] Consden, Kenyon, *J.C.S.*, **1935**, 1596.
[9] Chattaway, Garton, Parkes, *ibid.*, 1924, **125**, 1980.   See also Algerino, *Gazz.*, 1932, **62**, 1145.   Iododichlorides.

CHAPTER VI

REACTIONS OF THE DIAZO-COMPOUNDS. CLASS B. DERIVATIVES IN WHICH THE DIAZO-FUNCTION DISAPPEARS BUT THE DIAZO-NITROGEN ATOMS REMAIN IN THE NEW MOLECULE

GROUP 1. THE COUPLING REACTION OF DIAZO-COMPOUNDS

DIAZO-COMPOUNDS are said to "couple" with substances the normal mode of reaction of which is to donate a hydrogen atom attached to carbon :—

$$\text{ArN}_2\text{X} + \text{HR} = \text{ArN}_2\text{R} + \text{HX}$$

Compounds thus formed by attachment of the terminal nitrogen atom of a diazo-compound to a carbon atom of another radical comprise the important class of azo-compounds. These are stable substances built up with co-valent links, and are non-ionised. Diazo-compounds can also become attached to the nitrogen of amino-compounds, thus forming the diazoamino-compounds (see Chapter VII), or to oxygen or sulphur atoms. The three latter classes of substance are quite different in properties from the azo-compounds proper, and in the case of highly acid phenols are ionised salts. It is a convenient usage to denote such compounds as N-azo-, O-azo-, and S-azo-compounds.

Whatever may be the structure of the original diazo-compound, there is no doubt that the two nitrogen atoms which make the azo-link in the completed and stable azo-compound are both trivalent, a fact which is proved by reductive scission of the link to produce two molecules of amine :—

$$\text{ArN}{=}\text{NR} \xrightarrow{\;2\text{H}_2\;} \text{ArNH}_2 + \text{RNH}_2$$

But though the azo-link is usually written as above —N=N—, it will be shown below that it may function as a hydrazone link, =N—NH—, in molecules which have quinonoid tautomers. Further, all the bonds between the nitrogen atoms cannot lie in one plane, hence there is the possibility of *cis–trans* isomerism, but recent measurements of the dipole moments of azobenzene and some of its derivatives have shown that only the *trans*-configuration exists, nor is it likely, for steric reasons, that examples of the *cis*-form in a stable state are likely to be found.[1] The labile form of azobenzene described by C. V. and R. A. Gortner [2] was shown by Hartley and Stuart to be impure azobenzene,[3] and it can now be regarded as established that the structure of azo-benzene as seen in profile is ⌐N═N⌐ .

The coupling reaction was discovered in 1870 by Kekulé and Hidegh,[4] and the substances which will couple with diazo-compounds in the sense of the above equation are included in the following classes :—

1. Phenols and naphthols.
2. Aromatic amines.
3. Naphthol-, naphthylamine-, and aminonaphthol-sulphonic acids.
4. Substances containing reactive methylene groups.

To these must be added two classes which only afford coupling products under exceptional conditions or with specific diazo-compounds :—

5. Phenol ethers.
6. Hydrocarbons.

The azo-compounds are coloured, the simplest monazo-compounds being ordinarily yellow to red, though by choosing appropriate diazo-compounds and coupling components monazo-dyes in shade as deep as blue may be made. As more complex molecules are built up by incorporating the azo-link twice or more, so an array of compounds is marshalled in which all the colours of the visible spectrum are found. Many hundreds of these substances are used as dyestuffs for every purpose, and constitute the great class of azo-dyestuffs.

There are a number of reactions by which azo-compounds can be produced—for instance, the parent substance azobenzene, $Ph\cdot N{=}N\cdot Ph$, was made by Mitscherlich by distilling nitrobenzene with alcoholic potash twenty-four years before Griess discovered the diazo-compounds,[5] but the manufacture of nearly all the azo-compounds which are used as dyestuffs depends on the coupling reaction, while the number of azo-compounds which could be made by coupling all the known diazo-compounds with all the known phenols, amines, and substances having reactive methylene groups would run to many millions. The task in this chapter is therefore neither to discuss azo-compounds as such nor to catalogue known examples, but to consider the main features of the coupling reaction of diazo-compounds and arrive, if possible, at some general conclusions.

A factor which has a dominating influence on the coupling of any particular diazo-compound with any particular second component is the acidity of the solution, a factor to which the diazo-compound is especially sensitive. As will be shown in Chapter X, there is a somewhat complicated equilibrium between the diazonium salt and the diazo-compound, which for the present can be adequately expressed in the form :—

Diazonium salt $\rightleftharpoons$ Diazo-compound

As Goldschmidt first pointed out,[6] it is the diazohydroxide formed by hydrolysis of the diazo-salt or normal metallic diazotate which is active in coupling, and hence it is in the absence of strong mineral acids (which prevent conversion of the diazonium salt to the diazo-hydroxide or diazotate) that the coupling reaction takes place. In the graph of stability on page 272 the area in which coupling occurs is roughly that between p_H 3·5 and p_H 7·0 for amines and p_H 5·0 to p_H 9·0 for phenols. As this is also the area where stability falls to a low value, the coupling reaction must always be looked on as a race between azo-compound formation and decomposition of the diazo-compound, so much so that the latter sometimes far outstrips the desired coupling. Some diazo-compounds are so sensitive to this factor that rigid control of the p_H is necessary to obtain consistent results in the dyeing of textiles.[7]

The main support for the knowledge of the existence of the diaz-onium diazo-equilibrium rests on coupling experiments, and an idea of the p_H' at which the diazonium salt begins to be converted to the diazo-compound may be gained by carrying out coupling at different degrees of acidity. When this is done it is found that as negative substituents increase in the molecule, so the diazo-compound is able to couple in increasingly acid solution, until at last coupling occurs in strong acid. Schoutissen took a series of twenty-four diazo-compounds, commencing with diazobenzene, and attempted to couple with β-naphthol in a mixture of one part of sulphuric acid, sp. gr. 1·84, and two parts of phosphoric acid, sp. gr. 1·7. 2 : 4 : 6-Trichlorodiazobenzene first gave indication of coupling, 2 : 4-dinitrodiazobenzene coupled strongly, while the series culminated in 2 : 4 : 6-trinitrodiazobenzene. Equal with the latter was p-tetrazobenzene, which coupled once only, the second diazo-group not coupling until the acid had been neutralised. Not only was Schoutissen thus able to obtain asymmetric disazo-compounds, but at the same time he demonstrated that in tetrazo-compounds where both groups are attached to the same aromatic ring one diazo-group is in the diazonium form and one in the diazo-.[8] m-Tetrazobenzene salts behave in the same way.[9]

The Coupling of Phenols and Naphthols.

The position from which the diazo-compound first detaches a hydrogen atom when coupling with a phenol is *para* to the hydroxy-group. In the case of phenol itself a small proportion of the *ortho*-hydroxy-azo-compound is also formed simultaneously.[10] If the *para* position is occupied, then the attack is transferred to the *ortho* position, and this transference occurs if the *para* position has already been occupied by the azo-group, hence disazo-compounds result. The tendency for this to occur is pronounced in thymol and carvacrol;[11]

α-naphthol also couples twice, first in the 4-position and then in the 2-position. Ultimately, if the solution is sufficiently alkaline, phenol couples three times, forming 2 : 4 : 6-trisazophenol compounds.[12]

The power of phenols to couple is naturally affected by substituents; negative substituents making coupling difficult, as in salicylic acid or 4-nitro-β-naphthol. Frequently such substituents prevent coupling altogether. Conversely positive substituents increase the speed with which coupling occurs, and hence resorcinol couples more easily than phenol, and, like phenol, affords trisazo-compounds.[13] Such trisazo-compounds may be formed from three molecules of the same diazo-compound, or different diazo-compounds may be successively attached.[14] For long it was considered that resorcinol is the only dihydric phenol which will couple, but catechol couples under the correct conditions, and azo-compounds can be obtained from hydroquinone by benzoylating one of the hydroxy-groups.[15]

Seven of the principal mono- and poly-hydric phenols can be arranged in the following descending order of coupling power :

Phloroglucinol, α-naphthol, resorcinol, β-naphthol, catechol, phenol, salicylic acid.

The phenol which is paramount in importance for the manufacture of azo-colours, and particularly of insoluble azo-pigments, is β-naphthol and its derivatives. Coupling can only occur once, in the 1-position in the naphthalene ring, and the hydroxy-group in the resulting azo-compound is no longer able to form salts, hence the colours are not affected by alkalis or soap. α-Naphthol, if substituted in the 4-position by an acetyl group, so that coupling must occur in the 2-position, gives azo-compounds which behave in the same way. To account for the loss of salt-forming power in the azo-derivatives of β-naphthol, Mason advanced the explanation that the phenolic hydrogen chelates with the azo-link,[16] while Elkins and Hunter have recently demonstrated the chelating function of the azo-link unassisted by any substituents.[17]

By analogy with α-naphthol it might be expected that 1 : 5-dihydroxynaphthalene would couple no less than four times. Yet while it is one of the most sensitive of the naphthols to coupling conditions it is difficult to attach more than one azo-link. O. Fischer and Bauer succeeded in attaching two molecules of strongly coupling diazo-compounds both in the same ring at positions 2 and 4. Weakly coupling diazo-compounds attach themselves once only, and that in position 4 under mildly alkaline conditions, and in position 2 when caustic alkali is present.[18] The valuable acid chrome dyestuff, Diamond Black PV, is made by coupling diazotised o-aminophenolsulphonic acid to 1 : 5-dihydroxynaphthalene under alkaline conditions, so that coupling occurs in the 2-position, and thus the link in the azo-dyestuff molecule has two *ortho*-hydroxy-groups :—

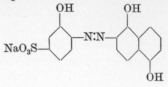

It would be an interesting experiment to try 1 : 5-dihydroxy-naphthalene with one of the very strongly coupling diazo-compounds from Schoutissen's list.

The hydroxyazo-compounds made by coupling diazo-compounds to naphthols may be formed in another way—namely, by making the corresponding arylhydrazone of the naphthoquinone; the products of both reactions are identical. For example, the phenylhydrazone of α-naphthoquinone is identical with the coupling product of diazobenzene and α-naphthol :— [19]

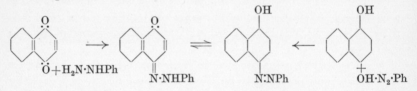

There can be no doubt on this evidence that the hydroxyazo-compounds and the quinone hydrazones are tautomeric. The ethers and salts (if the metal is attached to oxygen) must possess the azo-configuration, but the constitution of the free azo-compounds was a subject of keen debate in the last decade of the nineteenth century, the problem being attacked by both chemical and physical means without decisive result. Recently further work has been published by Lauer and Miller,[20] by Kuhn and Bär,[21] and by Burawoy.[22] These workers have shown that the azohydrazone equilibrium is mobile, as its position is altered both by substituents and by the solvent in which the substance is dissolved. In pyridine the azo-form of benzene-azo-α-naphthol predominates, in nitrobenzene the hydrazone, while in benzene the azo- and hydroazone tautomers are present in equal proportions. This subject is of fundamental importance in the theory of colour, and for an extended discussion books on colour chemistry should be consulted.

The Coupling of Amino-Compounds.

Though amines in their coupling reactions show the same general behaviour as phenols, they are differentiated by a lower level of reactivity. Thus aniline rarely yields aminoazo-compounds directly, and those monoamines which couple easily do not show the same capacity to form polyazo-compounds as is shown by the phenols.

When the free hydrogen atom is not available in the *para* position to the amino-group the *ortho* position is rarely attacked, so that amines such as dimethyl-*p*-toluidine refuse to couple.[23] Substitution of tertiary aromatic amines in the *o*-position also prevents coupling in the *para* position, and dimethyl-*o*-toluidine is well known for its inertness to all reagents, though it has been said to couple with 2 : 5-dichlorodiazobenzene.[24]

While the *ortho*-aminoazo-compounds have to be made indirectly in the benzene series,[25] such are easily obtained in the naphthalene series by coupling diazo-compounds with β-naphthylamine, which couples in the 1-position. The amino-group in azo-derivatives of β-naphthylamine cannot be diazotised, as it is apparently chelated in the same way as the oxy-group in the azo-derivatives of β-naphthol.

Positive substituents in the *meta* position to the amino-group enhance coupling power, so that *m*-toluidine, *p*-xylidine, and cresidine couple easily in the position *para* to the amino-group. α-Naphthylamine couples in both the 2- and the 4-position.

Just as resorcinol couples better than phenol, so the *m*-diamines couple with more facility than the monoamines, but stable trisazo-derivatives are not yet known. Both monochloro- and mononitro-*m*-phenylenediamines couple well and are used as intermediates for azo-dyestuffs. Morgan and his co-workers have made a detailed study of the effects of substitution on the coupling of *m*-diamines.[26]

The coupling power of primary amines may be enhanced not only by substituents in the benzene ring, but also by replacement of the primary aminohydrogen atoms by alkyl or aryl groups. Both dimethylaniline and diphenylamine couple more easily than aniline, while the aryl-naphthylamines have been closely studied by Levi and Faldino.[27] An easier way of securing the effect of alkylation is to warm together equivalent parts of amine, formaldehyde (as aqueous solution), and bisulphite solution, whereupon the base dissolves and a clear solution of the methyl-ω-sulphonate is obtained :—

$$ArNH_2 + OHCH_2SO_3Na \longrightarrow ArNH \cdot CH_2SO_3Na + H_2O$$

Aniline, after conversion to the methyl-ω-sulphonate, couples readily, and as the methyl-ω-sulphonate group is easily removed by hydrolysis, this is a method used technically to make *p*-aminoazo-compounds. The introduction of the sulphuric acid or nitric acid radicals into the amino-group to form sulphamic or nitramic acids, $ArNH \cdot SO_3Na$ and $ArNH \cdot NO_2$, has the same effect, and it has been stated that α-sulphaminonaphthalene,

NHSO$_3$Na

couples exclusively in the 4-position, and so affords purer amino-azo-compounds than does α-naphthylamine itself,[28] in which a certain amount of unwanted coupling in the 2-position also occurs. The characteristic of both the groups just mentioned is that they are easily removed, so much so that though they thus direct coupling, they do not hinder subsequent diazotisation of the product (see p. 17). Acyl groups, on the other hand, remove from primary amines the power to couple, just as they prevent diazotisation. Exceptions are the azo-compounds which can be made by coupling p-nitrodiazobenzene with the p-toluenesulphonamides of α- and β-naphthylamines,[29] and also the internal sulphonamide, 1 : 8-naphthasultam.[30]

Although aniline will not form azo-compounds by direct coupling with diazo-compounds, the primary products being diazoamino-compounds, yet aniline can be coupled with diazobenzene to form p-amino-azobenzene. The coupling medium is a mixture of aniline hydrochloride and aniline. To carry out the reaction sodium nitrite (1 mol.) is added to an excess of aniline (2 mols.) and aniline hydrochloride (2 mols.), whereupon an equivalent of aniline is diazotised, and at once combines with the excess aniline to form diazoaminobenzene. Such of this latter as is dissolved in the aniline and aniline hydrochloride is in equilibrium with a small amount of diazobenzene chloride formed by the action of the acid. The diazobenzene slowly couples with the aniline, and, being continually replaced from the reservoir of diazo-aminobenzene, coupling goes on until it is complete, and the reaction mass consists of p-aminoazobenzene hydrochloride partly dissolved in aniline. The optimum temperature is 35—40°. (For references to the controversies as to the course of this reaction see the chapter on Diazoamino-compounds.)

The essence of success in this coupling is, in fact, the stabilisation of the diazobenzene as its diazoamino-compound during the long period necessary for coupling, and such a coupling can only be made where a diazo-compound is to be coupled to its own amine. Thus o- and m-aminoazotoluenes are formed from o- and m-toluidines in the same way as p-aminoazobenzene. The bugbear of the process is the final separation of the p-aminoazo-compound and the excess base, and on the technical scale efforts are made to keep this excess as small as possible.

The Coupling of Naphthylamine-, Naphthol-, and Amino-naphthol-sulphonic Acids.

For the purpose of making pure azo-compounds free from by-products which may have deleterious properties, it is desirable to be able to control the position of entry of the azo-link in molecules where coupling can occur in more than one position. This is particularly the case among the naphthylamine-, naphthol-, and aminonaphthol-sulphonic acids, where azo-compounds of entirely different properties are formed according to the factor which influences the coupling, and where the influence of the sulphonic acid group goes deeper than merely acting as a group directly blocking coupling in certain positions and as a solubilising agent.

No comment is necessary in the case of the β-naphthylamine- and β-naphthol-sulphonic acids; they couple exclusively in the 1-position with any diazo-compound.

If the amino- or hydroxyl group is in the 1-position, then the diazo-compound attacks in the 4-position, unless (1) the 4-position is occupied or (2) a sulphonic acid group is in position 3 or 5, in which cases the attack is directed to the 2-position. But though this is the general rule, there are exceptions, which suggests that the diazo-compound itself causes variation of the point of excitation in the molecule with which it couples. 1-Naphthylamine-5-sulphonic acid is attacked in the 4-position by diazo-compounds with negative substituents, except diazotised sulphanilic acid, which enters exclusively *ortho-* to the amino-group. Moreover, acidity in the coupling medium tends to direct attachment of the azo-link to the 2-position.[31] Similar conditions apply in the case of α-naphthol-3-sulphonic acid, with which weak diazo-compounds couple in position 2 and strong diazo-compounds in position 4.[32] Lastly it may be mentioned that diazotised 1-amino-2-naphthol-4-sulphonic acid attacks α-naphthol exclusively in the 2-position, thereby affording a well-known black chrome dyestuff.[33]

Fierz-David has shown how variation in the destination of the diazo-group can happen with α-naphthol-5-sulphonic acid even with one and the same diazo-compound.[34] If this acid is treated with a diazo-compound in acid solution, a sparingly soluble diazonium sulphonate can be isolated, and this by careful treatment with mild alkali goes over entirely into the *ortho*-azo-dye, but if caustic soda is used, then a proportion of coupling in the 4-position occurs :—

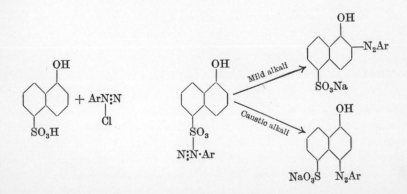

Among the aminonaphtholsulphonic acids the point of attachment of the diazo-compound is determined entirely by the acidity of the solution in which coupling takes place. In acid solutions it is the positions activated by the amino-group to which the azo-link is attached; in alkaline solution the hydroxyl group is the controlling factor. This is a matter of great technical importance, because the dyestuffs obtained by one way are entirely different in shade and fastness properties from those obtained by the other. Some aminonaphtholsulphonic acids can thus be made to couple twice, once on the amino-side and once on the hydroxy-side, as in the case of H-acid (1 : 8-aminonaphthol-3 : 6-di-sulphonic acid). The sulphonic acid groups cause coupling to take place in the 2- and 7-positions, so that the dyes belong to the useful *ortho*amino- and *ortho*hydroxy-azo-type.

γ-Acid (2 : 8-aminonaphthol-6-sulphonic acid) and J-acid (2 : 5-amino-7-sulphonic acid) will only couple once, but that single coupling may be made in either acid or alkaline solution :—

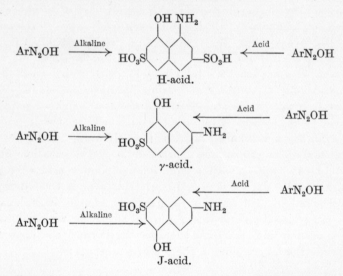

For lists of aminonaphtholsulphonic acids and their coupling positions one of the numerous books on dyestuff chemistry should be consulted.

The Coupling of Substances having Reactive Methylene Groups.

As might be expected, those substances of the aliphatic series which have tautomeric keto-enol constitutions are able to supply the necessary hydrogen atom to diazo-compounds and thereby couple to form azo-compounds. V. Meyer discovered as long ago as 1876 that acetoacetic ester dissolved in aqueous alkali couples with diazobenzene,[35] while three years earlier he had prepared benzeneazonitroethane.[36] Azo-compounds of this type are sometimes known as "mixed" azo-compounds, because an aromatic radical is linked to one of the aliphatic series by the azo-link. As with the azo-derivatives of the phenols, the number known is so great that no attempt can be made to give a list, but beside acetoacetic ester and its arylamides, the following substances of this type may be mentioned : malonic ester,[37] acetylacetone,[38] ethyl acetopyruvate,[39] acetone dicarboxylic acid,[40] acetone disulphonic acid,[41] cyclic-β-diketones,[42] and pyrazolones, which last are of great importance for the manufacture of many dyestuffs.

The original interest in these azo-compounds lay in the point as to whether they are to be regarded as true azo-compounds, for not only are the two forms tautomeric :—

$$\underset{\overset{|}{\text{N:N·Ar}}}{\text{MeCO·CH·CO}_2\text{Et}} \quad \rightleftharpoons \quad \underset{\overset{||}{\text{N·NHAr}}}{\text{MeCO·C·CO}_2\text{Et}}$$

but, as with the hydroxy-azo-compounds, the same compound is obtained whether a diazo-compound is coupled to a keto-enol tautomer or a hydrazine acts on a ketone. For example, the coupling product of diazobenzene with malonic ester is identical with the phenylhydrazone of mesoxalic ester.[43]

At the time of this discovery the matter was of considerable moment, because views as to the constitution of the diazo-compounds were in a fluid state, and the imprint left on the thought of that period is still sensible (see p. 182).

In passing, it may be said of the controversy as to the constitution of these substances that Bülow supported the true azo-structure because he was unable to acetylate the benzeneazoacetoacetic ester, nor could he bring it to react with benzoyl chloride or methyl iodide,[44] nor did he find any difference in the compound whether made from the normal or the isodiazotate of benzene.[45]

Japp and Klingemann, on the other hand, believed benzeneazo-acetone to be a hydrazone, because when treated with sodium ethoxide and ethyl chloroacetate the product of reductive scission was phenyl-glycine :—

$$\underset{\text{Cl·CH}_2\text{·CO}_2\text{Et}}{\overset{\text{MeCO·CH}=\text{N·NHPh}}{+}} \quad \rightarrow \quad \underset{\text{CH}_2\text{·CO}_2\text{Et}}{\overset{|}{\text{MeCO·CH}=\text{N·NPh}}} \quad \rightarrow \quad \underset{\text{Phenylglycine.}}{\overset{\text{(MeCO·CH}_2\text{·NH}_2)}{\text{PhNH·CH}_2\text{·CO}_2\text{H}}}$$

It was argued that had the benzeneazoacetone the constitution of an azo-compound the ethyl acetate could not have become attached to nitrogen, as the evidence showed it had, but to carbon. Such methods, however, are rarely decisive in attempts to settle the constitution of tautomers, and the view of v. Pechmann and Jennisch that the hydrogen is labile tallies with present-day ideas. It should be remarked that the ketone group in many of these azo-compounds retains its activity and condenses with hydrazines.

In general, there is among the reactive methylene compounds nothing analogous to the tris coupling of phenol. Malonic acid, however, can react with three molecules of diazobenzene forming first formazyl or its carboxylic acid and finally formazylazobenzene :—

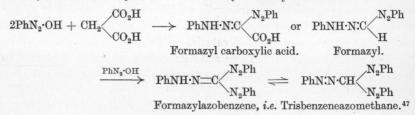

Formazyl carboxylic acid.   Formazyl.

Formazylazobenzene, *i.e.* Trisbenzeneazomethane.[47]

The azo-compounds derived from the substances having reactive methylene-groups resemble those derived from phenol, in that they form salts with weak caustic alkalis. This is a serious technical disadvantage, but the arylamides of acetoacetic ester, $MeCO \cdot CH_2 \cdot CONHAr$, are exceptions in this respect, affording azo-compounds which are used in quantity for making yellow pigments, the best being obtained by coupling with *o*-nitrodiazo-compounds,[48] while bisacetoacet-*o*-tolidide,

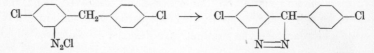

is the premier " naphthol " used in the various processes employed for obtaining yellow azoic colours.

Lastly, in the *endo*-azo-compounds of Duval an internal azo-compound is formed by the coupling of a diazo-compound derived from an *o*-aminodiphenylmethane with the central methane radical, the hydrogen atom being doubtless activated by the two phenyl nuclei. Both mono- and bis-*endo*azo-compounds have been described :—

They are typical azo-compounds, yellow or red in colour and insoluble in water.[49]

The Coupling of Phenol Ethers.

K. H. Meyer, on account of his views as to the mechanism of the coupling reaction, tried to couple diazo-compounds to phenol ethers. The ethers, being insoluble in alkali, were dissolved in glacial acetic acid, and in this medium it was found that, given sufficient time, strongly coupling diazo-compounds, like *p*-nitrodiazobenzene, would form azo-compounds, not indeed with monohydric phenol ethers like anisol, but with resorcinol ethers and, better still, with phloroglucinol ethers, with which latter even diazobenzene itself yielded azo-compounds.[50]   Later by using the still more strongly coupling 2 : 4-dinitro-diazobenzene, azo-compounds of anisol and phenetol were obtained.[51] The subject was also studied by Auwers, chiefly from the standpoint of substitution of the ethers and the point of entry of the diazo-compound.[52]   The notable characteristic of this coupling is, however, that it proceeds with partial or complete removal of the alkyl group of the phenol ether, a remarkable occurrence, because phenol ethers are by no means easily hydrolysed.   The proportion of the alkyl group which is removed varies with the diazo-compound, but no attempt has been made to ascertain what other factors are involved.   Generally speaking, the yields of azo-compounds are low.   Mason studied the coupling of 2-methoxy-3-naphthoic acid and determined the proportion of un-hydrolysed methoxyl remaining in the azo-compounds he prepared. He condensed his results into the following table :— [53]

TABLE XVII

Products of Coupling 2-Methoxy-3-naphthoic Acid

Diazo-Compound from :—	Methoxyl Groups remaining in Azo-Compound (proportion of one molecule).
p-Chloroaniline.	nil
2 : 6-Dichloroaniline.	nil
o-Nitroaniline.	0·5 mol.
m- ,,	0·5 ,,
p- ,,	nil
4-Nitro-o-anisidine.	1·0 mol.
5- ,,	2·0 mol., *i.e.* no hydrolysis had occurred.
Sulphanilic acid.	0·5 mol.
Benzidine.	nil
o-Tolidine.	nil

No guiding generalities can be deduced from the above list, and it is apparent that opportunities for research in this matter are by no means exhausted.   It would, for example, be interesting to study, in any particular pair of coupling components, the proportion of alkyl group lost when coupling is carried out in different solvents, and to look for a connection with the azo-hydrazo-equilibrium in that solvent.

The Coupling of Hydrocarbons.

To K. H. Meyer belongs the credit of first preparing crystalline azo-compounds by the union of a diazo-salt with a hydrocarbon, though Thiele had long before shown that some reaction leading to coloured substances takes place between diazo-compounds and *cyclo*pentadiene.[54] Meyer's first attempts were failures, but on persevering he found that

I

strongly coupling diazo-compounds yield derivatives with hydrocarbons of the butadiene series.[55]   Butadiene, isoprene, α-methylbutadiene, and β : γ-dimethylbutadiene all couple, the last-named the most easily either in glacial acetic acid or alcohol, with *p*-nitrodiazobenzene or 2 : 4-dinitrodiazobenzene. A method of determining conjugated dienes in admixture with other hydrocarbons is based on this coupling reaction.[55a] The azo-compounds preserve the unsaturated butadiene radical intact as shown by their forming tetrabromides by the addition of bromine. Unstable hydrazo-compounds are produced from the azo-compounds by the action of reducing agents.

The expectation that a still more strongly coupling diazo-compound would attack benzenoid hydrocarbons was realised when 2 : 4 : 6-trinitrodiazobenzene was combined with mesitylene and a crystalline azo-compound isolated.[56]   Benzene shows no sign of coupling even with this most avid of the diazo-compounds; toluene, *m*-xylene, and α-methylnaphthalene give colours, but no crystalline azo-compound.   This work has been extended by Smith and Paden, who coupled the same diazo-compound in sulphuric acid–glacial acetic acid with isodurene and pentamethylbenzene.   Durene and bromodurene refused to couple.[57]

Even ethylene hydrocarbons can be activated sufficiently to couple.[58] An intermediate carbenium salt formed by addition at the double bond can be isolated, and goes over either spontaneously or by the action of acid-binding agents to the azo-compound.   The patentees represent the reaction thus :—

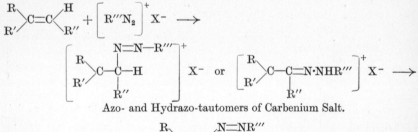

Azo- and Hydrazo-tautomers of Carbenium Salt.

Tetradiaminodiphenylethylene and dianisylethylene are mentioned in the examples as coupling with 2-diazonaphthalene-6 : 8-disulphonic acid and *p*-nitrodiazobenzene respectively.   The azo-dyestuffs are sensitive to acid and alkalis.

The Elimination of Substituents in Coupling.

As was mentioned above, all or part of an alkoxy-group may be split off a phenol ether in the coupling reaction, even though the azo-link does not become finally attached to the molecule in that position.

So great is the energy available for the consummation of the coupling reaction (see p. 78) that substituents occupying positions to which the azo-link would normally attach itself are sometimes ejected, and the azo-compound formed despite the blocking group. This is seen where halogen, sulphonic, carboxyl, or methylene groups occupy the 1-position in β-naphthol. In the case of the halogenated β-naphthols Pollack and Gebauer-Fulnegg have isolated intermediate compounds, apparently addition compounds,[59] which go over with elimination of hydrogen halide as noticed by several previous investigators.[60] Technical use has been made of the 1-sulphonic acid, as it offers a means of obtaining β-naphthol in a neutral or only faintly alkaline solution.[61] The ejection of the methylene group from β-dinaphthol methane by diazo-compounds was the first observed case of this reaction.[62] These substances have also been put to use in compounding printing mixtures (see p. 51).

Karrer described the removal of an alkyl group in the coupling of di-n-butylaniline and diisoamylaniline,[63] but Reilly and Hickinbottom have since coupled the former tertiary amine without loss of an alkyl group.[64] König [65] has shown that N-alkyl-2-methylenedihydroquinolines lose the alkyl group attached to nitrogen on coupling.

The Effect of Pyridine on the Coupling Reaction.

One type of azo-dyestuff, which includes some much-used direct cotton blues of good fastness, is made by coupling a diazo-compound to an amino-compound, re-diazotising the aminoazo-compound, coupling again, and so building up a chain of aromatic nuclei united by azo-links. This process cannot be continued indefinitely, and difficulties are encountered, and increase after the third repetition of the cycle. It is sometimes said of the diazo-compounds of these long-chain azo-compounds that they lack " coupling energy," which means to say that when they are added to the coupling component decomposition takes place much more quickly than coupling, so that only a small yield of the desired dyestuff is obtained. In these circumstances a great improvement in the yield results if the coupling medium is a mixture of pyridine and water.[66]

In what manner the pyridine acts so as to bring about this exaltation of the coupling power of the diazo-compound is not known, or at least not published. No academic investigation of the matter has been published, but it hardly seems to be a mere buffering action controlling the p_H. More probably there is some kind of loose combination between the diazo-compound and the pyridine which stabilises the diazo-compound during the long time necessary for coupling in the same way that diazobenzene is conserved in the coupling with aniline to form aminoazobenzene. To some degree the action of pyridine can be reproduced by a mixture of acetone and ammonia.[67] One may also hazard the guess that there has been for a long period empirical knowledge of this action of pyridine, and possibly of its homologues, in the laboratories of Germany, for Heller [68] mentions the beneficial effect of quinoline in the tris coupling of resorcinol, but says that pyridine and diethylamine did not show the effect. Fischer and Bauer [19] also mention that they tried pyridine to improve the coupling of 1 : 5-dihydroxynaphthalene.

An elucidation of this matter would be a considerable service to the knowledge of the chemistry of the diazo-compounds.

Migration of the Diazo-Group.

The attempt to couple primary aromatic amines with diazo-compounds in weakly acid solution sometimes fails to yield a single azo-compound, but instead there is obtained a mixture of two aminoazo-compounds. Thus :—

$$ArN_2X + Ar'NH_2 \quad \text{yields} \quad ArN_2Ar'NH_2 \quad \text{and} \quad Ar'N_2ArNH_2$$

The reaction is sometimes referred to among dyestuff chemists as " diazo-exchange," and it can be a source of annoyance when a useful compound is contaminated with one of inferior properties for the use in view.

A partial or complete exchange of the diazo-group between the two amines may precede the subsequent two-fold coupling, and Griess first observed such an exchange on mixing diazotised sulphanilic acid and p-toluidine hydrochloride when he recovered the sulphanilic acid and found p-diazotoluene chloride in the solution.[70] Similarly diazobenzene chloride can be obtained if aniline is used instead of p-toluidine, while p- or m-nitrodiazobenzene chloride will diazotise p-toluidine. The reverse reaction will not, however, occur,[71] and one might at first sight believe that diazo-compounds with negative substituents can always pass the diazo-group to amines with less negative substituents (compare E.P. 433,878, p. 139), but at least one exception to such a rule is known, for diazobenzene chloride exchanges its diazo-group with p-bromo-aniline.[72]

The readiest explanation is that an equilibrium exists between diazo-salt, amine salt, and nitrous acid. The equilibrium can, moreover, be approached from the diazo-side, for both Bamberger [73] and Bucherer and Wolff [74] found that a purified isodiazotate salt when acidified gives a diazo-salt solution in which the presence of nitrous acid can be demonstrated, the only apparent source of which is hydrolysis of the diazo-salt. Such observations support the case of those who would look on diazo-compounds as anilides of nitrous acid (see p. 176).

But though at first sight the inclination is to suppose that diazo-exchange precedes aberration of the coupling, yet it has recently been shown that azo-compounds can be attacked by diazo-compounds, and an exchange of the components already incorporated in the molecule is effected. A valuable paper on this subject has been published by Filippytschew and Tschekalin.[75] They ascribe the power of one diazo-compound to eject another from an azo-compound to be due to their relative coupling activity. Thus *p*-nitrodiazobenzene displaces diazotised sulphanilic acid, tetrazotised benzidine or diazobenzene, but no *p*-nitrodiazobenzene can be eliminated from an azo-compound into the composition of which it has entered by treatment with diazotised sulphanilic acid, whilst a diazo-compound of low activity like *p*-diazo-salicylic acid cannot eject any other nucleus. As an example of the reaction may be cited the action of tetrazotised benzidine on the azo-compound made by coupling diazobenzene to acetyl H-acid. At $N/10$ concentration at 0° in sodium carbonate solution exchange is complete in an hour, and an 80% yield of diazobenzene can be recovered from the solution. The authors of the paper believe the fundamental cause of the exchange to lie in keto-enol tautomerism, and as this is more pronounced in the naphthalene series than in the benzene series, so the exchange takes place more frequently in the dyes of the naphthalene series. They picture the reaction as proceeding by addition followed by scission of an unstable quinonoid addition product :—

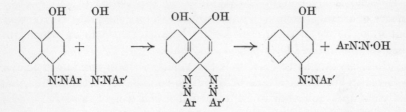

Rowe and Dangerfield [76] have shown that some azo-dyes can be hydrolysed back to diazo-compounds and coupling component merely by boiling with water.

The Kinetics of the Coupling Reaction.

This aspect of the coupling reaction has been studied extensively by Goldschmidt and his school, who found that the reaction is essentially bimolecular, though corrections for various factors are necessary. That such should be the case is hardly surprising, for complications are introduced by the tautomeric forms of the diazo-compounds which require time to change one into the other, and by the fact that it is not the sodium salt of the phenol which couples, but free phenol produced by hydrolysis of the salt.[77] Veley studied the rate of formation of Bismarck Brown in dilute aqueous solution by acting on *m*-diamines with nitrous acid and measuring the rate of formation of the dyestuff by the colorimeter. He also showed that the bimolecular law is followed.[78]

Conant and Peterson obtained more concordant results than Goldschmidt by buffering the coupling solution so as to prevent variation of the p_H as the reaction proceeded.[79] They used the colorimetric method to measure the rate of production of the azo-compound, and found the reaction to be bimolecular over a wide range. In the twenty pairs of diazo-compounds and phenols studied they found the coupling rate to be a simple function of the hydrogen-ion activity, and each pair was characterised by a " coupling value " defined as the p_H for a given temperature and salt concentration at which $\log k = 1$. Blumberger [80] has also determined experimentally the relationship between coupling speed and p_H.

The Mechanism of the Coupling Reaction.

The mainspring of much research on the coupling reaction has been the search for evidence to support theoretical views as to its mechanism. Broadly there have been two schools of thought : that which believed that the diazo-compound first attaches itself to the hydroxy- or aminogroup and thence migrates to the carbon atom, and against it the school which held that the diazo-compound first adds to a double bond.[81] Both schools are now in process of being superseded by the electron theory of organic reactions which provides a more adequate explanation, but some notice of them is necessary because the facts on which the theories are founded have permanent value.

Goldschmidt, as the result of the kinetic studies mentioned above, believed in the direct attack of the diazo-compound on the phenol, but his view does not seem to have carried much weight, and succeeding investigators worked on the hypothesis that reaction must proceed through an intermediate stage.

Dimroth, working on the action of diazo-compounds on aliphatic substances which show keto-enol tautomerism and in which the separate tautomers can be isolated, started the intermediate compound theory.[82] He used diacetsuccinic ester and acetyldibenzoyl methane, coupling in alcohol solution with p-nitrodiazobenzene*iso*diazotate. He showed that the keto-form does not couple, nor can direct replacement of hydrogen occur, because in the enol form of acetyldibenzoyl methane, $MeC(OH){=}C{<}^{COPh}_{COPh}$, there is no hydrogen atom available at the methane carbon atom to which the azo-link eventually becomes attached. The reaction must therefore go through the O-azo-compound. Such O-azo-compounds, which are colourless, were isolated by Dimroth and Hartmann,[83] and are easily recognised by their instability, and that when dissolved they show the reactions of a diazo-compound by coupling with β-naphthol, and hence they may be regarded as oxygen analogues of the diazoamino-compounds. When warmed with alkali the true red C-azo-compound is formed, and this again, when heated alone, undergoes a migration of the acetyl group, so that the final stable substance is a hydrazone.[84] From this hydrazone sodium ethoxide will remove the acetyl group regenerating a C-azo-compound having one acyl group less than the first. The four stages in acetyldibenzoyl methane occur thus :—

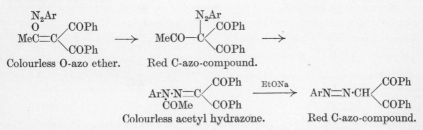

O-azo-compounds of phenols similar to the above O-azo-compounds are well known, and they are formed by negatively substituted phenols such as p-nitrophenol,[85] o-chlorophenol,[86] or picric acid (see p. 124). Here the phenolic hydrogen has become so acidic that it effectively plays the part of an anion to the diazonium cation. Dimroth examined a series of phenols of descending acidity[87] to find where the break from diazonium salt to O-azo-compound occurs, using as criterion the electrical conductivity of the solution in 80% acetone–water. In this solvent diazonium salts are ionised, whereas O-azo-compounds are not. In the following table is given a selection of values for conductivity against different acids and phenols when mixed with an equivalent of the diazo-compound from benzoyl-1 : 4-naphthylenediamine. The break between acidic phenols which form salts and those forming non-ionised O-azo-compounds is apparent.

TABLE XVI

Conductivities of Phenolic Diazo-Salts and O-Azo-Compounds of 4-Benzoylamino-1-diazonaphthalene

Phenols and Acids.	Conductivity.
Hydrochloric acid.	31·37
Trichloroacetic acid.	26·2
Picric acid.	30·48
2 : 4-Dinitrophenol.	22·00
p-Nitrophenol.	2·20
Acetyldibenzoyl methane.	0·26
Pentamethyl phenol.	0·41

Dimroth, moreover, showed that the colourless O-azo-compound from p-nitrophenol and p-bromodiazobenzene can be made to rearrange to the red *ortho*-hydroxyazo-compound, thus realising the two stages in the purely aromatic series :—

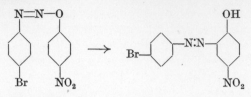

A defect of Dimroth's theory was that it could not accommodate the coupling of phenol ethers or hydrocarbons, and to fit these facts Meyer postulated addition at a double bond and an intermediate quinonoid addition product :—

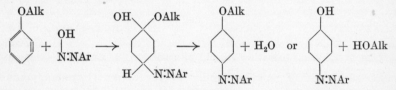

Thus the partial or complete hydrolysis of a phenol ether can be explained. This theory easily explained the coupling of aromatic hydrocarbons and unsaturated aliphatic hydrocarbons like the butadienes.

Karrer [88] considered the formation of intermediate oxonium or ammonium salts to be the mechanism of coupling as providing an explanation of the hydrolysis of phenol ethers :—

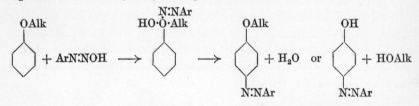

As proof of the actuality of such intermediate stages in the coupling of amines, Fierz-David has published a beautiful set of photomicrographs showing the intermediate stages in the coupling of diazotised sulphanilic acid to *m*-phenylenediamine to form Sulpho Chrysoidine.[89]

Hantzsch's theoretical views on the coupling reaction also included an intermediate addition product, but he believed such addition products to be derived from diazonium hydroxides, on account of the particular capacity of diazonium compounds to form addition complexes :—[90]

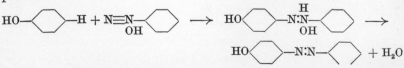

But, as has already been pointed out, few diazonium compounds are stable in the conditions under which coupling is carried out, and such complexes, if formed, would be very evanescent. It will be noted, however, that Hantzsch conceived of the diazonium hydroxide attacking directly the hydrogen atom to be eliminated.

In the light of the electronic theory, with its provision of induced polarity, the need for any such roundabout theories as those outlined above vanishes, and the original direct coupling suggested by Gold-schmidt comes to its own. The phenolic oxygen or amino-nitrogen atom induces sufficient polarisation in the *para* or *ortho* hydrogen atom for it to be expelled on the approach of the cationoid diazo-compound, which accepts the proffered electron. The same state obtains in conjugated dienes, where two ethylene linkages greatly enhance the anionoid nature of the molecule, so that combination occurs by direct expulsion of a hydrogen atom when a diazo-compound of sufficient electron accepting strength is present (see Robinson, Lecture, p. 21). In the coupling of aromatic hydrocarbons it will be observed that it is only those having the mesitylene structure which have been reported as coupling. In mesitylene the three methyl groups are jointly able to cause polarisation of a hydrogen atom, whereas in durene the inductive effects of only two *ortho*-methyl groups are insufficient to polarise either of the two possible coupling positions, which is also the case with *m*-xylene.

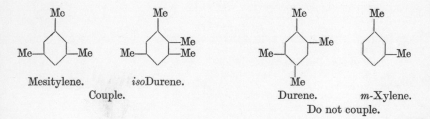

Mesitylene.   *iso*Durene.   Durene.   *m*-Xylene.
        Couple.   Do not couple.

Of Dimroth's experiments it may be remarked that though indeed he isolated intermediate O-azo-compounds, he was able to achieve the result rather as an abnormality by utilising molecules in which the coupling position is under the direct influence of cationoid groups, so that the normal coupling function is suppressed. For instance, the enol form of acetyldibenzoylmethane is seen to be a neutralised catio-enoid system fundamentally different from poly-enoid or hetero-enoid systems, in which the inductive effect is centred on a carbon atom :—

Diazo-Compounds and Proteins.

In their capacity to couple, diazo-compounds are of interest to the biochemist, for they combine with proteins both by virtue of the phenolic hydroxy-group present in structural units of the tyrosine family and the indole in tryptophane units. If the protein has suffered hydrolysis the products have a very high combining capacity for diazo-compounds as triazenes are formed as well as azo-compounds. Ehrlich's diazo-reaction [91] consists in the use of a diazo-compound, such as diazobenzene-*p*-sulphonic acid, to detect albumen in the urine in certain pathological conditions.[92] Further, artificial sera have been made by coupling diazo-compounds with proteins,[93] and such sera have been used in the study of immunity.[94] Similar substances can be employed as the vehicles for metals, such as gold and silver, for medicinal purposes by using the diazo-derivatives of the gold and silver salts of mercapto-*p*-aminobenzoic acid coupled to proteins.[95]

REFERENCES

[1] Bergmann, Engel, Sándor, *Ber.*, 1930, **63**, 2572.
[2] C. V. and R. A. Gortner, *J.Am.C.S.*, 1910, **32**, 1294.
[3] Hartley, Stuart, *J.C.S.*, 1914, **105**, 309.
[4] Kekulé, Hidegh, *Ber.*, 1870, **3**, 233.
[5] Mitscherlich, *Ann.*, 1834, **12**, 311.
[6] Goldschmidt, *Ber.*, 1895, **28**, 2020.
[7] S.C.I., E.P. 441,590; Anm. G. 88,238; F.P. 787,483.
[8] Schoutissen, *J.Am.C.S.*, 1933, **55**, 4541. See also Pelagatti, Ricci, *Ann. Chim. Appl.*, 1935, **25**, 603.
[9] Schoutissen, *Rec. trav. chim.*, 1935, **54**, 381.
[10] Bamberger, *Ber.*, 1900, **33**, 3188.
[11] Mazzara, Pozzetto, *Gazz.*, 1885, **15**, 52, 214.
[12] Grandmougin, Freimann, *Ber.*, 1907, **40**, 2662; *J. pr. Chem.*, 1908, ii, **78**, 384. Heller, Nötzel, *ibid.*, 1907, ii, **76**, 58. Heller, *ibid.*, 1908, **77**, 189; 1910, **81**, 184. Chattaway, Hill, *J.C.S.*, 1922, **122**, 2756.
[13] Orndorff, Ray, *Ber.*, 1907, **40**, 2662; Muhlert, *Zeit. angew. Chem.*, 1908, **21**, 2611.
[14] I.C.I., E.P. 441,398, 441,400; F.P. 792,699, 792,700.
[15] Witt, Johnson, *Ber.*, 1893, **26**, 1905. Witt, Meyer, *ibid.*, p. 1072.
[16] Mason, *J.S.D.C.*, 1932, **48**, 293.
[17] Elkins, Hunter, *J.C.S.*, **1935**, 1598.
[18] O. Fischer, Bauer, *J. pr. Chem.*, 1916, ii, **94**, 13; 1917, **95**, 264.
[19] Zincke, Bindewald, *Ber.*, 1884, **17**, 3026.
[20] Lauer, Miller, *J.Am.C.S.*, 1935, **57**, 520. See also Uemura, Manura, *Bull. Chem. Soc. Japan*, 1935, **10**, 169.
[21] Kuhn, Bär, *Ann.*, 1935, **516**, 144.
[22] Burawoy, *Ber.*, 1930, **63**, 3155; 1931, **64**, 462; 1933, **66**, 228.
[23] Scharwin, Kalianoff, *ibid.*, 1908, **41**, 2056.
[24] Rohner, D.R.P. 193,211 (Fr., **9**, 336).

[25] Witt, *Ber.*, 1912, **45**, 2380.
[26] Morgan, *J.C.S.*, 1900, **77**, 1205; 1902, **81**, 86, 650, 1376. Morgan, Wootton, *ibid.*, 1905, **87**, 935. Morgan, Clayton, *ibid.*, 1906, **89**, 1054. Morgan, Micklethwaite, *ibid.*, 1907, **91**, 368.
[27] Levi, Faldino, *Gazz.*, 1924, **54**, 818.
[28] Bayer, E.P. 238,683.
[29] Witt, Schmitt, *Ber.*, 1894, **27**, 2372. König, Kohler, *ibid.*, 1921, **54**, 981.
[30] König, Kohler, *ibid.*, 1922, **55**, 2139.
[31] Gattermann, Liebermann, *Ann.*, 1912, **394**, 198.
[32] Gattermann, Schulze, *Ber.*, 1897, **30**, 50. For an explanation on the basis of the electron theory, see Robinson, Lecture, p. 42.
[33] Fierz-David, Brütsch, *Helv. Chim. Acta*, 1921, **4**, 880.
[34] Fierz-David, *Angew. Chem.*, 1936, **49**, 24.
[35] V. Meyer, Ambuhl, *Ber.*, 1876, **9**, 384; 1878, **11**, 2418; 1884, **17**, 1928.
[36] V. Meyer, Ambuhl, *ibid.*, 1875, **8**, 751, 1053.
[37] V. Meyer, Munzer, *ibid.*, 1878, **11**, 1417.
[38] Bülow, Schlotterbeck, *ibid.*, 1902, **35**, 2187.
[39] Favrel, Jean, *Bull. Soc. chim.*, 1925, iv, **37**, 1238.
[40] v. Pechmann, Jennisch, *Ber.*, 1893, **24**, 3255.
[41] Parks, Fisher, *J.C.S.*, **1936**, 83.
[42] Sen, Gosh, *J. Indian C.S.*, 1927, **4**, 477.
[43] Beyer, Claisen, *Ber.*, 1888, **21**, 1697.
[44] Bülow, *ibid.*, 1899, **32**, 197.
[45] Bülow, *ibid.*, 1898, **31**, 3122.
[46] Japp, Klingemann, *ibid.*, 1887, **20**, 2942, 3284, 3398.
[47] Busch, Wolbring, *J. pr. Chem.*, 1905, ii, **71**, 366. Bamberger, Müller, *Ber.*, 1894, **27**, 147. v. Pechmann, *ibid.*, 1892, **25**, 3175.
[48] Rowe, *J.S.D.C.*, 1926, **42**, 80; 1928, **44**, 205. Fierz-David, *Helv. Chim. Acta*, 1928, **11**, 776.
[49] Duval, *Compt. rend.*, 1907, **144**, 222; 1908, **146**, 1407; 1912, **154**, 780.
[50] Meyer, Lenhardt, *Ann.*, 1913, **398**, 74.
[51] Meyer, Irschik, *Ber.*, 1914, **47**, 1741.
[52] Auwers, Michaelis, *ibid.*, p. 1281; Auwers, Borsche, *ibid.*, 1915, **48**, 1791.
[53] Mason, Jambuserwala, *J.S.D.C.*, 1930, **46**, 339.
[54] Thiele, *Ber.*, 1900, **33**, 668.
[55] Meyer, Scholler, *ibid.*, 1914, **47**, 1711; 1919, **52**, 1468.
[55a] Terentiev, *Compt. rend. Acad. Sci. U.S.S.R.*, 1935, **4**, 267; *Cent.*, 1936, **107**, 1, 4043.
[56] Meyer, Tochtermann, *Ber.*, 1921, **54**, 2283.
[57] Smith, Paden, *J.Am.C.S.*, 1934, **56**, 2169.
[58] I.G., E.P. 435,449; F.P. 769,113.
[59] Pollack, Gebauer-Fulnegg, *Monats.*, 1928, **50**, 310.
[60] Hewitt, Mitchell, *J.C.S.*, 1906, **89**, 1167. Smith, *ibid.*, p. 1515. Wahl, Lantz, *Bull. Soc. chim.*, 1923, iv, **33**, 93. Vesely, Stursa, *Chem. Listy*, 1933, **27**, 125.
[61] Calico Printers Assoc., D.R.P. 204,702 (Fr., **9**, 408). Heilmann, Battegay, D.R.P. 238,841 (Fr., **10**, 924).
[62] Möhlau, Strohbach, *Ber.*, 1900, **33**, 804. Strohbach, *ibid.*, 1901, **34**, 4162.
[63] Karrer, *ibid.*, 1915, **48**, 1398.
[64] Reilly, Hickinbottom, *J.C.S.*, 1918, **113**, 99.
[65] König, *Ber.*, 1923, **56**, 1543.
[66] I.G., E.P. 248,230; D.R.P. 450,998 (Fr., **15**, 521); D.R.P. 453,133 (Fr., **15**, 522); E.P. 287,232, 298,518. S.C.I., E.P. 347,742, Example 2.
[67] I.C.I., E.P. 374,498.
[68] Heller, *J. pr. Chem.*, 1908, ii, **77**, 190.
[69] Fischer, Bauer, *ibid.*, p. 190.
[70] Griess, *Ber.*, 1882, **15**, 2190. Fierz-David, "Kunstliche Organische Farbstoffe," p. 97.
[71] Schraube, Fritsch, *Ber.*, 1896, **29**, 287.
[72] Hantzsch, F. M. Perkin, *ibid.*, 1909, **42**, 1412.
[73] Bamberger, *ibid.*, 1895, **28**, 826.
[74] Bucherer, Wolff, *ibid.*, 1909, **42**, 881, 1852.

[75] Filippytschew, Tschekalin, *Anilinokras. Prom.*, 1935, **5**, 76; *Cent.*, 1935, ii, 2129. Compare Suais, *Bull. Soc. Ind. Mulhouse*, 1907, **77**, 75. Scission of the triphenylmethane molecule by *p*-nitrodiazobenzene.

[76] Rowe, Dangerfield, *J.S.D.C.*, 1936, **52**, 48. See also Grippa, Pieroni, *Gazz.*, 1936, **65**, 1250.

[77] Goldschmidt, Merz, *Ber.*, 1897, **30**, 670. Goldschmidt, Buss, *ibid.*, p. 2075. Goldschmidt, Keppler, *ibid.*, 1900, **33**, 893. Goldschmidt, Keller, *ibid.*, 1902, **35**, 3534.

[78] Veley, *J.C.S.*, 1909, **95**, 1186.

[79] Conant, Peterson, *J.Am.C.S.*, 1930, **52**, 1220.

[80] Blumberger, *Rec. trav. chim.*, 1930, **49**, 280.

[81] Summaries of views current at respective dates : Walker, *J.S.D.C.*, 1923, **39**, 293. Blumberger, *Chem. Wkbld.*, 1926, **23**, 106.

[82] Dimroth, *Ber.*, 1907, **40**, 2404.

[83] Dimroth, Hartmann, *ibid.*, 1908, **41**, 4012.

[84] Dimroth, Hartmann, *ibid.*, 1907, **40**, 4460.

[85] Griess, *ibid.*, 1884, **17**, 334.

[86] Auwers, *ibid.*, 1908, **41**, 4304.

[87] Dimroth, Leichtlin, Friedmann, *ibid.*, 1917, **50**, 1534.

[88] Karrer, *ibid.*, 1915, **48**, 1398.

[89] Fierz-David, " Kunstliche Organische Farbstoffe " (Springer), p. 96.

[90] Hantzsch, *Ber.*, 1908, **41**, 3532; 1909, **42**, 394, 2137.

[91] P. Ehrlich, *Charité-Annalen*, 1883, **8**. Literature survey, Clemens, *Deut. Arch. Klin. Med.*, **63**, 74. Huber, *Dissertation, Bern*, 1910.

[92] Hermanns, Sachs, *Zeit. physiol. Chem.*, 1921, **114**, 79, 88; *ibid.*, 1922, **122**, 98.

[93] Van Veen, *Chem. Wkbld.*, 1934, **31**, 567.

[94] den Dooren de Jong, *ibid.*, 1935, **32**, 590.

[95] I.G., D.P.P. Anm., 151,165.

CHAPTER VII

REACTIONS OF THE DIAZO-COMPOUNDS. CLASS B
(continued)

GROUP 2. OXIDATION PRODUCTS OF DIAZO-COMPOUNDS

DIAZO-COMPOUNDS can be oxidised in aqueous solution under carefully regulated conditions to form substances which Bamberger called "diazoic acids." These substances are, in fact, the aryl nitroamines, $Ar \cdot NH \cdot NO_2$, and are more suitably named as such rather than by a name which would be appropriate to the diazohydroxides and with which it might be easily confounded.

Oxidising agents which are effective under alkaline conditions are most suitable for the purpose, and here is provided yet another example of the way in which diazo-compounds in alkaline solution behave as if they had the nitrosamine structure—$Ar \cdot NH \cdot NO \longrightarrow Ar \cdot NH \cdot NO_2$.

Bamberger and Storch in the first instance carried out the oxidation with potassium ferricyanide,[1] and Bamberger found that potassium benzene*iso*diazotate gives a better yield than the normal salt.[2] Permanganate[3] and hydrogen peroxide[4] can also be used, while for technical purposes sodium hypochlorite is usually selected and reaction carried out in a weakly alkaline solution,[5] though care is necessary to avoid by-products.

Bamberger demonstrated that his diazoic acid is a nitroamine by showing the identity of the oxidation product of diazobenzene with the substance obtained by acting on aniline in ethereal solution with nitrogen pentoxide :—

$$2PhNH_2 + N_2O_5 \longrightarrow 2PhNH \cdot NO_2 + H_2O \quad [6]$$

That the nitro-group is attached to the amino-nitrogen atom is shown by its scission on diazotisation, when diazobenzene is obtained, and by its migration under acid conditions, when *o*- and *p*-nitroaniline are produced :—

The hydrogen atom of the imino-group in nitroamines can be replaced by chlorine by treatment with hypochlorite forming a chloro-imide in which both chlorine and nitro-group can migrate to the ring :—

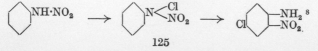

125

By reduction with zinc and acetic acid the nitroamines can be reduced back to the parent diazo-compound. Zinc dust and ammonium chloride converts them back to the *iso*diazotate,[9] but sodium amalgam gives the hydrazine.

Like the diazo-compounds from which they are derived, the nitroamines are tautomeric, though there is no doubt that their tautomerism is structural :—

$$Ar \cdot NH \cdot NO_2 \longrightarrow Ar \cdot N = NO_2H$$

The sodium and silver salts when treated with methyl iodide give two different ethers, just as do the diazotates. The ether derived from the sodium salt has the methyl group attached to nitrogen, while the ether derived from the silver salt is an *O*-ether. These facts gave rise to a controversy as to the constitution of the nitroamines much on the same lines as that touching the constitution of the diazo-compounds.[10] The nitroamines are one of the best examples of the substances called pseudo-acids by Hantzsch, being neutral as the free substance and only reverting to a salt-forming tautomer in the presence of bases.

REFERENCES

[1] Bamberger, Storch, *Ber.*, 1893, **26**, 471; Bamberger, *ibid.*, 1894, **27**, 359; M.L.B., D.R.P. 70,813 (Fr., **3**, 995).
[2] Bamberger, *ibid.*, 1894, **27**, 914; M.L.B., D.R.P. 77,397 (Fr., **4**, 1333).
[3] Bamberger, Landsteiner, *ibid.*, 1893, **26**, 482.
[4] Bamberger, Baudisch, *ibid.*, 1909, **42**, 3568.
[5] Zincke, Kuchenbecker, *Ann.*, 1903, **330**, 1; S.C.I., E.P. 447,514; D.R.P., 630,907; F.P. 783,305; Sw.P. 175,350, 176,018. Anthraquinone series : M.L.B., D.R.P. 156,803 (Fr., **8**, 286).
[6] Bamberger, *Ber.*, 1894, **27**, 584.
[7] Bradfield, Orton, *J.C.S.*, **1929**, 915.
[8] Bamberger, *Ber.*, 1894, **27**, 361.
[9] Bamberger, *ibid.*, 1920, **53**, 2321.
[10] Bamberger, *ibid.*, 1894, **27**, 2601; 1897, **30**, 1248; *Ann.*, 1900, **311**, 49. Hantzsch, *Ber.*, 1894, **27**, 1729; 1898, **31**, 177; 1899, **32**, 1722; 1902, **35**, 258.

GROUP 3. REDUCTION PRODUCTS OF THE DIAZO-COMPOUNDS. ARYL HYDRAZINES

Reducing agents which do not detach the nitrogen atoms from the aryl nucleus convert diazo-compounds to arylhydrazines, $Ar \cdot NH \cdot NH_2$, whether reduction is carried out in acid or in alkaline solution. The reagent most commonly used for the purpose is sulphurous acid or alkali sulphite, and various hydrazine sulphonic acids may appear as intermediate stages in the reduction. The first stage of the action of sulphite on diazo-compounds is the diazosulphonate, $ArN = N \cdot SO_3Na$, but Davies [1] has shown that substituents in the diazo-compound affect the reaction, and diazobenzene and *p*-nitrodiazobenzene are differentiated as follows :—

$$Ph \cdot N_2Cl + 2Na_2SO_3 + H_2O = Ph \cdot NH \cdot NHSO_3Na + NaCl + Na_2SO_4$$
$$NO_2 \cdot C_6H_4 \cdot N_2Cl + 2Na_2SO_3 + H_2O = NO_2 \cdot C_6H_4 \cdot N_2H(SO_3Na)_2 + NaCl + NaOH$$

The first reaction is the one known since 1871, when it was discovered by Strecker and Römer,[2] and was the basis of E. Fischer's synthesis of phenylhydrazine, in which he removed the β-sulphonic acid group by hydrolysis with weak acid, and then liberated the base with alkali.[3] This has been the standard process used industrially to manufacture the arylhydrazines, though it was for long not appreciated that cases of failure may have been due to want of correct conditions for the progress of the second reaction cited above. Not only is reduction with sulphite applicable in the benzene and naphthalene series, but also in the anthraquinone series.[4]

When reduction is carried out under more acid conditions with bisulphite, the sulphur may combine directly with the aryl radical, nitrogen being lost. The sulphinic acid which results then condenses with the hydrazine to form a sulphazide, $Ar \cdot NH \cdot NH \cdot SO_2Ar$.[5] The sulphazides are really sulphonhydrazides, and can be made by condensing arylhydrazines with sulphon chlorides.

Diazonium salts can be reduced direct to hydrazines with stannous chloride which is often the most convenient way of preparing hydrazines in small quantity for laboratory purposes :—[6]

$$ArN_2Cl + 2SnCl_2 + 4HCl = ArNHNH_2 \cdot HCl + 2SnCl_4$$

The action of zinc diethyl on benzenediazonium chloride suspended in dry ether at $-15°$ is also one of reduction, the principal product being $\alpha : \beta$-diethylphenylhydrazine.[7]

In caustic alkaline solution the metallic diazotates can be reduced to hydrazines by sodium amalgam,[8] but if the amalgam is used in acetic acid, then the amine is regenerated, and this, combining with unreduced diazo-compound, produces the diazoamino-compound.[9] Hydrosulphite can also be used in alkaline solution, but this reagent carries reduction only to the stage of the β-sulphonic acid, and an acid hydrolysis is afterwards necessary.[10]

Lastly, Angeli and Jolles have obtained hydrazine derivatives with sodium stannite, a reducing agent which normally removes the nitrogen and produces the hydrocarbon. Believing that this reduction proceeds through phenyldi-imide, $PhN = NH$ (unknown), which decomposes into benzene and nitrogen, they added sodium benzene diazotate to sodium stannite with alcohol and benzaldehyde, and obtained benzoylphenylhydrazine, due, in their opinion, to the condensation of the intermediate di-imide and aldehyde :—[11]

$$PhN{=}NH + HOC \cdot Ph = PhNH \cdot NHCOPh$$

The arylhydrazines are strongly basic substances usually low-melting solids, though some, like phenylhydrazine itself, are oils. They are characterised by strong reducing power for silver and copper salts. If boiled with cupric salts, the nitrogen is quantitatively evolved, a reaction which serves both as a means of analysis and also of generating the parent hydrocarbon of the diazo-compound.[12]

REFERENCES

[1] Davies, *J.C.S.*, 1922, **121**, 715.
[2] Strecker, Römer, *Ber.*, 1871, **4**, 784.
[3] E. Fischer, *ibid.*, 1875, **8**, 589; *Ann.*, 1878, **190**, 77.
[4] Bayer, D.R.P. 163,447; Möhlau, *Ber.*, 1912, **45**, 2233.
[5] Königs, *ibid.*, 1877, **10**, 1531; Limpricht, *ibid.*, 1887, **20**, 1233.
[6] V. Meyer, Lecco, *ibid.*, 1883, **16**, 2976.
[7] Bamberger, Tichwinski, *ibid.*, 1902, **35**, 4179.
[8] Bamberger, *ibid.*, 1898, **29**, 473. Hantzsch, *ibid.*, 1897, **30**, 340; 1899, **32**, 1719.
[9] Walther, *J. pr. Chem.*, 1895, ii, **53**, 467.
[10] Grandmougin, *Ber.*, 1907, **40**, 422.
[11] Angeli, Jolles, *ibid.*, 1929, **62**, 2099.
[12] Baeyer, Pfitzinger, *ibid.*, 1885, **18**, 90, 786.

GROUP 4. THE DIAZOAMINO- AND DIAZOIMINO-COMPOUNDS OR TRIAZENES AND THEIR USE AS STABILISED DIAZO-COMPOUNDS

The diazoamino-compounds have been known as long as the diazo-compounds themselves, for they were discovered by Griess, who observed their formation when the attempt is made to diazotise an amine with insufficient acid.[1] So easy is their formation, provided that the hydrogen-ion concentration is kept low, that Earl has shown that diazoaminobenzene is formed almost quantitatively when carbon dioxide is passed into an emulsion of aniline in sodium nitrite solution.[2] They arise by the attack of a diazocompound on an aminohydrogen atom, and are stable under neutral or alkaline conditions, but are split back more or less easily by acids to diazo-salt and amine. Their mode of formation shows that the central core of the molecule of the diazo-amino-compounds consists of a chain of three nitrogen atoms, two being united by a double bond, $-N=N\cdot N<$.

All the members of this large family are derived from the unknown base $HN=N\cdot NH_2$ by substitution of one, two, or three of the hydrogen atoms. The systematic name given to the base is triazene, and in a completely rational nomenclature all members of the family would be named as triazenes. The names diazoamino and diazoimino are therefore, strictly speaking, trivial names, but as their genesis and usage are older and more strongly entrenched than the systematic name, they will be retained here and used interchangeably with the name triazene, whichever is the most concise. In the older nomenclature diazoamino-compounds comprise substances derived from a diazo-compound and a primary amine, and diazoimino-compounds those derived from secondary amines. While in some respects the two groups resemble each other, the labile hydrogen atom present in the diazoamino-compounds causes the problems associated with tautomerism to be manifested, and from the day of their discovery they have attracted the inquiries of chemists.

The subsequent discussion will be simplified if the various known permutations which arise from substitution in the triazene nucleus are set out in a form available for reference. In the list below aromatic nuclei are denoted by Ar, which in any molecule may be the same or different if occurring more than once, and the aliphatic by A, to which the same proviso applies.

1. Aromatic and mixed aliphatic diazoamino-compounds; $ArN\!\!=\!\!N\cdot NHAr$, $ArN\!\!=\!\!N\cdot NHA$.

2. Bisdiazoamino-compounds: $(Ar'N\!\!=\!\!N)_2NAr$, $(ArN\!\!=\!\!N)_2NA$, $(ArN\!\!=\!\!N)_2NH$.

3. Aliphatic diazoamino-compounds : $AN\!\!=\!\!N\cdot NHA$.

4. Diazoimino-compounds :

$$ArN\!\!=\!\!N\cdot N\!\!\begin{array}{c}\diagup Ar \\ \diagdown Ar\end{array} \quad ArN\!\!=\!\!N\cdot N\!\!\begin{array}{c}\diagup Ar \\ \diagdown A\end{array} \quad ArN\!\!=\!\!N\cdot N\!\!\begin{array}{c}\diagup A \\ \diagdown A\end{array} \quad ArN\!\!=\!\!N\cdot N\!\!\begin{array}{c}\diagup A \\ \diagdown A\end{array}$$

At various times the difficulties of explaining the reactions of the diazoamino-compounds have caused structures other than the above to be mooted, such as $\underset{\text{NH}}{\overset{\text{ArN}\!\!-\!\!\text{NAr}}{\diagdown\!\!\diagup}}$ and $\underset{\text{N}}{\overset{\text{ArN}\!\!-\!\!\text{NHAr}}{|||}}$. Neither of these can be supported. The former structure cannot properly account for the diazoimino-compounds, while as to the latter there is no evidence to support the presence of a non-ionised pentavalent nitrogen atom in the molecule.

When a diazo-compound acts on a primary amine, either aromatic or aliphatic, under neutral or alkaline conditions, the triazene system is formed, except in certain cases where a carbon atom has been activated, so that coupling occurs to form an azo-compound as in m-toluidine, xylidines, naphthylamines, and m-diamines. If coupling is prevented by suitably placed substituents, diazoamino-compounds are formed, howbeit sometimes with great difficulty.[3] Griess first made unsymmetrical diazoamino-compounds from diazobenzene nitrate and p-bromoaniline and p-toluidine. At the same time he discovered that whether diazobenzene acts on p-toluidine or diazo-p-toluene on aniline the products of both reactions are identical.[4]

Where the object is to make symmetrical aromatic diazoamino-compounds, this is easily done by acting on the amine with but half the quantity of nitrite and mineral acid necessary to secure diazotisation, whereupon the diazoamino-compound is formed in one operation by the union of the diazo-compound with the unchanged amine, and the diazoamino-compound separates from solution as a light-coloured precipitate, which can be collected, dried, and crystallised.[5] Many variations of the method have been published, and solvents other than

K

water can be employed. Aniline dissolved in ether can be acted on by amyl nitrite [6] or by nitrosyl chloride [7] or solid benzenediazonium chloride can be added to excess of aniline.[8]

When a primary aliphatic amine is presented to the diazo-compound the tendency is for the bisdiazoamino-compound to be formed according to the equation :—

$$3AlkNH_2 + 2ArN_2Cl = 2AlkNH_2 \cdot HCl + (ArN{=}N)_2Alk.\,[9]$$

Dimroth had considerable difficulty in finding conditions under which benzenediazonium chloride will unite with primary alkylamines to form the phenylalkyl triazenes, $Ph \cdot N{=}N \cdot NHAlk$,[10] while Busch and his co-workers have found that the aliphatic amino-acids such as glycine only afford diazoamino-compounds in poor yield.[11] Nitrosoacetaryl-amines (see p. 96) with primary aromatic amines in non-hydroxylic solvents afford diazoamino-compounds in neutral conditions, and bis-diazoamino-compounds if alkali is present.[12]

Phenyltriazene, $PhN{=}N \cdot NH$, which should be the first product of reaction of diazobenzene and ammonia, can only be made by reducing phenylazoimide (see p. 140) with stannous chloride,[13] for if it is sought to use ammonia instead of an amine to make triazenes, a more complex series of reactions occurs, and the first products are not isolable. Griess investigated the matter, and identified diazoaminobenzene as a main part of the reaction product, aniline having been regenerated.[14] A yellow acidic substance was also formed, and remained in the filtrate, which deposited powerfully explosive crystals on evaporation to dry-ness. v. Pechmann and Frobenius showed this substance in the case of diazo-p-toluene to be the bisdiazoamide, $(C_7H_7 \cdot N{=}N)_2NH$.[15] They confirmed the probability of this structure by methylation, when the product was found to be identical with that obtained from two mole-cules of diazo-p-toluene and one of methylamine. They showed, too, how ammonia brings about changes not common to the alkylamines, for, like other alkalis, it converts the diazo-compound to the diazotate, and then brings about its destruction by the agency of ammonium salts. Thus Nitrosamine Red was found to decompose with ammonium chloride :—

$$NO_2 \cdot C_6H_4 \cdot NO \cdot NNa + NH_4Cl = NO_2 \cdot C_6H_4 \cdot NH_2 + N_2 + NaCl + H_2O$$

Unconverted diazo-compound at once combines with the amine thus produced, and so the upshot of the reaction is the production of the diazoamino-compound, as Griess found.

The purely aliphatic triazenes form a small group, and are distin-guished by great instability. Long unknown, they were the fruit of the discovery by Dimroth of a general method of preparing diazoamino-compounds by the action of a Grignard reagent on azoimides :— [16]

$$ArN_3 + Ar'MgBr \longrightarrow Ar'N(MgBr){-}N{=}N \cdot Ar \longrightarrow Ar'NH \cdot N{=}NAr + MgBrOH$$

Thus dimethyltriazene is produced from methylazoimide and methyl-magnesium bromide. It is exceedingly unstable even in ethereal solution below 0°, and is a liquid, m. p. — 12° and b. p. 92°, having a peculiar alkaloidal smell and causing headache by inhalation of the vapour.

The diazoamino-compounds are usually colourless to yellow or orange solids when pure, and often brown if " technical " products. If free from sulphonic or carboxylic groups they are insoluble in water, but soluble in organic solvents, and they are stable, as mentioned, only under neutral or alkaline conditions. Aqueous acids at once split them into their components, amine and diazo-compound, which latter may be recognised only after it has changed further.

Thus hot weak acids give phenol, amine, and nitrogen :—

$$Ar·N{=}N·NHAr' + H_2O = ArOH + Ar'NH_2 + N_2$$

If the aryl radicals are different, then two phenols and two amines are found.

Concentrated hydrogen halides, particularly if cuprous salts are present, give the aryl halides :—

$$Ar·N{=}N·NHAr' + HCl = ArCl + Ar'NH_2·HCl + N_2$$

If reduced, hydrazine and amine result, but again if the diazoamino-compound is asymmetric two amines and two hydrazines are formed.

They have been said to form salts with anhydrous acids in non-ionising solvents, but it is difficult to be sure that these are not really mixtures of the amine salt with the diazonium salt. They are sufficiently basic to form salts with platinum chloride. On the other hand, the imine hydrogen may be replaced by metals; copper, silver, and mercury form stable and easily handled salts, while alkali metal salts may be made in ethereal solution.[17, 18] The colour changes in the indicator dye, Clayton Yellow, which is a diazoamino-compound of dehydrothio-toluidine, may be due to similar salt formation in aqueous solution.

o- and p-Aminodiphenyl or their homologues result from the controlled pyrogenic decomposition of aromatic diazoamino-compounds,[19, 20, 21] while Graebe and Ullmann's synthesis of carbazole from o-aminodiphenylamine is based on the decomposition by heat of an internal diazoimino-compound :—

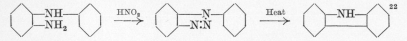

In respect of the constitution of the diazoamino-compounds the striking fact that in many cases only one substance, and that bearing all the marks of chemical individuality, is obtained from two dissimilar amines, no matter which is diazotised and combined with the other, early attracted the attention of chemists, and an account of the diazoamino-compounds would be incomplete without mention of the numerous researches which have been undertaken to ascertain the movement of the hydrogen atom.

In the case of phenyl-*p*-tolyltriazene fruitless results followed attempts by Nölting and Binder to trace the change by means of reactions such as acid splitting, reduction, acetylation, and alkylation.[23] Meldola and Streatfeild were more fortunate in the choice of *m*-nitrophenyl-*p*-nitrophenyltriazene (made from *m*- and *p*-nitroanilines and their diazo-compounds) for the subject of a series of researches based on fixation of the imine hydrogen by alkylation. They were able to isolate three isomeric alkyl derivatives :—

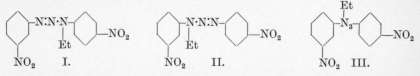

The first of these was obtained by coupling diazotised *m*-nitroaniline with ethyl-*p*-nitroaniline, the second by coupling diazotised *p*-nitroaniline with ethyl-*m*-nitroaniline, and the third by alkylation of the diazoamino-compound as made either from *p*-nitrodiazobenzene and *m*-nitroaniline, or vice versa. As the last was identical with an equimolecular mixture of I and II, they concluded the original diazoamino-compound to be also an equimolecular mixture.[24] In this they were supported by Smith and Watts with data derived from absorption spectra.[25]

Goldschmidt and his school conducted another sustained attack on the problem, starting from the assumption that the imine hydrogen would not be labile in non-hydroxylic solvents. In such solvents they fixed it by combination with phenylcarbimide, and then hydrolysed the resulting urea. The scheme set out below shows how such a procedure can locate the imine hydrogen by the comparison of the hydrolysis products when Ar and Ar′ are two different radicals :—

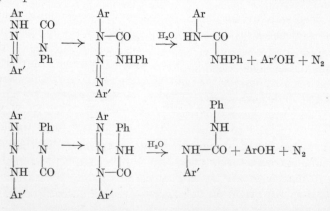

Thus the urea found after hydrolysis will have one composition or another, according to the position in which the phenylcarbimide found the hydrogen atom to which it attached itself. Goldschmidt and Holm [26] used phenylbenzyltriazene (made from diazobenzene and mono-benzylamine), $Ph \cdot N = N \cdot NHCH_2Ph$, as a test case, and their hydrolysis products were phenylbenzyl urea, phenol, nitrogen, and benzyl chloride. They dismissed the latter as a by-product, and allotted to the triazene the structure given above. They examined a number of other triazenes derived from benzylamine, and always found the double bond next to the aromatic residue, and later Goldschmidt and Molinari laid it down that the double bond is always to be found next to the most negative radical.[27]

Dimroth sought to settle the question for his mixed triazenes such as phenylmethyltriazene. But whereas acids indicated the structure $MeN = N \cdot NHPh$, acetylation and the reaction with phenylcarbimide just as definitely indicated the reverse, $MeNH \cdot N = NPh$, and he was ready to believe in the impossibility of distinguishing between either form.[28] With Eble and Gruhl he considered the still more difficult case of the bisdiazoamino-compounds, pointing out that diphenyl-methyltriazene, generally supposed to be $\begin{matrix} PhN=N \\ PhN=N \end{matrix} > NMe$, might have

an alternative structure $\begin{matrix} PhN \cdot N = NMe \\ | \\ N = NPh \end{matrix}$, because when treated with cold hydrochloric acid it affords one molecule of diazobenzene chloride, one of aniline hydrochloride, methyl chloride and nitrogen. To carry the investigation further, asymmetric bisdiazoamino-compounds were made for which, beside the symmetrical structure, two possible alternatives exist :—

$$\begin{matrix} Ar'N-N=NMe \\ | \\ N=NAr'' \end{matrix} \qquad \text{and} \qquad \begin{matrix} Ar'N=N \\ | \\ MeN=N-NAr'' \end{matrix}$$

These, when split by cold acid, should give different diazo-compounds if the asymmetric structures exist, but on experiment it was found that however the bisdiazoamino-compound was made the scission products were always the same. These results therefore caused Dimroth and his collaborators to support the symmetrical structure for the bisdiazoamino-compounds, but nevertheless inclined them somewhat to agree with Goldschmidt that phenylmethyltriazene is indeed $Ph \cdot N = N \cdot NHMe$.[29] Nevertheless in camphorylphenyltriazene Forster and Garland discovered a case which could reconcile Dimroth's contradictory data. They found agreement in the structure both as indicated by acid scission and by phenylcarbimide, and they produced evidence to show that this was due to wandering of the phenylcarbamic radical after attachment to the triazene molecule, a transference which they said in the other cases must have been too rapid to observe :—

$$C_8H_{14} \Big\langle \begin{matrix} CH\cdot N{=}N\cdot NPh \\ | \\ CO \end{matrix} \quad \begin{matrix} | \\ CO\cdot NHPh \end{matrix} \quad \longrightarrow \quad C_8H_{14} \Big\langle \begin{matrix} CH\cdot N\cdot N{=}NPh \\ | \quad\quad | \\ CO \quad CO\cdot NHPh \end{matrix}$$

They argued that since in this triazene the double bond lay next to the alkyl radical, it probably occupies this position when lower aliphatic radicals are the substituents, and therefore such triazenes are correctly formulated as $PhNH\cdot N{=}N\cdot Alk$.[30]   That Goldschmidt and Molinari may have been deceived by the uncertainty of phenylcarbimide as a reagent for ascertaining structure has been more recently suggested by a patent in which use is made of the wandering of the imine hydrogen atom to secure a technical effect.[31]   According to this invention a negatively substituted water-soluble amine is diazotised and combined with a less negatively substituted amine not having solubilising substituents.   A water-soluble diazoamino-compound results, and is dissolved with a coupling component, such as Naphthol AS, in alkaline solution, thickened and printed.   On treating the print with an acid, an insoluble pigment is formed by combination of the naphthol and the diazo-compound of the water-insoluble amine.   For instance, when 4-sulphoanthranilic acid is diazotised, combined with p-toluidine, and the diazoamino-compound split with acid, the product is diazo-p-toluene, formed thus :—

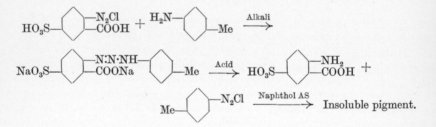

A similar series of reactions is reported by Veinberg, p-nitrodiazo-benzene giving diazoamino-compounds with various aminosulphonic acids, these then rearranging to the diazosulphonic acids and p-nitro-aniline.[32]

From the foregoing one cannot conclude that the investigators of the structure of the diazoamino-compounds arrived at such definite results as they might have hoped to reach, and something yet remains to be discovered of the intramolecular forces which operate in such tautomeric substances.

The aromatic diazoamino-compounds on gentle treatment with acids can undergo a rearrangement of which aminoazo-compounds are the result :—

$$Ar\cdot N{=}N\cdot NHAr \quad \longrightarrow \quad Ar\cdot N{=}N\cdot Ar\cdot NH_2$$

This is the usual technical method of manufacture used for p-amino-azobenzene, and much experimentation has been made to discover whether the reaction is one of intramolecular rearrangement or whether the acid causes scission into diazo-compound and amine followed by coupling. The azo-link attaches itself to the p-position to the amino-group, though conditions are known under which a small amount of *ortho*-coupling occurs,[33] and the reaction cannot occur if substituents already occupy the p-position. If excess amine is present the reaction proceeds more smoothly and completely; diazoaminobenzene is usually converted to p-aminoazobenzene in a solution of aniline and aniline hydrochloride. Baeyer and Caro suggested p-nitrosoaniline as an inter-mediate in the rearrangement,[34] but Friswell and Green [35] examined the reaction, and asserted that the diazo-compound is actually formed as free molecules, which then recombine with the aniline to form the azo-compound. Goldschmidt and his school continued the study of this reaction over a long period of years, using dynamic methods and a variety of catalysts. They found the reaction velocity to be that of a unimolecular reaction,[36] and while at first acid ions were believed to be the catalytic agent responsible, they later thought it not impossible that an ammonium ion, $PhNH_3'$, might play the part.[37] They generally used a large excess of aniline, the diazoamino-compound being dis-solved at a concentration of 0·25 molar and 0·1 molar for the acid. They considered that the results showed that the reaction could not be other than one of intramolecular change.

Japanese workers have shown that in aniline solution diazoamino-benzene can form salts; this salt formation is postulated as the step preceding scission and recoupling.[38] Rearrangement can also occur in alcoholic hydrochloric acid, but the presence of aniline improves the yield.[39] Rosenhauer and Unger used dimethylaniline as the reaction medium instead of aniline, and obtained a considerable part of the reaction product as p-dimethylaminoazobenzene; this could only arise if diazobenzene has been first formed.[40] Rosenhauer agreed with the Japanese that scission is initiated by addition of acid to the imino-group.[41]

Hantzsch and later Orloff both said that diazoamino-compounds can exist in stereoisomeric forms, but Bamberger showed definitely that Hantzsch was in error, and though the possibility of stereoisomerism exists, the isomers yet remain to be isolated.[42]

Diazoimino-compounds are formed when a diazo-compound acts under alkaline conditions on a secondary amine, which may be either aromatic, aliphatic, hydroaromatic, or cyclic. The number to which reference may be found in the literature is large, and dates from the days of Griess. Baeyer and Jäger made the diazoimino-compound from diazobenzene and dimethylamine; [43] Wallach that from piper-

idine; [44] Bernthsen and Goske from monomethylaniline and mono-
ethylaniline; [45] Bamberger and Wulz from monomethyl-*p*-toluidine [46]
and from tetrahydroquinoline and its homologues.[47] Compounds such
as those described above are colourless to pale-coloured crystalline
substances insoluble in water and stable when heated up to about 100°.
With no labile hydrogen atom remaining in the molecule, tautomeric
phenomena are not possible, nor are salts formed. On solution in cold
acid the base and the diazo-compound are regenerated, so that, as
Wallach first remarked, such a solution behaves exactly as one of the
diazo-salt; the ease with which scission occurs varies considerably
among different individuals. Like the diazoamino-compounds, rearrangement succeeds acid treatment if the molecule contains an
aromatic residue in which a coupling position is available; for example,
diazoamino-compounds in the tetrahydroquinoline series give azo-
compounds coupled in the 6-position.

If a diazo-compound is free to combine with either an amino- or an
imino-group, as in the amidines, then the combination is with the
primary amino-group.[48]

Both diazoamino- and diazoimino-compounds can split off the diazo-
group to form an azo-dyestuff if warmed in solution with a phenol of
sufficiently strong coupling power.[49, 50] The solvent can be omitted,
for by melting together diazoaminobenzene and phenol, *p*-oxyazo-
benzene and aniline result, a process which was actually suggested fifty
years ago as a means of obtaining prints of insoluble azo-colours on
calico.[51, 52] Nevertheless, it is only within the last decade that technical
processes based on the use of diazoamino- and diazoimino-compounds
have come into practice, a circumstance that may well excite the
curiosity of those interested in the genesis of chemical invention.

The making of azo-compounds on the fibre by the use of Wallach's
reaction as the source of the necessary diazo-salt has been patented,[53, 54]
and had matters remained there, the triazenes would have continued
to be without great technical significance, but a far-reaching step was
taken when the diazo-salts used for Ice Colours were converted to the
diazoimino-compounds of secondary amines carrying sulphonic acid
or carboxylic acid groups, so that the resulting diazoimino-compounds
have solubility in water or weak alkalis. In this form they are specially
suitable for calico printing, for they can be dissolved with the naphthol,
with which no coupling occurs under alkaline conditions, and the
thickened solution can be printed on calico and dried without change,
nor will any change occur until the print is brought into an acid
medium. In this respect they differ from the nitrosamine salts, which,
given sufficient time, will couple to completion under alkaline conditions. When the print of the diazoimino-compound and naphthol is
acidified the diazo-compound is regenerated, and at once couples with

the naphthol, which is finely divided and in intimate contact with the diazo-salt. An insoluble pigment is thus formed in the fibre. The acid treatment is usually applied either by immersing the print in a hot solution of sodium sulphate acidified with acetic and formic acids, or by ageing with steam carrying acetic acid vapour. On soaping off the print the imino-compound which acted as " carrier " or " stabiliser " for the diazo-salt is washed out and passes away with the soap. Based on the above principle a complete range of shades is now available, and forms the Rapidogen series of the I.G. Company.

The diazoimino-compounds are formed as easily as the coupling of diazo-compounds with a component which affords an azo-dye. The following example is typical of the preparation of a diazoimino-compound suitable for a printing mixture :—

Into an aqueous solution of piperidine-3-sulphonic acid (17 g.) and sodium carbonate (20 g.) is allowed to run at 15° the diazo-solution made from 1-amino-2-methoxy-5-chlorobenzene (11·4 g.). The reaction is soon complete, and the yellow diazoimino-compound is salted out with sodium chloride collected, and dried.[55]

Special conditions to improve the ease of formation of such diazo-imino-compounds have been patented using phthalates as buffers.[56]

Although this splitting and coupling on the fibre is an entirely general reaction, search has been made over a wide field to meet the demands of technical usage, for experience invariably shows that components can by no means be selected at random out of a general class, but choice must be made according to fine differences in properties only to be found by experiment. For example, two important desiderata for diazoimino-compounds suitable for use as components of printing mixtures are proper solubility and correct speed of scission and coupling which will ensure even development in a composite print. A considerable patent literature dealing with such products has therefore come into existence.

When formaldehyde-bisulphite acts on primary amines, alkyl-ω-sulphonates are formed :—

$$\begin{array}{c} \text{Alk} \\ \diagdown \\ \diagup \\ \text{H} \end{array} \text{N·CH}_2\text{·O·SO}_3\text{Na,}$$

and from these water-soluble diazoimino-compounds have been made.[57]

Imines of a more general type are represented by the general formula $\text{HN} \diagup^{R}_{R'}$, where R and R′ are the same or different radicals, one or both carrying one or more sulphonic or carboxylic acid groups. Diazoimino-compounds derived from methylaniline-4-sulphonic acid, ethyl-4-toluidine-3-sulphonic acid, sarcosine, dibenzylaminesulphonic acid, and similar substances here come into consideration.[58]

Primary aromatic amines which are water-soluble and unable to couple in the nucleus can also be employed, and these form diazoamino-compounds best with those diazo-compounds which are substituted by strong negative groups.[59, 60, 61] A patent for the diazoimino-compounds derived from aliphatic amines solubilised by sulphonic acid groups, including compounds such as methyl taurine and its congeners, has been allowed to become void,[62] but cyclic amines are represented by piperidine sulphonic acids and carboxylic acids as well as indole-, tetrahydrocarbazole-, and tetrahydroquinoline-sulphonic acids.[63, 64]

Proline (pyrrole-α-carboxylic acid) and hydroxyproline, both commonly obtained from the hydrolysis products of proteins or glue, have been claimed independently in America [65] and in England,[66] while an ingenious means of obtaining water-solubility is the use of the secondary sugar amines :—

$$HN{\Large<}_{CH_2(CHOH)_xCH_2OH}^{R} \text{ (where } x = 3 \text{ or } 4).^{67}$$

The imine derived from two molecules of β-bromolactic acid and one of ammonia has also been suggested,[68] while piperazine has been employed by utilising one imino-group for the attachment of a water-solubilising group and the other for the attachment of the diazo-compound.[69]

Lastly, it has long been known that cyanamide forms diazoimino-compounds,[70] and these have likewise been pressed into the service of the Ice Colours.[71]

For therapeutic tests a large number of triazenes containing arsenic, chiefly derived from arsanilic acid, have been prepared, but apparently none have been found of value.[72]

REFERENCES

[1] Griess, *Ann.*, 1862, **121**, 258; 1866, **137**, 36; *J.C.S.*, 1866, **20**, 57.
[2] Earl, *Chem. and Ind.*, 1936, **55**, 192.
[3] Morgan, *J.C.S.*, 1905, **87**, 86. Morgan, Wootton, *ibid.*, p. 935.
[4] Griess, *Ber.*, 1874, **7**, 1618.
[5] Fischer, *ibid.*, 1884, **17**, 641. Vaubel, *Chem. Zeit.*, 1911, **35**, 1238.
[6] V. Meyer, Ambuhl, *Ber.*, 1875, **8**, 1074.
[7] Tilden, Miller, *Chem. News*, **69**, 142.
[8] Goldschmidt, Burdach, *Ber.*, 1892, **25**, 1369.
[9] Goldschmidt, Badl, *ibid.*, 1889, **22**, 933.
[10] Dimroth, *ibid.*, 1905, **38**, 2328.
[11] Busch, *J. prakt. Chem.*, 1935, **140**, 127.
[12] v. Pechmann, Frobenius, *Ber.*, 1894, **27**, 656, 703.
[13] Dimroth, *ibid.*, 1907, **40**, 2376.
[14] Griess, *Ann.*, 1866, **137**, 80.
[15] v. Pechmann, Frobenius, *Ber.*, 1894, **27**, 898; *ibid.*, 1895, **28**, 170.
[16] Dimroth, *ibid.*, 1906, **39**, 3905.
[17] Watt, Fernelius, *Z. anorg. Chem.*, 1934, **221**, 187.
[18] Beckh, Tafel, *Ber.*, 1894, **27**, 2315.
[19] Heusler, *Ann.*, 1890, **260**, 227.
[20] Hirsch, *Ber.*, 1892, **25**, 1973.

THE DIAZOAMINO- AND DIAZOIMINO-COMPOUNDS 139

[21] Morgan, Walls, *J.C.S.*, **1930**, 1503.
[22] Graebe, Ullmann, *Ann.*, 1896, **291**, 16. Ullmann, *Ber.*, 1898, **31**, 1697.
[23] Nölting, Binder, *ibid.*, 1887, **20**, 3004.
[24] Meldola, Streatfeild, *J.C.S.*, 1886, **49**, 624; 1887, **51**, 102, 434; 1888, **53**, 664; 1889, **55**, 412; 1890, **57**, 785.
[25] Smith, Watts, *ibid.*, 1910, **97**, 562.
[26] Goldschmidt, Holm, *Ber.*, 1888, **21**, 1016.
[27] Goldschmidt, Molinari, *ibid.*, p. 2578.
[28] Dimroth, *ibid.*, 1905, **38**, 670.
[29] Dimroth, Eble, Gruhl, *ibid.*, 1907, **40**, 2390.
[30] Forster, Garland, *J.C.S.*, 1909, **95**, 2051.
[31] I.G., E.P. 433,878; Anm. I. 46,720; F.P. 769,838; Sw.P. 175,677; Ital.P. 318,926; Ind.P., 20,706.
[32] Veinberg, *Anilinokras. Prom.*, 1934, **4**, 281; B., **1934**, 793.
[33] Witt, *Ber.*, 1913, **46**, 2557.
[34] Baeyer, Caro, *ibid.*, 1874, **7**, 966.
[35] Friswell, Green, *J.C.S.*, 1885, **47**, 917.
[36] Goldschmidt, Reinders, *Ber.*, 1896, **29**, 1369, 1899; *Zeit. physiol. Chem.*, 1899, **29**, 89.
[37] Goldschmidt, Johnsen, Overwien, *ibid.*, 1924, **110**, 251.
[38] Suizu, Yokojima, *J. Soc. Chem. Ind. Japan*, 1926, **29**, 32; A., **1926**, 831.
[39] Earl, *Ber.*, 1930, **63**, 1666.
[40] Rosenhauer, Unger, *ibid.*, 1928, **61**, 392.
[41] Rosenhauer, *ibid.*, 1930, **63**, 1065; 1931, **64**, 1438.
[42] Hantzsch, *ibid.*, 1894, **27**, 1857. Orloff, *Cent.*, 1906, ii, 1569. Bamberger, *Ber.*, 1894, **27**, 2596.
[43] Baeyer, Jäger, *ibid.*, 1875, **8**, 148.
[44] Wallach, *Ann.*, 1886, **235**, 233.
[45] Bernthsen, Goske, *Ber.*, 1887, **20**, 925.
[46] Bamberger, Wulz, *ibid.*, 1891, **24**, 2055.
[47] Bamberger, Wulz, *ibid.*, p. 2055.
[48] Pinner, *ibid.*, 1889, **22**, 1609.
[49] Weselsky, *ibid.*, 1875, **8**, 968. Weselsky, Benedikt, *ibid.*, 1879, **12**, 226.
[50] Heumann, Oekonomides, *ibid.*, 1887, **20**, 372, 904.
[51] Fischer, Michaelis, D.R.P. 40,890 (Fr., **1**, 548).
[52] Fischer, Wimmer, *Ber.*, 1887, **20**, 1577.
[53] I.G., E.P. 306,844; U.S.P. 1,880,522.
[54] I.G., E.P. 308,660.
[55] I.G., Sw.P. 171,587.
[56] Kuhlmann, F.P. 735,698. F.P. 800,876.
[57] I.G., E.P. 309,610; D.R.P. 502,334 (Fr., **17**, 1065); U.S.P. 1,879,424; F.P. 673,052; Sw.P. 143,022, 144,753—4.
[58] I.G., E.P. 320,324; D.R.P. 500,437, 510,441 (Fr., **17**, 1058, 1060); U.S.P. 1,879,424; F.P. 674,195, 674,637; Sw.P. 143,023, 144,850, 148,341—3.
[59] I.G., E.P. 324,041; D.R.P. 513,209 (Fr., **17**, 1062); D.R.P. 531,008, 532,401, 535,076 (Fr., **18**, 1055—1058); U.S.P. 1,867,088, 1,871,850, 1,874,524; F.P. 677,579, 37,909, 37,246; Sw.P. 145,151, 149,889, 150,784—5, 150,173—4, 150,786—7, 151,141.
[60] I.G., E.P. 329,353; U.S.P. 1,858,623.
[61] I.G., E.P. 334,529; D.R.P. 534,640 (Fr., **18**, 1046); U.S.P. 1,882,561; F.P. 690,395.
[62] I.G., E.P. 388,721; D.R.P. 530,396 (Fr., **18**, 1046).
[63] I.G., E.P. 407,840; F.P. 43,580; Sw.P. 169,351, 271,586—9, 171,590—1.
[64] I.G., E.P. 427,803.
[65] Pharma Chemical Co., U.S.P. 1,982,681.
[66] DuPont, E.P. 422,195; F.P. 758,889.
[67] DuPont, E.P. 429,618; F.P. 764,755.
[68] DuPont, U.S.P. 1,979,327.
[69] I.C.I., E.P. 423,587; F.P. 775,097.
[70] Pierron, *Bull. Soc. chim.*, 1902, **27**, (3), 785; *ibid.*, 1906, **35**, (3), 1114.
[71] I.G., E.P. 443,222; D.R.P. 614,198, 615,846; F.P. 777,401; Sw.P. 177,932.
[72] Jacobs, Heidelberger, *J.Am.C.S.*, 1921, **43**, 1632.

GROUP 5. REACTIONS WITH NITROGEN BASES. AZOIMIDES AND RELATED COMPOUNDS

Diazo-compounds condense with many nitrogen bases which are able to give up a hydrogen atom attached to nitrogen, and the diazo-amino-compounds which have just been discussed represent but one case out of many. Such condensations of nitrogen bases with diazo-compounds necessarily involve the formation of a chain of at least three nitrogen atoms, and in such chains there is a marked tendency to reach a more stable state by forming a ring, if such is possible.

Thus it comes about that the aryl azoimides, $Ar \cdot N \underset{N}{\overset{N}{\diagdown}}$, appear as the chief products of a number of condensations, different molecules being eliminated from the primary condensation product to form the above ring of three nitrogen atoms in each case.

Phenyl azoimide, $Ph \cdot N \underset{N}{\overset{N}{\diagdown}}$, the type substance, cannot be obtained in more than traces from diazobenzene and ammonia, because the former condenses twice with one molecule of ammonia, even in presence of excess of the latter, to form bisdiazobenzene amide, which, being unable to form a ring, breaks up. Nor can the azoimide be obtained from diazobenzene picrate and ammonia.[1] The necessary directive force can, however, be exerted by using diazobenzene *per*bromide and ammonia, which affords phenylazoimide thus :—

$$PhN_2Br_3 + 4NH_3 \longrightarrow [PhNBrN{=}NH] \longrightarrow PhN\underset{N}{\overset{N}{\diagdown}} + 3NH_3 \ [2]$$

Instead of ammonia, phenylhydrazine can be used,[3] while a small yield can be obtained by acting on diazobenzene with chloroamine.[4]

If hydroxylamine is used in place of ammonia, the arylazoimides can be obtained directly from the diazo-salts without the necessity of forming the diazo-*per*bromide, and this is the only satisfactory synthesis of the hydroxyphenylazoimides.[5] Mai[6] showed that there are two possibilities in this reaction which lead either to regeneration of the amine or production of the azoimide :—

$$ArN_2Cl + OHNH_2 = (ArN{=}N \cdot O \cdot NH_2) \begin{cases} \nearrow ArNH_2 + N_2O \\ \searrow ArN\underset{N}{\overset{N}{\diagdown}} + H_2O \end{cases}$$

By running the diazo-salt into alkaline hydroxylamine, high yields of the amine can be recovered, but if the diazo-solution and hydroxylamine are mixed and then made alkaline, the azoimide is the chief product. With the alkyl- and aryl-hydroxylamines diazo-compounds attach themselves to the amino-group, and form stable hydroxydiazo-amino-compounds of the type $\begin{array}{c} ArN\!\!=\!\!N\cdot NAr' \\ OH \end{array}$.[7] These are so stable to acid that they are not easily broken up to their original components in the way common to most diazoamino-compounds, but instead afford nitrogen, phenols, and other decomposition products.[8] Similar diazo-amino-compounds of the anthraquinone series, prepared from 1-diazo-anthraquinone-2-sulphonic acid and hydroxylamine or hydrazine, when treated with strong sulphuric acid are transformed by loss of nitrogen and migration of the hydroxyl group to 1-amino-4-hydroxyanthra-quinone-2-sulphonic acid :— [9]

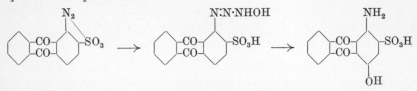

Oximes condense in a similar way to hydroxylamine, except that two molecules condense with each one of the diazo-compound. Thus diazobenzene condenses with two molecules of acetone oxime to give a substance to which Bamberger assigned the constitution :— [10]

$$\begin{array}{c} Me_2C\!\!-\!\!N\cdot N_2Ar \\ | \quad\quad | \\ Me_2C\!\!:\!\!N\cdot O \quad OH \end{array}$$

These condensation products when treated with acids form azoimides.

With hydrazine or the arylhydrazines the reactions are rather more complicated, as the chain of four nitrogen atoms which is formed can break up in either of two places. Thus when Griess treated phenyl-hydrazine with m-diazobenzoic acid, he obtained phenylazoimide, m-carboxyphenylazoimide, aniline, and m-aminobenzoic acid,[11] and the same products from diazobenzene and m-hydrazinobenzoic acid. Curtius, acting on hydrazine itself with diazobenzene, obtained phenyl-azoimide and hydrazoic acid, [12]

$$PhN\!\!=\!\!N\cdot NHNH_2 \Big\langle \begin{array}{c} PhNH_2 + HN_3 \\ PhN_3 + NH_3 \end{array} .$$

The effects of this interchange can only be avoided when the hydrazine and the diazo-compound have the same aryl nucleus as when E. Fischer acted on phenylhydrazine with diazobenzene sulphate :— [13]

$$PhN_2SO_4 + PhNHNH_2 = PhN_3 + PhNH_2\cdot H_2SO_4$$

Diazobenzene can also attack the imino-group of phenylhydrazine, and there results a fairly stable diazoimino-compound, diazobenzene phenylhydrazide, $\begin{array}{c} PhN\!\!=\!\!N\cdot N\cdot NH_2 \\ | \\ Ph \end{array}$.[14]

By substituting one of the hydrogen atoms in ammonia with an arylsulphonyl group, better yields of the arylazoimides are obtained than from chloroamine. The main reaction of diazo-compounds on alkaline sulphonamides proceeds thus :—

$$ArSO_2NH_2 + Ar'N_2Cl = ArSO_2H + Ar'N_3 + HCl$$

A side-reaction which complicates the matter is the condensation of the sulphinic acid with the unused diazo-compound to form diazo-sulphone, and the reaction serves better for the synthesis of sulphinic acids than azoimides.[15] The reaction proceeds with especial readiness with methane sulphonamide.[16]

Lastly, when diazo-compounds react with hydrazoic acid (azoimide), HN_3, arylazoimides are formed, but at the cost of the loss of the nitrogen atoms from the diazo-compound :— [17]

$$ArN_2Cl + HN_3 = ArN_3 + N_2 + HCl$$

This route is the only one by which β-naphthylazoimide may be prepared.[18]

The azoimides which are free from carboxy- or sulphonic acid groups are oils or low-melting solids, volatile with steam and often, like phenylazoimide, having an objectionable smell. They are unstable to acids, hydrochloric acid breaking phenylazoimide down to chloro-benzene and nitrogen,[19] while with sulphuric acid aminophenol results.[20] The arylazoimides are unstable to heat and explode when heated suddenly.

REFERENCES

[1] Silberrad, Rotter, *J.C.S.*, 1906, **89**, 167.
[2] Griess, *Ann.*, 1866, **137**, 81.
[3] Oddo, *Gazz.*, 1890, **20**, 789.
[4] Forster, *J.C.S.*, 1915, **107**, 263.
[5] Forster, Fierz, *ibid.*, 1907, **91**, 1350.
[6] Mai, *Ber.*, 1892, **25**, 373 ; 1893, **26**, 1271.
[7] Bamberger, *ibid.*, 1896, **29**, 103.   Bamberger, Renaud, *ibid.*, 1897, **30**, 2280.
[8] Bamberger, *Ann.*, 1920, **420**, 137.
[9] Wacker, *Ber.*, 1902, **35**, 2600.
[10] Mai, *ibid.*, 1891, **24**, 3418; 1892, **25**, 1187. Bamberger, *ibid.*, 1899, **32**,
        1546. See also Mangini, *R.A.L.*, 1935, vi, **22**, 452.
[11] Griess, *ibid.*, 1876, **9**, 1659.
[12] Curtius, *ibid.*, 1893, **26**, 1264.
[13] E. Fischer, *ibid.*, 1877, **10**, 1334; *Ann.*, 1877, **190**, 94.
[14] Wohl, Schiff, *Ber.*, 1900, **33**, 2741.
[15] Dutt, Whitehead, Wormall, *J.C.S.*, 1921, **120**, 2088 ; Kay, Dutt, *ibid.*,
        1928, 2035.
[16] Dutt, *ibid.*, 1924, **125**, 1463.
[17] Noelting, Michel, *Ber.*, 1893, **26**, 88.
[18] Forster, Fierz, *J.C.S.*, 1907, **91**, 1942.
[19] Griess, *Ber.*, 1886, **19**, 313.
[20] Friedländer, Zeitlin, *ibid.*, 1894, **27**, 192.

GROUP 6. AZOTHIOPHENOLS AND AZOMERCAPTANS

Diazo-compounds do not couple with thiophenols or thionaphthols, but form thioethers which have the general constitution $Ar \cdot SN = N \cdot Ar'$.[1] These stable thioethers are analogous to the much less stable O-azo-compounds derived from diazo-compounds and phenols, which have been mentioned in connection with the coupling reaction. Combination with the diazo-group is a general function of the mercapto-group, and is exhibited by the aliphatic mercaptans as well as by hydrogen sulphide itself. The latter gives different products according to the conditions of the reaction. Thus if hydrogen sulphide is passed into a neutral solution of p-nitrodiazobenzene, two molecules become attached to each atom of sulphur forming the diazo-sulphide $(NO_2C_6H_4N_2)_2S$. If the solution is acid, a disulphide is formed through the intermediary of an acid sulphide :— [2]

$$NO_2C_6H_5N_2 \cdot SH \cdot H_2S \longrightarrow (NO_2C_6H_4N_2)_2S_2$$

Diazo-sulphides of the above type are of low stability, and a severe explosion due to a substance of this class has come under the notice of the author.

Diazo-compounds which contain a mercapto-group in the *ortho* position form internal sulphides, sometimes called thiodiazoles,[3] such as

The thiodiazoles are colourless, but the diazo-sulphides are yellow solids. By padding cotton with an alkaline solution of a thiol and developing with p-nitrodiazobenzene, a beautiful yellow shade can be obtained. It is, however, useless as a dyestuff, as the diazothio-ether decomposes at the temperature of boiling water.[4]

REFERENCES

[1] Hantzsch, Freese, *Ber.*, 1895, **28**, 3227. Dunn, Fletcher, *Trans. Kansas. Acad. Sci.*, 1934, **37**, 123.
[2] Bamberger, Kraus, *Ber.*, 1896, **29**, 272.
[3] Jacobsen, *Ann.*, 1893, **209**, 219, 232, 237.
[4] Pollak, Gebauer-Fulnegg, *Monats.*, 1928, **50**. 310.

CHAPTER VIII

REACTIONS OF THE DIAZO-COMPOUNDS.   CLASS C. DERIVATIVES FORMED BY REPLACEMENT OF THE DIAZO-GROUP

The great usefulness of the diazo-compounds in synthesis is due to the extensiveness of this class of reaction in which the nitrogen is eliminated and another element or radical becomes attached to the same carbon atom of the aromatic nucleus.

GROUP 1.   REPLACEMENT OF THE DIAZO-GROUP BY HYDROGEN

The diazo-group is replaced by hydrogen by a process of reduction, but this process is to be distinguished from that by which hydrazines are formed, in that to form hydrazines the diazo-compound accepts hydrogen from a powerful reducing agent, whereas when hydrogen replaces nitrogen the diazo-compound acts as an oxygen donor to a weak reducing agent.   The Italian school has gone so far as to suggest a direct parallelism in oxidising function between hydrogen peroxide, hydroxylamine, and the metallic diazotates.[1]

The agent frequently used to effect the reduction is ethyl alcohol, which is itself oxidised to acetaldehyde, a reaction discovered by Griess.[2] The method of operation is to isolate and dry a diazonium salt, and then warm it with dry alcohol.   Isolation as the nitrate should be avoided, as the nitric acid may nitrate the reaction products.   The course of the reaction is by no means simple, although it is usually represented by the equation :—

$$ArN_2X + EtOH = ArH + CH_3 \cdot CHO + N_2$$

At best this merely indicates the stoicheiometric proportions of the reactants and resultants.   Moreover, the reaction is not general, for as the action of water on diazonium salts leads to phenols, so the action of alcohols normally leads to phenol ethers.   Whether hydrocarbons or phenol ethers will result from the action of alcohol depends largely on the substituents in the aromatic nucleus and partly on the alcohol. In general, negative groups in the *ortho* position to the diazo-group favour replacement by hydrogen, and their influence diminishes through the *meta* position to the *para*.   Thus *ortho*diazobenzoic acid affords benzoic acid with ethyl alcohol, but the *meta-* and *para*-diazobenzoic

144

acids both give the ethoxybenzoic acids.[3] Nitro-diazo-compounds nearly always give the corresponding substituted hydrocarbon,[4] as do also the diazophenols.[5] Further, as might be expected, the product is often a mixture of hydrocarbon (or substituted hydrocarbon) and phenol ether, as in the case of the α- and β-diazonaphthalenes.[6]

As to the fate of the alcohol, the amount of the various aldehydes produced by the reduction of benzenediazonium sulphate has been determined quantitatively by Hodgson and Kershaw :— [7]

Alcohol.	Aldehyde.
Benzyl alcohol . . .	19·5 mol.-%
Methyl alcohol . . .	0·0 ,,
Ethyl alcohol . . .	9·4 ,,
n-Propyl alcohol . . .	4·7 ,,
isoPropyl alcohol . .	5·0 ,,
isoPropyl alcohol + Water .	3·6 ,,
n-Butyl alcohol . . .	1·25 ,,

The course of the reaction is altered so that the hydrocarbon is the sole product if diazonium salts are replaced by diazohydroxides or diazotates, as is well illustrated by the following table, due to Chamberlain.[8]

TABLE XVIII

Reaction Products of p-*Toluenediazonium Nitrate and Sulphate with Methyl Alcohol*

	Diazo-Nitrate.		Diazo-Sulphate.	
	p-Cresol Me Ether.	Toluene.	p-Cresol Me Ether.	Toluene.
Boiling MeOH 760 mm. Hg . .	29%	trace	66%	trace
,, ,, 250 ,, . .	22	10%	77	—
,, ,, 1250 ,, . .	39	—	61	—
,, ,, with sodium methoxide .	—	36	—	32%
,, ,, ,, caustic potash .	—	44	—	59
,, ,, ,, pot. carbonate .	—	53	—	44
,, ,, ,, zinc dust . .	—	45	—	46
,, ,, ,, zinc oxide . .	17	22	20	48

Other investigators have obtained results similar to the above with other diazo-compounds,[9] and the tetrazo-compounds of the diphenyl series afford dialkoxy-compounds in acid solution and diaryls in alkaline.[10] The tetrazodiphenyls can be reduced step-wise if desired.[11]

Because of the uncertainty of the reducing action of alcohol and the necessity of employing the diazo-compounds in the dry state, other reducing agents have been introduced. Friedländer found sodium

L

stannite in aqueous solution effective,[12] and it has also been used by Eibner,[13] as well as by Hantzsch and Vock (see p. 77). Maw [14] first employed hypophosphorous acid, and it has recently been used by Raiford and Oberst.[15] Formates and formic acid also afford the hydrocarbon,[16] but alkaline ferrous sulphate gives a mixture which includes both hydrocarbon and diaryl.[17] The curious case of the diazo-derivative of ethyl gallate which is reduced by heating with water is probably due to self-reduction.[18]

When finely-divided metals are used in this reaction they are employed in conjunction with alcohol, which they appear to activate in some way rather than themselves be responsible for direct attack on the diazo-compound. Thus Morgan and Evens used alcohol and aluminium to prepare 4-nitro-2-naphthol from 4-nitro-1-diazo-2-naphthol, finding it more effective than either zinc or copper,[19] but alcohol alone proved more effective with 1-diazo-2-naphthol-4-sulphonic acid when reducing it to β-naphthol-4-sulphonic acid,[20] and cuprous oxide and alcohol for the reduction of the 6-nitro-derivative of the same diazo-compound.[21] Parsons and Bailar [22] prepared 4-methylazobenzene by removing a diazo-group in the 4'-position by boiling with alcohol and copper bronze. In short, in each case where this reaction is to be applied the optimum conditions must be sought by experimental trial and error.

REFERENCES

[1] Angeli, R.A.L., 1930, vi, 11, 542.
[2] Griess, Phil. Trans., 1864, 164, 683.
[3] Griess, Ber., 1888, 21, 978. See also Wroblensky, ibid., 1884, 17, 2704.
[4] Remsen, Graham, Amer. Chem. J., 1889, 11, 319. Orndorff, Cauffmann, ibid., 1892, 14, 45. Weida, ibid., 1897, 19, 561.
[5] Cameron, ibid., 1898, 20, 229.
[6] Orndorff, Kortwright, ibid., 1891, 13, 153.
[7] Hodgson, Kershaw, J.C.S., 1930, 2784.
[8] Chamberlain, Amer. Chem. J., 1897, 19, 531.
[9] Beeson, ibid., 1894, 16, 235. Griffin, ibid., 1897, 19, 163. Moale, ibid., 1898, 20, 298.
[10] Winston, ibid., 1904, 31, 119.
[11] Cain, Ber., 1898, 31, 479.
[12] Friedländer, ibid., 1889, 22, 587.
[13] Eibner, ibid., 1903, 36, 2065.
[14] Maw, ibid., 1902, 35, 162.
[15] Raiford, Oberst, Amer. J. Pharm., 1935, 107, 242.
[16] Gasiorowsky, Waijss, Ber., 1885, 18, 337. Tobias, ibid., 1890, 23, 1632.
[17] Jolles, Busoni, Gazz., 1932, 62, 1150.
[18] Power, Sheddon, J.C.S., 1902, 81, 77.
[19] Morgan, Evens, ibid., 1919, 115, 1132.
[20] Morgan, Jones, J.S.C.I., 1923, 42, 97T.
[21] Ruggli, Knapp, Merz, Zimmermann, Helv. Chim. Acta, 1929, 12, 1034.
[22] Parsons, Bailar, J.Am.C.S., 1935, 58, 269.

GROUP 2. THE FORMATION OF DIARYLS FROM DIAZO-COMPOUNDS

Two distinct classes of diaryls can be made by the agency of diazo-compounds :—

A. Symmetrical diaryls.

B. Asymmetrical diaryls.

These classes will be treated separately because they are different types, the reactions leading to the symmetrical diaryls being undoubtedly ionic in their earlier stages, whereas it has been more than once suggested that those leading to the asymmetrical diaryls indicate the activities of free radicals.

A. Symmetrical Diaryls.

Mention of the detection of diaryls in small quantities among the products of reaction or decomposition of diazo-compounds are numerous, and the isolation of diphenyl from this source was first announced by Griess.[1]

Where symmetrical diaryls are sought as the major product of reaction, the best agencies by which to effect reduction are finely-divided metals such as copper or zinc in acid solution or cuprous salts in alkaline solution.

The use of finely-divided copper was introduced by Gattermann, and the reaction is commonly named after him.[2]

Gattermann carried out the reaction as follows :—

Aniline (31 g.) is dissolved in water (150 c.c.) and sulphuric acid (40 g., sp. gr. 1·80) and diazotised at 0—2° with sodium nitrite (23 g.) dissolved in water (55 c.c.). To the diazo-solution is then added alcohol (100 g.), then copper (50 g.) (prepared by precipitating from copper sulphate solution with zinc dust). Nitrogen is given off freely and the temperature rises to 30—40°. An hour later the solution is steam distilled. Alcohol goes over first, then an oil immiscible with water (benzene ?), then the solid diphenyl. The yield is 6—7 g., *i.e.* approx. 25% of theory.

The inclusion of alcohol is not really necessary, and is likely to lead to the formation of benzene as a by-product, though it was included by Gattermann, probably because he believed that it was the actual reducing agent, the copper acting as a catalyst or activator. Hantzsch was also of opinion that Gattermann's copper acts " catalytically," whereas cuprous salts bring about transformations by intermediate compound formation. The reaction is, however, essentially one of reduction by the copper, and in many cases the presence of alcohol is deleterious. Zinc and iron can be used instead of copper for the reduction, but are usually not as effective, possibly because the grains of metal are covered with an oxide film, whereas the copper can be freshly prepared by precipitation with zinc. Ullmann showed that the copper bronze of commerce which is used for many synthetic purposes is also effective here,[3] while Chattaway used zinc and alcohol to make β : β'-dinaphthyl from β-diazonaphthalene.[4] In the anthraquinone series Scholl and Kunz have made 2 : 2'-dimethyl-1 : 1'-dianthraquinonyl from 1-diazo-2-methylanthraquinone.[5]

As might be expected, substituents in the diazo-compound have a profound effect on the reaction, negative substituents in the *ortho* position being the most favourable to diaryl formation. The fact that *o*-nitrodiazobenzene affords 2 : 2'-dinitrodiphenyl proves that the two aryl radicals unite in the positions occupied by the diazo-groups, while the fact that Niementowski obtained *o*-chloronitrobenzene as a by-product from the reaction shows that the copper does not remain in Hantzsch's " catalytic " isolation, but is converted to cuprous chloride in reducing the diazo-compound, and the cuprous chloride produces the chloro-compound by Sandmeyer's reaction.[6] Ullmann and Forgan actually used cuprous chloride as the reducing agent in this reaction, and obtained a slightly higher yield of 2 : 2'-dinitrodiphenyl than Niementowski, possibly because the nitro-group slowed up the competing Sandmeyer reaction.[7]

When alkaline cuprous oxide is used as the reducing agent, the products may be either diaryls or azo-compounds, according to the substituents in the diazo-compound. Halogens, hydroxyl, ether, or alkyl groups cause the azo-compound to be formed; nitro-, cyano-, aldehyde, or acidic groups induce diaryl formation. Diazotised anthranilic acid affords high yields of diphenyl-2 : 2'-dicarboxylic acid,[8] but the most important technical application of the reaction is in the naphthalene series, where α-naphthylamine-8-carboxylic acid is converted by ammoniacal cuprous oxide to 1 : 1'-dinaphthyl-8 : 8'-dicarboxylic acid, an important intermediate from which by ring closure anthanthrone, the parent of a series of vat dyes, is obtained :— [9]

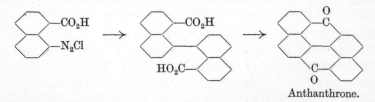

Anthanthrone.

Where the formation of diaryls occurs in solution, one must imagine the molecules to be somehow oriented in close proximity to each other, so that when deprived of their anions by the reducing agent, the charged residues, from which the nitrogen has been eliminated, can unite, for were such residues left at random in the solution large yields of tar might be expected. Union may result in the generation of a pole at the *p*-position in one of the radicals, and to this another nucleus may attach itself, chains of aryl nuclei being thus formed. This accounts for the isolation of ter-, tetra-, and penta-phenyl from the reduction products of diazobenzene.[10] The azo-compounds are most probably formed by a process exactly analogous to the coupling reaction, the loss of a diazo-group in one nucleus leaving a charged pole equivalent to that *para* to the hydroxy-group in a phenol, and to this an undecomposed diazo-molecule attaches itself. There seem to be no intermediate steps in diaryl formation, but both diaryl and azo-compound formation can proceed together, as is shown by the production and isolation of benzene-azodiphenyl,[11] while water is not essential to symmetrical diaryl forma-tion, as Möhlau obtained a 50% yield of diphenyl from solid benzene diazonium sulphate and copper powder in benzene,[12] and Griess obtained a good yield of 4 : 4'-dihydroxydiphenyl by the thermal decomposition of the double chloride of diazobenzene chloride and stannic chloride.[13] Such reactions as the two latter indicate a mechanism involving free radicals,[13a] and are probably special cases of Class B.

B. Asymmetric Diaryls.

Asymmetric or asymmetrically substituted diaryls are formed when the nucleus of a diazo-compound substitutes itself for hydrogen in another compound, the nitrogen atoms being eliminated in the process. The characteristic of such reactions is that they proceed in non-hydroxylic solvents, the active form of the diazo-compound being a diazohydroxide or a derivative thereof, which combines with mole-cules of the solvent. Further, if the diazo-compounds enters an aromatic nucleus already containing a substituent, then, as Grieve and Hey have pointed out, no matter what the usual directive effect of that substituent, the diazo-residue invariably enters in its *ortho-* or *para-* position.[14]

Despite their great solubility in water, diazo-compounds can be extracted from solution by other liquids immiscible with water. Hirsch extracted diazobenzene from water with phenol using slightly acid conditions, so that no coupling occurred. On drying the phenol solution and removing that solvent by distillation, he recovered a mixture of 2- and 4-hydroxydiphenyl in yield up to half the weight of aniline taken to make the original diazobenzene.[15] Aniline can be used in place of phenol, when 2- and 4-aminodiphenyl are obtained,[16] a reaction remi-niscent of Heusler's synthesis of the same compounds from diazoamino-benzene (see p. 131). Norris, Macintire, and Corse decomposed di-azonium salts by phenol and, like Hirsch, obtained 2- and 4-hydroxy-diphenyl in somewhat greater yield by working at a lower temperature.[17]

In the above case the diazo-compound can be supposed to be removed from the water by virtue of compound formation with the solvent, and the investigators mentioned did indeed suppose O-diazo-compounds and diazoamino-compounds to be the precursors of nitrogen loss and diphenyl formation. The diazo-compounds can, however, be extracted by liquid hydrocarbons or heterocyclic compounds like pyridine; loss of nitrogen ensues, and the nucleus of the diazo-compound is found attached to the solvent. The technique of carrying out this reaction is due to Gomberg and his co-workers.[18] The amine is diazotised in the smallest possible volume of water, the liquid with which it is to be combined is added, and the two phases are mixed by a powerful stirrer while caustic alkali is added to form the diazotate. After stirring cold for some twenty-four hours, the diazo-compound is usually found to have disappeared, and the products of reaction are recovered by distillation of the solvent. The yield is rarely good, being of the order of 15%, much diazo-compound being lost as tar. p-Bromoaniline and benzene afford 4-bromodiphenyl in nearly 40% yield, and is one of the best examples of this reaction.[19] Pyridine affords the 4-arylpyridines, but in very poor yield.

Instead of relying on the extractive effect of the solvent to remove the diazo-compound from water, dry metallic diazotates may be employed, the diazohydroxide being liberated by reagents such as acid chlorides. Kuhling[20] carried out this reaction with sodium p-nitrobenzene iso-diazotate and benzoyl chloride in benzene, hoping to make the benzoyl derivative of the diazotate under more favourable conditions than in aqueous solution (see p. 96). Doubtless the diazobenzene benzoyl ether was formed, but it at once decomposed, and the product obtained was 4-nitrodiphenyl. Reaction occurs similarly in toluene with acetyl chloride in place of benzoyl chloride, 4-nitro-4'-methyldiphenyl being formed. Bamberger showed that Kuhling's reaction could be brought about simply by liberating the diazohydroxide with an equivalent of anhydrous organic acid, and Kuhling followed it up by preparing 4'-nitrophenyl-1-naphthalene from sodium p-nitrobenzeneisodiazotate and molten naphthalene.[21] Bamberger also showed that p-nitrodiazo-benzene methyl ether will react with benzene,[22] as do also diazo-anhydrides,[23] while it has been already remarked that nitrosoacet-anilide reacts with benzene, pyridine, thiophene, and similar substances. In fine, the active compound in this class of reaction is the diazohydr-oxide, whether it be employed as such or as an acyl or alkyl ether or its anhydride. The poor yields and the large amounts of tar-like by-products support the view of Grieve and Hey that free radicals formed by the break up of the diazohydroxide are the active agents. Free radicals may also be responsible for the diaryls which Möhlau and Berger obtained from diazonium chlorides and aluminium chloride suspended in hydrocarbons.[24]

Lastly, when aqueous alkaline diazobenzene solutions act on quinone, the diazo-nucleus enters the quinone nucleus, forming phenylquinone, which on reduction affords 2 : 4-dihydroxydiphenyl.[25] The reaction is general, and has been carried out with a number of diazo-compounds and benzoquinone and naphthoquinone.[26]   From p-benzoquinone mon-oxime, which behaves similarly, Borsche isolated the compound in which two phenyl radicals have entered the quinone in both *ortho* positions to the oxygen atom.[27]

REFERENCES

[1] Griess, *Ann.*, 1866, **137**, 39.
[2] Gattermann, *Ber.*, 1890, **23**, 1218.   See also Tobias, *ibid.*, p. 1628.   Sand-meyer, *ibid.*, p. 1880.
[3] Ullmann, *ibid.*, 1896, **29**, 1878.
[4] Chattaway, *J.C.S.*, 1895, **67**, 656.
[5] Scholl, Kunz, *Ber.*, 1907, **40**, 1697; E.P. 14,578/05; D.R.P. 180,157 (Fr., **8**, 355); U.S.P. 856,811; F.P. 357,239.
[6] Niementowski, *Ber.*, 1901, **34**, 3331.
[7] Ullmann, Forgan, *ibid.*, p. 3802; D.R.P. 126,961 (Fr., **6**, 55).
[8] Vorländer, Meyer, *Ann.*, 1901, **320**, 122.   Niementowski, *Ber.*, 1901, **34**, 3325.
[9] I.G., E.P. 278,100; D.R.P. 445,390 (Fr., **15**, 300); U.S.P. 1,684,272; F.P. 618,222.
[10] Gerngross, Dunkel, *Ber.*, 1924, **57**, 739.   Gerngross, Schachnow, Jonas, *ibid.*, p. 747.
[11] Locher, *ibid.*, 1888, **21**, 911.   Börnstein, *ibid.*, 1901, **34**, 3968.
[12] Möhlau, *ibid.*, 1895, **28**, 2049.
[13] Griess, *ibid.*, 1885, **18**, 965.
[13a] Waters, "Physical Aspects of Organic Chemistry," p. 147.   Routledge, London, 1935.
[14] Grieve, Hey, *J.C.S.*, **1934**, 1797.
[15] Hirsch, *Ber.*, 1890, **23**, 3705.
[16] Hirsch, *ibid.*, 1892, **25**, 1196.
[17] Norris, Macintire, Corse, *Amer. Chem. J.*, 1903, **29**, 120.
[18] Gomberg, Bachmann, *J.Am.C.S.*, 1924, **46**, 2339.   Gomberg, Pernert, *ibid.*, 1926, **48**, 1372.
[19] "Organic Syntheses," Collected Volume 1, 109.
[20] Kuhling, *Ber.*, 1895, **28**, 41, 523.
[21] Kuhling, *ibid.*, 1896, **29**, 168.
[22] Bamberger, *ibid.*, 1895, **28**, 403.
[23] Bamberger, *ibid.*, 1896, **29**, 470.
[24] Möhlau, Berger, *ibid.*, 1893, **26**, 1196, 1994.
[25] I.G., E.P. 390,029; D.R.P. 508,395 (Fr., **17**, 557); U.S.P. 1,735,432; F.P. 739,053.
[26] Kvalnes, *J.Am.C.S.*, 1934, **56**, 2478.
[27] Borsche, *Ber.*, 1899, **32**, 2935; *Ann.*, 1899, **312**, 211.

GROUP 3.   REPLACEMENT OF THE DIAZO-GROUP BY HYDROXYL.   FORMATION OF PHENOLS AND PHENOL ETHERS

Phenols are the result of the normal course of decomposition of diaz-onium salts in aqueous solution, a reaction which it is impossible to prevent entirely by cooling, and which proceeds with rapidity in boiling water.   The decomposition of benzene diazonium sulphate is typical of all other salts :— [1]

$$PhN_2SO_4H + H_2O = PhOH + H_2SO_4 + N_2$$

But few cases of complete failure are known, though 3 : 3'-dichloro-benzidine and dianisidine may be mentioned.[2]   Nor do substituents prevent reaction of the diazo-compound except in so far as by increasing the stability the time and temperature necessary to attain complete conversion to the phenol may be increased. If two diazo-groups are present in one molecule, a substituent may cause differential decomposition, so that one diazo-group is converted before the other, as in the case of the tetrazo-compound from 3-ethoxybenzidine, where the ethoxy-group protects the diazo-group to which it is contiguous,[3] otherwise polydiazo-compounds pass smoothly to the polyhydroxy-compounds.[4]

Various modifications of the technique for carrying out the operation are practised in order to avoid unwanted side reactions. One such side reaction, which proceeds when a large bulk of liquid is heated slowly, is the formation of azo-compounds due to the coupling of the diazo-compound with the phenol already formed. Reaction time can be shortened by running cold diazo-solution in a thin stream into boiling acid, or by boiling the solution of the amine salt and adding a solution of nitrite slowly, when the diazo-compound decomposes as quickly as formed.[5] If instead of running the diazo-solution into boiling water it is run into a boiling salt bath containing acid, higher temperatures can be reached—sometimes so high that the phenol boils away and is preserved by removal from the reaction sphere. Guaiacol can be thus obtained from o-methoxydiazobenzene using a bath of sulphuric acid and sodium sulphate at 140°.[6] The method has been extended successfully in the hands of Cain to prepare phenols from very stable diazo-compounds such as those from the di- and tri-chloro- and bromo-anilines.[7]

The very stable α- and β-anthraquinone diazonium chlorides, which can be crystallised from boiling water, can be converted to the hydroxy-anthraquinones by electrolysis at 0° with a mercury cathode and carbon anode.[8]

Just as water replaces the diazonium group by hydroxyl, so alcohols replace it by alkoxy-residues, forming phenol ethers :—

$$ArN_2X + AlkOH = ArOAlk + XH + N_2$$

The above is the normal reaction, and the appearance of hydrocarbons when negatively substituted diazo-compounds are treated with alcohols is the result of abnormal influences.[9] While the reaction has been studied almost exclusively in relation to the lower aliphatic monohydric alcohols, yet the formation of diphenyl ether from diazobenzene sulphate and dry phenol has been observed.[10]

The temperature usually selected for carrying out the reaction—viz., the boiling point of the alcohol at atmospheric pressure—is not necessarily the best, and Remsen and Dashiell found that as the boiling point is raised by increasing pressure so the yield of phenol ether improves. They obtained the following figures in the reaction between p-diazotoluene-o-sulphonic acid and ethyl alcohol :— [11]

Pressure, in mm. Hg .	120	210	300	400	500	600	700	800
Phenol ether formed, mol.-% . .	37·2	40·6	43·4	48·7	52·8	57·7	63·2	69·8

The same authors concluded that 15% is the maximum permissible amount of water in the alcohol.

The diazo-group can also be replaced by the acetoxy-group by heating the diazo-acetate. The yields from heating aqueous diazo-acetates are, however, very poor, as tar is the chief decomposition product.[12] The acetoxy-compound is obtained in good yield by adding nitrite to the glacial acetic acid solution at 60° of m-nitrobenzeneazo-β-naphthylamine. Nitrogen is given off, and on cooling, the acetyl derivative of m-nitrobenzeneazo-β-naphthol crystallises. The acetyl ether of m-chlorophenol can also be obtained in 50% yield from m-chloroaniline through the diazoborofluoride.[13]

As soon as mineral acid is removed from the reaction sphere when diazo-compounds interact with water or an alcohol, then phenols and phenol ethers are no longer formed. In the latter case reduction to the hydrocarbon invariably takes place, in the former pure products can rarely be isolated, though Justin-Mueller has shown that diazobenzene-p-sulphonic acid in acetic acid solution affords azoxybenzene-4 : 4'-disulphonic acid.[14]

If the solution is made fully alkaline so that metallic diazotates suffer decomposition, then resinous masses, which have been called " diazo-resins " by Jolles, are obtained.[15] Oddo and Indovina [16] have shown that the resins still contain nitrogen, and appear to be formed by chain condensations or coupling. As yet diazo-resins have not received any technical application.

REFERENCES

[1] Griess, *Ann.*, 1866, **137**, 67.   [2] Cain, *J.C.S.*, 1903, **83**, 688.
[3] Cain, *ibid.*, 1905, **87**, 5.
[4] E. Fischer, *Ann.*, 1878, **194**, 301—Rosaniline. Hirsch, *Ber.*, 1889, **22**, 335. Bülow, *ibid.*, 1898, **31**, 2577—Benzidine, tolidine.
[5] Witt, Nölting, Grandmougin, *ibid.*, 1890, **23**, 3635.
[6] Kalle, E.P. 7233/87; D.R.P. 95,339 (Fr., **4**, 124). Sandoz, F.P. 238,031. See also Usines du Rhone, D.R.P. 167,211 (Fr., **8**, 128); F.P. 361,734. Heinichen, *Ann.*, 1889, **258**, 281.
[7] Cain, Norman, *J.C.S.*, 1906, **89**, 19.
[8] Battegay, Béhar, *Bull. Soc. chim.*, 1923, iv, **33**, 1089.
[9] Hantzsch, Jochem., *Ber.*, 1901, **34**, 3337.
[10] Hofmeister, *Ann.*, 1871, **159**, 191.
[11] Remsen, Dashiell, *Amer. Chem. J.*, 1893, **15**, 105.
    On the conversion of diazo-compounds to phenol ethers see also : Remsen, *Ber.*, 1885, **18**, 65. Remsen, Palmer, *Amer. Chem. J.*, 1886, **8**, 243. Remsen, Orndorff, *ibid.*, 1887, **9**, 387. Parks, *ibid.*, 1893, **15**, 30. Metcalf, *ibid.*, p. 301. Shober, *ibid.*, p. 379. Shober, Kiefer, *ibid.*, 1895, **17**, 454. Bromwell, *ibid.*, 1897, **19**, 561.
[12] Orndorff, *ibid.*, 1888, **10**, 368.
[13] Meldola, East, *J.C.S.*, 1888, **53**, 464. Haller, Schaffer, *J.Am.C.S.*, 1933, **55**, 4954.
[14] Justin-Mueller, *Bull. Soc. chim.*, 1935, v, **2**, 1370.
[15] Jolles, *R.A.L.*, 1932, vi, **15**, 292, 395.   [16] Oddo, Indovina, *Gazz.*, 1935, **65**, 1037.

GROUP 4. REPLACEMENT OF THE DIAZO-GROUP BY THE HALOGEN ELEMENTS. THE SANDMEYER REACTION

If heated with halogen acids, the diazo-compounds decompose, nitrogen is given off, and is replaced by an atom of halogen. In aqueous solution, even with the strongest acid, the yields are poor except in the case of hydriodic acid, which affords the aryl iodides direct in high yield. Thus to convert a diazonium salt to the corresponding aryl iodide it is only necessary to add an alkali iodide to the acid solution and warm gently. Nitrogen is given off rapidly, the insoluble iodo-compound separates, and can be collected and purified.[1] An exception to this very general reaction has been recently reported by Cumming and Muir, who have found that 1-diazonaphthalene-8-sulphonic acid when treated with potassium iodide in pyridine solution affords not the iodo-compound, but naphthalene-1 : 8-sultone.[2]

If dry diazonium chlorides or bromides are heated, the yield is improved over that obtained in aqueous solution, aryl bromides in particular being obtained from the diazo-*per*bromides, and the process is brought under better control if double salts with metallic halides are employed. Griess observed chlorobenzene to be formed in the decomposition of dry diazobenzene platinichloride,[3] and later obtained it also from diazobenzene hexachlorostannate.[4] The technique of carrying out such dry decompositions has been improved by Schwechten,[5] so that it can be employed in the laboratory to prepare fair-sized specimens. Schwechten first precipitates the diazonium chloride or bromide as the double salt with mercuric chloride or bromide. This salt is collected, dried, and mixed with double its weight of potassium chloride or bromide. The dry powder, packed in a vertical tube, is gently heated from the top downwards, so distilling away the aryl halide into a receiver. Working in this way, 2 : 2'-dibromodiphenyl can be obtained in 80% yield and β-bromonaphthalene in 60% yield.

Had no better means than the above been found, it is doubtful whether the replacement of the diazo-group by chlorine and bromine could ever have become an industrial operation, but in 1884 Sandmeyer, in trying to prepare phenylacetylene from diazobenzene and copper acetylide, obtained chlorobenzene in good yield. Investigating further, he found the active agent in promoting the change to be cuprous chloride. Aniline (30 g.) diazotised and run into cuprous chloride solution (150 c.c. of 15% solution) afforded a yield of chlorobenzene (26 g.) far beyond anything to be obtained by heating the diazo-chloride with strong hydrochloric acid.[6]

The action of cuprous salts in bringing about this replacement of the diazo-group by other elements and radicals is specific, and the reaction is known as the " Sandmeyer reaction." That chemist himself tried cupric and ferrous salts, finding them without the same action as cuprous salts, while cupric salts merely accelerate decomposition.[7] Many other chemists have tried to find substances having the same action as cuprous ions and to explain the mechanism of the reaction. As far as replacement of the diazo-group by chlorine and bromine is concerned, nothing has been found to challenge cuprous chloride or bromide, and it is generally agreed that an unstable intermediate product is formed in the solution. Walther suggested that arylhydrazines might be the intermediates, but this is unlikely.[8] Sandmeyer was unable to isolate any kind of intermediate product,[9] but Lellmann and Remy were successful in isolating a red, crystalline substance from β-diazonaphthalene bromide and cuprous bromide,[10] while an analogous diazobenzene bromide—cuprous bromide—was obtained by Hantzsch.[11] These double salts readily decompose to the aryl halides.

Two pieces of evidence indicate that the halogen atom which replaces the diazo-group is derived from the cuprous salt. First, Hantzsch and Blagden [12] obtained p-chlorobromobenzene from p-bromobenzene diazonium bromide and cuprous chloride, and conversely p-dibromobenzene from p-bromobenzenediazonium chloride and cuprous bromide in methyl sulphide solution. Secondly, Hodgson and Walker have shown that replacement by chlorine, bromine, and iodine can be carried out even in concentrated sulphuric acid solution.[13] Nevertheless it is well known that in replacing the diazo-group by bromine a higher yield is often obtained if diazotisation is carried out with hydrobromic acid than if hydrochloric acid is used.

Gattermann believed free copper to be as effective as cuprous ions,[14] and Hantzsch thought the reaction might have two alternative courses, one via an intermediate compound and the other purely "catalytic," but when copper is used to bring about halogen replacement it is the cuprous ions first formed by the action of the acid on the copper which really do the work. The reaction only proceeds in acid solution, and hence appears to be a reaction of the diazonium salt, though Hantzsch considered any intermediate stages to be derived from the syndiazohydroxide.

The kinetics of the Sandmeyer reaction have been investigated by Waentig and Thomas.[15]

The reaction is one which has proved of very great service in synthetic chemistry, but every case requires individual study if the best yields are to be obtained. Erdmann's study of the preparation of o-chlorotoluene from o-toluidine is a good example.[16] In tetrazo-compounds both diazo-groups can be replaced by halogen, as in Erdmann's preparation of 1 : 2 : 4-dichlorotoluene.[17]

There seems to be no alternative to the separate preparation of the diazo-solution and the cuprous salt.[18]

Attempts have been made to utilise electrolysis of diazo-solutions with copper plates in order to avoid the preparation of cuprous salts and their subsequent recovery in large-scale operations, but apparently such processes have not enjoyed large technical use.[19]

The replacement of the diazo-group by fluorine is not influenced by copper, or, if influenced, the effect may be unfavourable, for Hantzsch and Vock obtained p-bromophenol by acting on p-bromobenzene-diazonium fluoride with copper.[20] Sparingly soluble diazo-compounds such as those derived from the aminobenzoic acids afford fluoro-compounds when the diazo-compound is added as a paste to strong hydrofluoric acid.[21] Another way of achieving the same end is to convert the diazo-compound to an insoluble diazoimino-compound with a base such as piperidine, and add the solid diazoimino-compound to strong hydrofluoric acid.[22] Heating diazo-chlorides with weak solutions of hydrofluoric acid will also give fluoro-compounds, but in yields of less than 20%, and it is doubtful if ferric chloride, which has been claimed as a catalyst, has great effectiveness.[23]

Hollemann and Beckmann made fluorobenzene by distilling it away as fast as generated from a stream of diazobenzene chloride solution run into warm hydrofluoric acid,[24] while Ekbom and Manzelius made α-fluoronaphthalene by adding potassium nitrite slowly to warm α-naphthylamine hydrofluoride.[25]

The discovery that diazonium fluorides are easily precipitated with fluoroboric acid gives a means of using the dry distillation method of decomposition which has been employed by Balz and Schiemann to make fluorobenzene,[26] and also extended to the preparation of m- and p-difluorobenzene.[27]

REFERENCES

[1] Griess, *Ann.*, 1866, **137**, 56; *Ber.*, 1868, **1**, 190; 1885, **18**, 961.
[2] Cumming, Muir, *J. Roy. Tech. Coll.*, 1936, **3**, 562.
[3] Griess, *Phil. Trans.*, 1864, **164**, 693.
[4] Griess, *Ber.*, 1885, **18**, 965.
[5] Schwechten, *ibid.*, 1932, **65**, 1605.
[6] Sandmeyer, *ibid.*, 1884, **17**, 1633.   Compare Neogi, Mitra, *J.C.S.*, **1928**, 1332—Use of copper hydride.
[7] Blumberger, *Rec. trav. chim.*, 1930, **49**, 267.
[8] Walther, *J. pr. Chem.*, 1896, ii, **53**, 427.
[9] Sandmeyer, *Ber.*, 1884, **17**, 2650.
[10] Lellmann, Remy, *ibid.*, 1886, **19**, 810.
[11] Hantzsch, *ibid.*, 1895, **28**, 1751.   See also Neumann, *Monats.*, 1894, **15**, 492.
[12] Hantzsch, Blagdon, *Ber.*, 1900, **33**, 2544.
[13] Hodgson, Walker, *J.C.S.* 1933, 162.
[14] Gattermann, Canzler, *Ber.*, 1892, **25**, 1091.
[15] Waentig, Thomas, *ibid.*, 1913, **46**, 3922.   See also Heller, Tischner, *ibid.*, 1911, **44**, 250.
[16] Erdmann, *Ann.*, 1892, **272**, 141.   See also Heller, *Zeit. angew. Chem.*, 1910, **23**, 389.
[17] Erdmann, *Ber.*, 1891, **24**, 2769.
[18] Behrend, Inssen, *Ann.*, 1892, **269**, 394.

[19] Votoček, Zeniseck, *Z. f. Electrochem.*, 1899, **5**, 458. Vesely, *Ber.*, 1905, **38**, 136.

[20] Hantzsch, Vock, *ibid.*, 1903, **36**, 2060.

[21] Lenz, *ibid.*, 1877, **10**, 1135; 1879, **12**, 580. Paterno, Olivieri, *Gazz.*, 1882, **12**, 85.

[22] Schmitt, Gehren, *J. pr. Chem.*, 1870, ii, **1**, 395. Baeyer, Jäger, *Ber.*, 1875, **8**, 893. Wallach, Heusler, *Ann.*, 1888, **243**, 219.

[23] Valentiner, Schwartz, E.P. 9827/97; D.R.P. 96,153 (Fr., **5**, 910); U.S.P. 656,229; F.P. 266,155. D.R.P. 186,005 (Fr., **8**, 1237)—Use of $FeCl_3$ as catalyst.

[24] Hollemann, Beckmann, *Rec. trav. chim.*, 1904, **23**, 232. Swarts, *ibid.*, 1908, **27**, 120.

[25] Ekbom, Manzelius, *Ber.*, 1889, **22**, 1846.

[26] Balz, Schiemann, *ibid.*, 1927, **60**, 1186.

[27] Balz, Schiemann, *ibid.*, 1929, **62**, 3035.

GROUP 5. REPLACEMENT OF THE DIAZO-GROUP BY NITROGEN-CONTAINING RADICALS : —CN, —CNO, —CNS, —NO$_2$, —NO, —NH$_2$

Both Sandmeyer's cuprous salts and Gattermann's copper powder are useful in this series of replacements, which take place in acid solution.

Sandmeyer [1] prepared benzonitrile from diazobenzene and copper cyanide, working as follows :—

Copper sulphate (25 g.) is dissolved in water (150 c.c.) to which is then added potassium cyanide (28 g., 96%). A precipitate is formed, but soon dissolves with evolution of hydrocyanic acid, and at 90° a solution of diazobenzene chloride is allowed to flow in slowly. The latter is made from aniline (9·3 g.) dissolved in water (80 c.c.) and hydrochloric acid (21 c.c., sp. gr. 1·17), and diazotised with a solution of sodium nitrite (7 g.). When all the nitrogen has been disengaged the whole is distilled and the oily layer of the distillate collected, washed with weak caustic soda, then with weak sulphuric acid and distilled. The yield is 6·3 g. of benzonitrile, b. p. 184°, uncorr.

A large number of nitriles have been made by this method, Sandmeyer's procedure being varied only in detail.[2]

In Gattermann's method solutions of the diazo-salt and potassium cyanide are mixed in the cold, and copper powder is then added. Nitrogen is evolved, and the aryl nitrile separates and is collected.[3] This is one of the most useful and frequently used transformations of the diazo-compounds, as subsequent hydrolysis of the nitriles affords carboxylic acids.

Gattermann and Canzler showed that phenyl*iso*cyanate, PhNCO, can be made from diazobenzene,[4] but the yields are poor, probably because it is impossible to prevent some reaction of the *iso*cyanate with water, and hence from 10 g. of aniline only 2 g. of the product can be obtained. The preparation of the thiocyanate using copper thiocyanate as catalyst is much smoother.[5] Replacement of the diazo-group by the nitrile and thiocyanate groups is one of the few cases where metals other than copper are effective catalysts. Cuprous cyanide can be replaced by the double cyanide of nickel and potassium, while cobalt thiocyanate gives good results in the preparation of thiocyanates. A double salt of the benzenediazothiocyanate and cobalt thiocyanate can be isolated as a malachite-green crystalline powder.[6] Zinc and iron have no catalytic effect on these replacements.

The decomposition of diazonium nitrites leads to the aryl nitro-compounds, and almost invariably copper is necessary either as metal or as cuprous or cupric salts. In order to ensure the presence of the diazo-nitrite, diazotisation is best carried out with nitric acid and excess nitrite, thus :—

Aniline (9 g.) is dissolved in water (50 g.) and nitric acid (20 g., sp. gr. 1·4) and diazotised at 0—5° with sodium nitrite (15 g.). The clear solution is added in portions to a solution of cuprous oxide in weak nitric acid, and when the evolution of nitrogen is finished the product is removed by steam. After washing out phenols with alkali nitrobenzene (5 g.) is obtained in 40% yield.[7]

By adding twenty molecular proportions of nitrite to tribromo-benzenediazonium sulphate in dilute solution, Orton obtained tribromo-nitrobenzene in 80% yield.[8]

Bucherer has suggested that the excess of nitrous acid reduces the diazo-nitrate to diazo-nitrite, which then decomposes to the aryl nitro-compound :—

$$\overset{\overset{..}{N}}{Ar\ddot{N}\cdot NO_3} + HNO_2 \longrightarrow \overset{\overset{..}{N}}{Ar\ddot{N}\cdot NO_2} + HNO_3 \longrightarrow ArNO_2 + N_2 \ [9]$$

Hantzsch and Blagdon decomposed the double salt of mercuric nitrate and benzenediazonium nitrate with copper powder, and obtained nitrobenzene, thus showing a similar transfer of the anion from the metallic salt to the aryl nucleus, as has already been noted as characterising halogens.[10] They also obtained nitro-compounds by adding a diazonium sulphate to cupro-cupric sulphite, and transferred the nitro-group from a nitrite which was added last.[11] Contardi, who made an extensive examination of this reaction, concluded that cupric salts are as effective as cuprous.[12] The reaction is, however, one of but limited application, and used only to effect synthesis where direct nitration fails, as in the case of β-nitronaphthalene.

The replacement of the diazo-group by the nitroso-group is a side reaction occurring to a very small extent in the oxidation of the diazotates (see p. 125).

The recovery of the original amine from a diazo-salt can be brought about by hydroxylamine, conversion of some of the diazo-compound to the arylazoimide taking place at the same time (see p. 140). Wacker has also recorded an anomalous case of decomposition of 1-diazo-anthraquinone-2-sulphonic acid, which when treated with ammonia loses nitrogen and gives back the original amino-compound.[13] Treatment of diazo-compounds with ammonia does in fact often give back the original amine, which appears as the diazoamino-compound, as has been already explained (see p. 130). Another example is the formation of Clayton Yellow, which is a diazoamino-compound, and can be obtained by diazotising dehydrothiotoluidine sulphonic acid, and adding ammonia, when nitrogen is given off and the dyestuff is formed by coupling of the undecomposed diazo-compound with the freshly formed amine.[14]

REFERENCES

[1] Sandmeyer, *Ber.*, 1884, **17**, 2650.
[2] Ahrens, *ibid.*, 1887, **20**, 2952—hydroxybenzonitriles. Sandmeyer, *loc. cit.*— nitrobenzonitriles, tolunitriles. Pinnow, Müller, *Ber.*, 1895, **28**, 151— *o*-nitrobenzonitrile. Ruggli, Caspar, *Helv. chim. Acta*, 1935, **18**, 1414— 4 : 6-dimethyl*iso*phthalodinitrile, from tetrazonium borofluoride.
[3] Gattermann, Canzler, *Ber.*, 1890, **23**, 1218.
[4] Gattermann, Canzler, *ibid.*, p. 1225; *ibid.*, 1892, **25**, 1086.
[5] Gattermann, Hausknecht, *ibid.*, 1890, **23**, 738.
[6] Korczynski, Mrozinski, Vielan, *Compt. rend.*, 1920, **171**, 182.
[7] Sandmeyer, *Ber.*, 1887, **20**, 1495.
[8] Orton, *J.C.S.*, 1903, **83**, 806.
[9] Bucherer, von der Recke, *J. pr. Chem.*, 1931, ii, **132**, 121.
[10] Hantzsch, Blagdon, *Ber.*, 1900, **33**, 2544.
[11] I.G., Anm. I. 48569. 3-Chloro-*o*-toluidine → 3-chloro-2-nitrotoluene.
[12] Contardi, *Ann. Chim. App.*, 1923, **7**, 13.
[13] Wacker, *Ber.*, 1902, **35**, 2593.
[14] Prof. A. G. Green, Private Communication.

GROUP 6. REPLACEMENT OF THE DIAZO-GROUP BY SULPHUR-CONTAINING RADICALS

Diazo-compounds when acted upon by sodium sulphide or hydrogen sulphide under such conditions that the nitrogen is eliminated give oily products,[1] which have been shown to be mixtures of diphenyl-sulphide and diphenyldisulphide.[2] Copper sulphides give only dark resinous substances.[3] Diazosulphonic acids with alkali sulphides afford the thiophenol sulphonic acid,[4] while anthranilic acid gives dithio-salicylic acid,[5] but the best reagent for the formation of thiophenols is potassium xanthate. The first product of reaction is an ester of dithiocarbonic acid, which can be split in either of two ways to form the thiophenol or its alkyl ether :— [6]

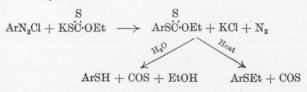

Analogous esters of dithiocarbamic acid have been prepared, $ArS\overset{S}{C}\cdot NR_2$.[7]

As might be expected from analogy with the alcohols, the mercaptans afford the thiophenol ethers,[8] and phenylthioglycollic acid is obtained from diazobenzene and thioglycollic acid.[9]

The production of sulphinic acids from the diazo-compounds with sulphur dioxide and copper powder is one of the most successful of the Gattermann syntheses.[10] A further favourable circumstance is that the isolation of the sulphinic acids can be brought about by adding ferric chloride to the reaction solution, the insoluble ferric sulphinate being precipitated.[11] While copper powder is the best reagent for the laboratory, other copper salts have been patented for technical use, including the sulphate,[12] the sulphide,[13] and sulphite.[14]

The diazo-group can be converted to the sulphonic acid group by heating with sulphurous acid and copper, but the yield recorded is only 20%.[15]

Selenium in the form of the selenocyano-group can be introduced in place of the diazo-group in the anthraquinone series. Anthraquinone-1-diazonium sulphate gives a red diazoselenocyanide when treated with potassium selenocyanide, and this substance quickly loses nitrogen, forming the orange anthraquinone-1-selenocyanide.[16]

REFERENCES

[1] Griess, *Ann.*, 1864, **119**, 142.
[2] Graebe, Mann, *Ber.*, 1882, **15**, 1683. Börnstein, *ibid.*, 1901, **34**, 3968.
[3] Blumberger, *Rec. trav. chim.*, 1930, **49**, 257.
[4] Klason, *Ber.*, 1887, **20**, 349.
[5] Henderson, *Amer. Chem. J.*, 1892, **21**, 206.
[6] Leukhardt, *J. pr. Chem.*, 1890, ii, **41**, 170.   Hartley, Smiles, *J.C.S.*, **1926**, 1824.
[7] Clifford, Lichty, *J.Am.C.S.*, 1932, **54**, 1163.
[8] Stadler, *Ber.*, 1884, **17**, 2078.
[9] Kalle, E.P. 22,736/05; D.R.P. 192,075 (Fr., **8**, 1371); U.S.P. 850,827; F.P. 359,398.
[10] Gattermann, *Ber.*, 1909, **32**, 1140.   Bayer, E.P., 26,139/96; D.R.P. 95,830 (Fr., **5**, 43); F.P. 252,787.
[11] Dreyfus, Clayton Aniline Co., E.P. 13,055/06. Thomas, *J.C.S.*, 1909, **95**, 342.
[12] S.C.I., E.P. 12,871/00; D.R.P. 130,119 (Fr., **6**, 64).
[13] Dreyfus, Clayton Aniline Co., E.P. 7288/05.
[14] Bayer, E.P. 23,047/97; D.R.P. 100,702 (Fr., **5**, 44).
[15] Landsberg, *Ber.*, 1890, **23**, 1454.
[16] Bayer, E.P. 23,164/12; D.R.P. 256,667 (Fr., **11**, 1128); U.S.P. 1,065,941; F.P. 453,208.

GROUP 7. REPLACEMENT OF THE DIAZO-GROUP BY RADICALS CONTAINING ARSENIC OR ANTIMONY

Under this heading falls Bart's reaction by which arylamines are converted to arylarsinic acids, a reaction of outstanding importance in the chemistry of the arsenical drugs.

Bart's reaction differs from the replacements heretofore considered in that it occurs in alkaline solution, whereas the Sandmeyer and Gattermann group of replacements occur in acid medium. The hydroxyl-ion concentration must not, however, be too high, or the only reaction is the oxidising action of the diazo-compound for arsenites observed by Gutmann.[1]

The reaction is carried out by allowing a diazonium salt to act on an alkali arsenite, and is well illustrated by the preparation of phenylarsinic acid itself.[2]

Aniline (4·65 g.) is dissolved in water (50 g.) and hydrochloric acid (17·5 c.c., sp. gr. 1·126) and diazotised with sodium nitrite (50 c.c. N-solution).

To this solution is added disodium arsenite (10 g.) dissolved in water (50 g.). The liquid becomes coloured greenish, a little nitrogen is given off, and some resin separates. Then caustic soda (12·5 c.c. $5N$-solution) is added, the temperature is allowed to rise to 15°, and stirring is continued until the diazobenzene has disappeared.

An alternative procedure is to run the diazo-solution into the mixed sodium arsenite and caustic soda solutions with cooling. The solution at once becomes coloured red, which colour is discharged as the nitrogen is given off, while a brown by-product separates.

The solution of crude phenylarsinic acid so obtained by either route is then made acid to Congo, paper filtered, boiled down to half volume with animal charcoal, filtered, and evaporated to dryness. The dry material is powdered, washed with water to remove inorganic salts, and the acids dissolved in weak ammonia and filtered from arsenious acid. Hydrogen peroxide is then added to oxidise any phenyl-arsenious acid, the solution is made acid, again boiled down with animal charcoal, and filtered. The free phenylarsinic acid may crystallise at small bulk, or the solution may be taken to dryness and the acid (which becomes insoluble in cold water once it has been dried) is washed clean with cold water. The yield is 5·8 g. Pure phenylarsinic acid crystallises from water in colourless prisms, softening at 158°.

No intermediate compound has been isolated in this reaction, but Bart assumed that such a compound has a transitory existence, and if such be the case it might be either an O-azo- or an As-azo-compound :—

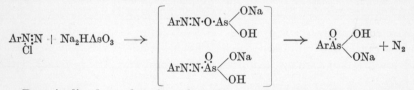

Bart inclined to the view that the reaction proceeds through the O-azo-compound, but Schmidt[3] to the alternative which he looked upon as an addition compound of the arsenic, providing the point at which the arsenic steps up from the trivalent condition of the alkali arsenite to the pentavalent condition of the arylarsinic acid. On this point Földi[4] suggested that the arsenic in arsenious acid is already pentavalent, and that the acid behaves towards diazonium salts as a monobasic acid, $H\left[O\text{:}As\!\!<^{OH}_{OH\cdot}\right]$

A characteristic red colour is formed on first mixing the diazonium chloride with the alkaline arsenite, and may be evidence of an azo intermediate, but if a diazotate is dissolved in alkaline arsenite no red colour appears, though the arylarsinic acid is formed. With increasing alkali concentration the red colour fades, and at the same time the yield of arylarsinic acid falls until under Gutmann's oxidation conditions only a trace is formed. The reaction also proceeds perfectly well with isodiazotates such as that obtained from p-nitrodiazobenzene.[5] Reaction also will proceed in acid solution with diazo-compounds having strong negative substituents, a fact which points to a mechanism involving the diazo- and not the diazonium tautomer.[6]

The double chlorides of diazonium chlorides and arsenic trichloride afford arylarsinic acids if treated with alkalis, but treated with copper powder a complex mixture is obtained.[7]

Bart's reaction has been applied to make many arylarsinic acids such as the benzenediarsinic acids from the tetrazobenzene salts,[8] arsanthrene [9]

stilbene arsinic acids, *e.g.* H_2AsO_3⟨⟩—CH=CH—⟨⟩—AsO_3H_2,[10] and the arsinic acids of the anthraquinone series.[11]

The arylstibinic acids are made from diazonium chlorides by adding a solution of antimony oxide in hydrochloric acid and subsequently treating with excess sodium hydroxide. The reaction is not prevented by even a large excess of hydroxide. May's double salts of antimony trichloride and diazonium chlorides also afford the stibinic acids when treated with alkali.[12] The mechanism is of precisely the same nature as that which operates in the formation of the arylarsinic acids. Arsenious and stibnic acids which are already substituted will also react with diazo-compounds,[13] while arsenic and antimony acids of the pyridine series can also be obtained by diazotising 3-aminopyridine in presence of arsenic or antimony chlorides and hydrolysing the product with alkali.[14]

The diazo-group cannot be replaced by the phosphorous acid radical. A thorough series of attempts to bring about the reaction has been made by Nijk with complete failure.[15]

REFERENCES

[1] Gutmann, *Ber.*, 1912, **45**, 821.
[2] Bart, *Ann.*, 1922, **429**, 55; E.P. 568/11; D.R.P. 250,264 (Fr., **10**, 1254).
[3] Schmidt, *Ann.*, 1920, **421**, 159.
[4] Földi, *Ber.*, 1923, **56**, 2489.
[5] Bart, *Ann.*, 1922, **429**, 103. Chem. Fab. von Heyden, D.R.P. 264,924 (Fr., **11**, 1030).
[6] M.L.B., E.P. 24,667/12; D.R.P. 266,944 (Fr., **11**, 1033); U.S.P., 1,075,537, 1,075,538.
[7] Földi, *loc. cit.* Compare Bart, D.R.P. 268,172 (Fr., **11**, 1032).
[8] Lieb, *Ber.*, 1921, **54**, 1511.
[9] Kalb, *Ann.*, 1921, **433**, 39.
[10] Karrer, *Ber.*, 1915, **48**, 310.
[11] Benda, *J. pr. Chem.*, 1919, ii, **95**, 74.
[12] Chem. Fab. von Heyden, E.P. 16,350/12; D.R.P. 254,421, 261,825 (Fr., **11**, 1084—7); U.S.P. 126,070.
[13] Chem. Fab. von Heyden, D.R.P. 269,205 (Fr., **11**, 1087).
[14] I.G., Anm., I. 51,515. See also Binz, v. Schickh, *Ber.*, 1936, **69**, 1527.
[15] Nijk, *Rec. trav. chim.*, 1922, **41**, 476.

GROUP 8.   REPLACEMENT OF THE DIAZO-GROUP BY METALS

The double salts of the diazonium halides with those of mercury, tin, and lead can be used not only to form aryl halides as described on p. 154, but under other conditions are intermediates for organo-metallic compounds.   The correct choice of solvent is the dominant factor, acetone being usually the best, while positive substituents in the diazonium compound favour the reaction, which consists essentially in the removal of the halogen by a metal.   Thus from the mercuric chloride double salts there may be produced either mercury diaryls or mercuric aryl halides according to the amount of copper used, as shown in the equations :—[1]

$$2ArN_2Cl \cdot HgCl_2 + 6Cu = ArHg + Hg + 3Cu_2Cl_2 + 2N_2$$
$$ArN_2Cl \cdot HgCl_2 + 2Cu = ArHgCl + Cu_2Cl_2 + N_2$$

The stannic chloride double salts are decomposed by tin in boiling ethylacetate :— [2]

$$(ArN_2Cl)_2 \cdot SnCl_4 + Sn = Ar_2SnCl_2 + SnCl_4 + N_2$$

Here tin is more effective than zinc or copper.

The lead chloride double salts afford lead triphenyl chloride, Ph_3PbCl, and lead diphenyl oxide, Ph_2PbO, in small yield.

REFERENCES

[1] Nesmejanov, *Ber.*, 1929, **62**, 1010.   Nesmejanov, Kalm, *ibid.*, p. 1018.
[2] Nesmejanov, Kozaschkov, Klimova, *ibid.*, 1935, **68**, 1877.
For failure of reaction in certain cases see :—
    Kotscheschkow, Nesmejanov, Gipp, *J. Gen. Chem. U.S.S.R.*, 1936, **6**, 172 ; A, 1936, 837.

CHAPTER IX

THE ACTION OF LIGHT ON DIAZO-COMPOUNDS

A VERY casual practical acquaintance with the diazo-compounds will indicate that they are sensitive to light, although in widely varying degrees. A solution standing in sunlight is seen to give off nitrogen bubbles more rapidly than a portion of the same solution in a shaded place, and a specimen of a solid diazo-compound will sooner or later become discoloured where it is illuminated. Closer observation has shown that light can also bring about interconversion of the diazo-tautomers, for example, converting the labile diazo-cyanide of 2 : 4 : 6-tribromodiazobenzene to the stable isomer,[1] the stable metallic *iso*-diazotates back to the normal diazotates[2] and the stable diazo-sulphonates into active diazo-compounds (see below).

Diazonium salts irradiated in solution are decomposed into phenol and nitrogen, a fact first demonstrated by Andresen[3] in the case of α- and β-diazonaphthalene. Seyewitz and Mounier[4] found the liberation of nitrogen to be proportional to the exposure to light up to 90% decomposition for diazotised sulphanilic acid. Water must be present in order that the decomposition to a phenol may take place, light bringing about the same reaction as heat :—

$$ArN_2Cl + H_2O = ArOH + HCl + N_2$$

Green, Cross, and Bevan,[5] who prior to Andresen had shown that the nitrogen is liberated quantitatively from diazo-Primuline, were not certain as to the nature of the residual molecule, for they disclosed that this diazo-compound, which, like diazo-dehydrothiotoluidinesulphonic acid, is extremely stable to both light and heat, is only markedly affected by light when in close association with a colloid such as gelatine or cellulose. Exposure in a thin film, whether wet or dry, as, for example, by smearing some of the precipitated diazo-compound on glass or cotton cloth, is accompanied by little or no action. It would appear therefore that for rapid decomposition by light water is necessary, and in some cases at least extension on a colloid is also needful. The much slower action of light on the solid substance probably brings about the same decomposition as heat, the aryl halide being produced.

$$ArN_2Cl = ArCl + N_2$$

Diazo-compounds can be arranged in a series of increasing resistance to the action of light, but detailed comparison of such series as published by various workers requires the greatest caution, because technique has a profound effect on the results, and no two workers have used the same methods, or even the same portion of the spectrum.

Ruff and Stein painted strips of paper with equimolecular solutions of various substituted diazobenzene compounds, and exposed successive portions to daylight for a series of fixed periods, so as to produce a cumulative effect at one end of the strip graded down to the unexposed residue at the other. The undestroyed diazo-compound was fixed by coupling, and the shades of the azo-compounds were compared.[6] Spencer [7] reduced Ruff and Stein's results to a common basis, and constructed the following table showing the relative times needed for complete destruction of the diazo-compounds derived from the several amines.

TABLE XIX

Decomposition of Diazo-compounds by Direct Sunlight

p-Aminophenol . . .	100 units of time
p-Nitroaniline . . .	125 ,, ,,
p-Aminobenzoic acid . .	150 ,, ,,
p-Chloroaniline . . .	175 ,, ,,
p-Toluidine	200 ,, ,,
m-Toluidine	125 ,, ,,
o-Toluidine	200 ,, ,,
Benzidine	75 ,, ,,
Diaminofluorene . . .	29 ,, ,,
Diaminocarbazole . . .	32 ,, ,,

Orton, Coates, and Burdett [8] irradiated diazo-solutions with daylight in glass, but the most recent experiments of this type have been made by Ljaschenko and Kirner,[9] who used the light of a mercury vapour lamp and irradiated diazo-solutions at 0° in both glass and quartz vessels. The irradiated solutions were agitated by a stream of carbon dioxide, and the nitrogen resulting from the decomposition collected and measured in a nitrometer. In the table, p. 166, are given the percentage molecular decompositions occurring in three hours.

Though light in decomposing diazo-compounds in the presence of water to phenol and nitrogen brings about the same reaction as that effected by heat, yet the order of increasing speed is almost the reverse of that shown in Snow's list (p. 69) for increasing speed of decomposition by heat. As a general rule it may be said that diazo-compounds having negative groups in the *ortho* or *para* positions are less stable to light than those having positive groups in the same positions. Compounds very stable to heat, such as 2 : 4 : 6-tribromodiazobenzene chloride, are easily and quantitatively decomposed by light. Further, Ruff and Stein found that tetrazodiphenyl decomposes at the same speed as a solution of equivalent concentration of 4-diazodiphenyl or diazobenzene, from which the conclusion can be drawn that the nucleus directly controls the speed of photolysis of a diazo-compound. Schmidt and Maier [10] have also examined diazo- and tetrazo-compounds using the nitrometer to measure the rate of decomposition, and have described the preparation of diazonium chlorides of substituted p-phenylene-diamines of the type used in photography and the stability of their double salts with mercurous, ferric, cadmium, and zinc chlorides.

TABLE XX

Decomposition of Diazo-compounds in Solution in Glass and Quartz by Mercury Vapour Light

Amine.	Glass (Mol.-% decomp.).	Quartz (Mol.-% decomp.).	Difference.
Anthranilic acid	3·7	17·0	13·3
Aniline	9·0	22·0	13·0
m-Nitroaniline	9·5	23·5	14·0
m-Aminobenzoic acid . .	9·7	24·0	14·3
Metanilic acid	13·0	27·0	14·0
m-Toluidine	15·0	29·0	13·5
o-Toluidine	19·0	33·5	14·5
o-Chloroaniline	21·0	34·0	14·5
o-Nitroaniline	26·8	40·5	13·2
o-Anisidine	27·0	41·0	14·0
m-Aminophenol . . .	30·4	44·0	13·6

While a beginning has been made in the investigation of the relation between wave-length of the light and decomposition of the diazo-compound, data are available for but few compounds. The diazo-oxide of 1-amino-2-hydroxynaphthalene-4-sulphonic acid and the diazonium salts of p-aminodiphenylamine have been examined because of their importance in photography. Schröter found the quantum yield independent within wide limits of other conditions, including temperature and concentration of the solution. The diazo-oxide is first attacked when the wave-length is 4500 Å. or less, but waves as short as X-rays do not cause decomposition.[11] Light between the wave-lengths 4500 Å. and 4000 Å. attacks many benzene- and naphthalene-diazonium salts,[12] and hence the marked destructive effect of the mercury lines at 4360 Å. and 4050 Å.[13]

The application of the photo-sensitivity of diazo-compounds has become an important part of photographic technology, surrounded with a patent literature the intricacies of which can only be appreciated by those skilled in the art, and full elucidation of which would require a considerable treatise. The most interesting information must, unfortunately, be stored away in the archives of commercial concerns, and all that can be attempted here is a broad survey.

Diazo-compounds can be used to make either positive or negative prints or pictures on textiles, paper, gelatine, or celluloid films, the picture being fixed generally by converting the diazo-compound to an azo-compound by coupling with a phenol or amine, and it will be understood here that such azo-compounds are insoluble in water unless otherwise stated.

The majority of diazotype processes utilise the destructive power of the light to remove the diazo-group in those areas which are illuminated. Subsequently to irradiation the undestroyed diazo-compound is fixed by coupling, and thus a positive is produced direct. Green, Cross, and Bevan [5] first appreciated the possibilities of the technique, and applied it to the printing of cloth with Primuline. The cloth was dyed with Primuline, a diazotisable direct cotton dyestuff, treated with nitrous acid and exposed to light under stencils. After exposure the cloth was run through a developing solution of β-naphthol or similar coupling component, when full development occurred only at those points which had been shielded from the light. Naturally by varying the period or intensity of the exposure the contrast with the fully developed shade could be made as sharp as desired, down to complete destruction of the diazo-compound on the exposed portions.

The established technique of continuous printing of textiles by means of engraved rollers was never seriously threatened by the diazo-type process, which laboured under the disadvantages that it must perforce be intermittent, as even in bright sunlight the cloth must remain stationary for at least half a minute during irradiation, and, as it could only print in monochrome, it offered no particular inducement to the more exclusive hand-block printing trade. From the very outset, however, it opened up prospects of improvement in the means of copying drawings and documents, though many difficulties had to be overcome before the present ascendancy over the blue print was attained. A copying paper which could be kept some time in the dark was prepared by Green, Cross, and Bevan by surfacing paper with a Primuline solution, diazotising, and drying. After exposure the copy was developed by brushing with a solution of β-naphthol or α-naphthylamine, and washed. The print was thus developed in red or purple.

While this process was indeed the precursor of those at present in use, it needed much improvement, because users demand at least four chief desiderata in a diazotype paper :—

1. Reproduction in black or dark colours, developing quickly and
      fast to light and water.
2. Clear whites.
3. The sensitive diazo-layer must not be unduly perishable nor
      have any effect on the paper.
4. The process of operation must be simple.

At the present time diazotype copying papers of two broad classes are in use :—

Class 1. Those employing the principle of Green, Cross, and Bevan, in which the diazo-compound alone is present in the paper and development is accomplished by treating the paper after exposure with a coupling component.

Class 2. Those papers in which both the diazo-compound and the coupling component, actual or potential, are present in the same layer and coupling is prevented prior to development either by the nature of the diazo-compound, by control of the acidity, or by protection of the phenol until the time for development.

Class 1. For making diazotype papers of this class diazo-compounds are needed which will give monazo-compounds of shade approaching black, and this need is supplied almost entirely by substances which can be looked on as derivatives of asymmetrically substituted p-phenylenediamine. They are incorporated in the film as diazonium salts, and mention is to be found of their stabilisation as metallic double salts or as borofluorides.[14] 3-Diazocarbazole was tried by Ruff and Stein, but present-day commercial papers contain diazotised p-aminoalkylanilines[15] and diazotised p-aminodiphenylamine (known in the trade as ZA).[16, 17] Substances of the type of 4-benzoylamino-2 : 5-diethoxyaniline[18] are also used, and mention has been made of halogenated benzylarylenediamines.[19] Mixtures of diazo-compounds can also be used with advantage when reproducing drawings having areas of different colour density.[20]

The chief among the phenols used for development is phloroglucinol, both because it will couple quickly, even with weakly coupling diazo-compounds such as some of the above, and because it affords deep shades which appear as blacks if sufficiently heavy. Resorcinol is used, and tends to give brown prints, often quite pleasing in shade.

The papers of this class are handicapped in competition with those of Class 2, in that to fix the print it must be treated with a solution of the coupling component, and special apparatus has been devised to facilitate handling of the exposed prints, passing them through the developing bath with the greatest expedition.[21] A bath and paper has also been devised from which, after development, the paper emerges dry to the touch, fillers having been precipitated into the paper to prevent its holding the developing solution.[22]

As the developing solution must be alkaline if it is to cause coupling, its removal or neutralisation presents a problem, as alkali is harmful to paper on long contact. As an alternative components are selected which will couple under faintly acid conditions,[23] diazotised p-aminodiphenylamine having this property. Acid layers can be incorporated in the paper to neutralise alkalis,[24] while the problem of keeping the whites clear has been solved by the application of various reducing agents.[24]

Class 2.   The papers of Class 2 were the first to become commercially practicable, Kögel of the firm of Kalle being chiefly responsible for their invention. Premature coupling of the diazo-compound within the sensitised layer is prevented by using a diazo-compound which in acid medium forms a diazo-oxide incapable of coupling with the phenol present with it in the layer.   1-Diazo-2-naphthol-4-sulphonic acid is the most important diazo-compound of this class,[26] but other o- and p-hydroxydiazo-compounds can be used,[27] and also diazo-compounds forming internal imines such as diazotised p-aminodiphenylamine.[28] For prevention of premature coupling the addition of titanium salts to the sensitised layer [29] or of boric acid [30] has been patented.

On exposure to light under a tracing the diazo-compound is destroyed, and development is brought about by bringing the paper into an alkaline medium, whereupon the undestroyed diazo-compound couples with the phenol present and the drawing is reproduced. An advantage over papers of Class 1 is that development can be brought about without wetting, as moist air, preferably warm, and charged with ammonia, will bring about coupling, and after a few minutes in a developing chamber the print emerges ready for use and free from added reagents.[31]

Inventors have sought to obtain the same effect with other diazo-compounds and to find means to prevent premature coupling other than by the use of a diazo-oxide.   Thus, phloroglucinol may be prevented from coupling with a diazonium salt in an acid medium by converting it to the oxime of its tautomeric ketonic form and by adding reducing agents to the layer,[32] while phenols have also been acetylated to prevent coupling before being acted upon by the alkaline developer.[33]   Another device is to keep the diazo-compound and coupling component in separate layers—for example, by dusting on the other components after the diazo-layer has been prepared.[34]

Beside the two foregoing there are other ways in which development of the photographic image may be carried out.   For instance, prints can be obtained when the sensitised layer contains a diazo-compound alone if it will couple with the phenol formed by its own decomposition. This was the principle underlying an early patent by Schoen, who used diazotised o-aminosalicylic acid,[35] and the same principle has been applied since, chiefly with 1-diazo-2-naphthol-4-sulphonic acid.   One process rests on the discovery that the light-decomposition product of the diazo-compound couples much more readily than the heat-decomposition product, although the published facts indicate that both are identical chemically.   Possibly the light-decomposition product is more finely divided or is left in a more active state immediately on formation. Hence after exposure under a negative for a time insufficient to destroy all the diazo-compound, colour formation takes place in those areas which have been irradiated on merely storing or warming in damp air. A positive picture is the result, and such a diazo-layer is said to be " self-developing." [36] In a very early patent it was proposed to degrade the diazo-compound completely to phenol and develop the picture in a diazo-bath, also with production of a positive from a negative.[37] Further, instead of the colour being produced by coupling the diazo-compound and phenol, the latter may be oxidised to dark-coloured substances either by the diazo-compound, in which case self-development occurs,[38] or by an external oxidising development bath.[39] Pictures may also be made by utilising the decomposition products of a diazo-compound to tan gelatine film, and so make a picture in hardened gelatine.[40]

Except where mention has been made to the contrary, the above diazotype papers give positives from positives, but negative diazotype papers are produced when a passive stabilised diazo-compound in admixture with a coupling component is irradiated. The light activates the passive diazo-compound, which immediately couples and forms the azo-compound in the irradiated areas. The print is fixed by washing away those portions of the other components which have not reacted. It is the diazosulphonates which lend themselves best to this process, because they are soluble in water, and are entirely without the power to couple, even on long storage, until light produces the active diazo-compound. Feer [41] first used diazosulphonates in this way, and the process has since been adapted to modern diazo-compounds for textile printing.[42]

Diazo-compounds have naturally found application in the sphere of colour photography, for by a suitable choice of diazo-compound and coupling component any colour in the spectrum may be formed. Thus Langgurth and Hummel [43] proposed to make three-colour prints by coating paper with a diazo-compound, exposing under a colour screen, developing that colour, again coating with a diazo-compound, and again exposing under another colour screen, and so on successively until the coloured picture had been built up, a laborious process which can be shortened if the paper is prepared with a number of superposed separate sensitised layers.[44] Layers on paper or films may also be sensitised with coloured diazo-compounds which, being sensitive only to light of their own colour, give a coloured picture direct after exposure under a coloured transparency.[45] Diazo-compounds can also be used in conjunction with silver halide emulsions,[46] while it has been claimed that better contrasts result if the silver salt is replaced by a mercurous salt.[47]

The chemistry of a process which Murray has described [48] depends on the combination of diazonium salts with silver iodide to form stable double salts insoluble in water. A coloured picture is made by analysing the primary in the usual way through screens to make three silver images corresponding to each of the three primary colours. The silver images are then bleached with cuprous chloride, washed, and immersed in a solution of a suitable diazonium salt, which is fixed only on the silver halide deposit. The excess is washed away, and the colour is developed in a bath containing a solvent for the silver, such as thiosulphate, and a coupling component to give the required shade. The three coloured images are then superposed and a picture in colours results.[49] *iso*-Diazotates can also be absorbed on the bleached silver image,[50] and coloured pictures produced by the above process.

REFERENCES

[1] Ciusa, *R.A.L.*, 1906, v, **15**, ii, 136.
[2] Oddo, Indovina, *Gazz.*, 1935, **65**, 1099.
[3] Andresen, " Photographische Correspondenz," 1895.
[4] Seyewitz, Mounier, *Compt. rend.*, 1928, **186**, 953.
[5] Green, Cross, Bevan, *J.S.C.I.*, 1890, **9**, 1001.
[6] Ruff, Stein, *Ber.*, 1901, **34**, 1668.
[7] Spencer, *Phot. Journ.*, 1928, **68**, 490.
[8] Orton, Coates, Burdett, *J.C.S.*, 1907, **91**, 35.
[9] Ljaschenko, Kirner, *Anilinokras. Prom.*, 1934, **4**, 272.
[10] Schmidt, Maier, *Ber.*, 1931, **64**, 767; *J. pr. Chem.*, 1932, ii, **132**, 153.
[11] Schröter, *Zeit. wiss. Phot.*, 1930, **28**, 1. See also Eggert, Schroter, *Zeit. Electro-chem.*, 1928, **34**, 602. Fukushima, Horio, *J. Soc. Chem. Ind. Japan*, 1931, **34**, 367.
[12] Horio, *ibid.*, 1934, **37**, 322B. Yamamoto, *ibid.*, 1935, **38**, 274B.
[13] Horio, Yamashita, *Zeit. wiss. Phot.*, 1935, **33**, 273.
[14] Kalle, E.P. 296,008; D.R.P. 461,603.
[15] Van der Grinten, E.P. 281,604.
[16] *Chem. Age*, 1936, **34**, 198.
[17] Kalle, E.P. 234,818; Harding, E.P. 443,995.
[18] Kalle, E.P. 347,430, 449,341.
[19] Kalle, E.P. 415,081; D.R.P. 605,553; F.P. 768,539; Sw.P. 172,751.
[20] Kalle, E.P. 296,725.
[21] Henriques, *Chem. Wkbld.*, 1936, **33**, 242.
[22] Harper, Powell, E.P. 435,874.
[23] Leuch, Harding, E.P. 425,235; Sw.P. 179,782.
[24] Murray, E.P. 320,395; 320,603.
[25] Kalle, E.P. 306,408. Murray, E.P. 317,199.
[26] Kalle, E.P. 210,826; D.R.P. 376,385, 381,551, 383,510.
[27] Kalle, E.P. 296,008; D.R.P. 461,603. Gay, E.P. 282,894.
[28] Kalle, E.P. 234,818.
[29] Kalle, E.P. 280,593; D.R.P. 462,399.
[30] Kalle, E.P. 294,247.
[31] Kalle, D.R.P. 419,978.
[32] Van der Grinten, E.P. 294,972.
[33] Gay, E.P. 283,274.
[34] Leuchs, Harding, E.P. 427,962, 438,805, 443,955. Philip's Gloeilampenfab., E.P. 433,999. Halden, E.P. 450,817.
[35] Schoen, D.R.P. 111,416.
[36] Philip's Gloeilampenfab., E.P. 434,761; F.P. 783,415. See also E.P. 433,586; F.P. 783,321.
[37] Agfa, D.R.P. 82,239.
[38] Philip's Gloeilampenfab., E.P. 391,970; U.S.P. 2,034,508.
[39] Kalle, E.P. 391,963.

[40] Kalle, E.P. 401,898.
[41] Feer, D.R.P. 53,455 (Fr., 2, 558).
[42] Ufer, E.P. 309,168.   St. Denis, F.P. 560,784; 45,829.
[43] Langgurth, Hummel, E.P. 274,129.
[44] I.G., E.P. 436,587.   See also Kalle, E.P. 299,010.
[45] Gaspar, E.P. 417,588.
[46] Lierg, E.P. 298,979.   Kalle, E.P. 390,616.
[47] Philip's Gloeilampenfab., E.P. 439,005; F.P. 785,041; Sw.P. 181,833.
[48] Murray, *Phot. Journ.*, 1933, April Supplement.
[49] Murray, Spencer, E.P. 363,616.
[50] I.G., E.P. 387,197.

CHAPTER X

THEORIES OF THE CONSTITUTION OF THE DIAZO-COMPOUNDS

THE description which has been given of the aromatic diazo-compounds, their preparation, reactions, and uses, has avoided as far as possible references to the theories which have been advanced to explain their behaviour in terms of chemical constitution. A huge body of literature has grown up on this subject of the constitution of the diazo-compounds, unhappily presenting the features of a morass in which the inexperienced reader may often feel the sensation of sinking helplessly in search of a solid basis of truth. Confusion would certainly result in the mind of the reader of a purely historical survey tracing every stage by which the accumulation has been formed. Not a few of the statements which have been made have been proved to be false, and the critical reader may well doubt others. Nor would it be just in a work such as this to take the easy course of expounding one theory, leaving others out of account, seeing that as yet no one theory is generally accepted. The aim, therefore, of the present author is to recount as concisely as possible the most important theories which have been advanced to explain the facts and to bring out those aspects of the truth which lie behind the façade of wordy polemics. Furthermore, it should be observed here that the word " theory " is employed more by conformity to general usage than by strict exactitude, for not one of the theories has as yet graduated beyond the stage of serving as a good working hypothesis.

Collecting together the descriptions given in earlier pages, an instructive summary can be made of the effects of the slow addition of caustic soda, at first with cooling, to a strongly acid solution in which the operation of diazotising a simple aromatic amine has been performed. As the acidity of the solution diminishes, marked changes in the properties of the diazo-compound can be detected, and change persists until the highest degree of alkalinity has been reached, although, as has been explained earlier (see p. 82), heat may be necessary to consummate the final conversion. Three broad zones can be clearly distinguished, and the chief characteristics which differentiate each are set out in tabular form, p. 174.

Little serious interest was shown by chemists in the question of the constitution of the diazo-compounds until the nineties, when the progress of discovery had brought to light most of the above facts. The acute

TABLE XXI

Changes in Acid Diazo-Solutions Brought About by Caustic Alkali

Zone.	Range of Stability (approx.).	Nature of Compound.	Reaction with Phenols.	Other Major Characteristics.
1 Diazonium salts.	Acid, up to p_H 3·5.	Strong salt-forming base; most salts unstable in solid state; free hydroxide never isolated.	Couples imperfectly.	Salts strongly ionised; forms double salts readily.
2 Normal Diazotates.	Neutrality, p_H 6·5—8·0.	Very weak acid; salts unstable; a few free hydroxides isolated, these very unstable.	Couples readily.	Salts hydrolytically dissociated; weakly ionised; decomposes with evolution of nitrogen; weak oxidising agent.
3 *iso*Diazotates.	Alkaline, p_H over 8·0.	Weak acid; salts stable; isolation of free hydroxide doubtful.	Does not couple or only very slowly in cold aqueous solution.	Undergoes most reactions of normal diazotate, but much more slowly.

problem then arose of offering an explanation as to how the constituents of a system consisting of an aromatic nucleus united to two nitrogen atoms could rearrange themselves so as to function at one time as a strong base and at others in two weakly acidic forms.

The Diazonium Salts.

To the first question—that of the structure of the strong base—a satisfactory answer had been given years before and forgotten. The circumstances were these. Griess named the substances he had discovered the " diazo "-compounds, because he believed two hydrogen in the benzene ring to have been substituted by nitrogen atoms. He wrote the radical $C_6H_4 \cdot N_2-$, and believed it to be a weak base forming salts by addition, $C_6H_4 \cdot N_2 \cdot HX$, and was inclined to leave it at that.[1] Wurtz, Erlenmeyer, and Butleroff all considered that the nitrogen atoms might be arranged in a ring :— [2]

Griess later speculated on the possibility of one pentavalent and one trivalent nitrogen atom in a chain, $C_6H_4=N:N,HX$.[3] Kekulé first perceived that these are strong bases forming salts by substitution, and he suggested that they have the same form as their best-known derivatives, the azo-compounds, the constitution of which had by then been determined. Adopting the latter configuration, he wrote the diazo-compounds $Ar \cdot N = N \cdot X$.[4] He differed from Griess in another particular, in that he believed the two nitrogen atoms to have but one point of attachment to the benzene ring, his reason being that the transformation products of the diazo-compounds are so often mono-derivatives of benzene. The matter was later clinched when penta-substituted anilines were found to diazotise without loss of any substituent.[5] But whereas the azo-compounds are substances of great stability, the diazo-compounds are notoriously unstable, so that it was protested that the diazo-compounds must differ essentially in structure from the azo-compounds. Strecker,[6] Erlenmeyer,[7] and Blomstrand [8] took this view; independently and in a short space of time they put forward the same proposal. Priority belongs to Blomstrand, and his proposition was based on the premise that for salt formation by substitution a pentavalent nitrogen atom must be present exactly as in the ammonium salts. He therefore wrote the diazo-compounds as $\begin{array}{c} \text{Ar·N·X} \\ ||| \\ \text{N} \end{array}$, where X is the ion of a strong monovalent acid or its equivalent. Strecker further pointed out that the salt-forming capacity of the pentavalent nitrogen atom might be just as well satisfied by an acidic group actually contained in the same molecule as the diazo-group—for example, in the diazo-compound of sulphanilic acid :—

Unfortunately Blomstrand published his idea in a book which did not have a large circulation, and where it remained forgotten for twenty-six years, while when first proposed it was somewhat summarily pushed into the background, because E. Fischer was unable to reconcile a substance having such a structure as being the parent by reduction of phenylhydrazine. The full extent of the labile nature of the diazo-compounds had not yet been revealed, and it was asserted at that period that a nitrogen atom once pentavalent remained pentavalent in such compounds. Hence it was argued that reduction of Blomstrand's compound must proceed as follows :—

$$\begin{array}{c} \text{PhN·Cl} \\ ||| \\ \text{N} \end{array} + 2H_2 \longrightarrow \begin{array}{c} \text{PhNH}_2\text{·HCl} \\ || \\ \text{NH} \end{array} \longrightarrow \begin{array}{c} \text{PhNH}_2 \\ || \\ \text{NH} \end{array}$$

Fischer proved that phenylhydrazine must be, not the above isomer, but Ph·NH·NH₂,[9] and nineteen years elapsed before Blomstrand parried with the remark that a completely reduced substance could not contain a double bond and that the reduction in question could be formulated :— [10]

$$\begin{array}{c} \text{Ph·N}\!\equiv\!\text{N} \\ \text{Cl} \end{array} + 2H_2 \longrightarrow \begin{array}{c} \text{Ph·NH·NH}_2 \\ \text{HCl} \end{array} \longrightarrow \text{Ph·NH·NH}_2$$

In 1895 Blomstrand's formula was almost simultaneously redis-covered by Bamberger [11] and by Hantzsch,[12] who at once recognised how correctly it interpreted the facts. By analogy with the ammonium radical, Hantzsch proposed the name " diazonium " radical, a proposal which was immediately accepted, and to this day Blomstrand's con-figuration containing the pentavalent nitrogen atom is known as the " diazonium " form, although Blomstrand himself suggested the clumsier name " azo-ammonium." This formula has entirely displaced those, such as v. Pechmann's, which denoted diazobenzene as the anilide of nitrous acid,[13] or that of Walther, who had the same basic idea,[14] or of Sieber, who viewed the diazonium compounds as substituted ammonium nitrite,[15] and it has only been seriously challenged by Cain. The constitution put forward by Oddo,[16] $ArN{\equiv}N{\cdot}X$, which contains pentacovalent nitrogen, is forbidden by the current electronic theory of valency, if on no other ground.[17]

While, therefore, the term diazo-compound is used as a generic term, and covers any form which a molecule of this species may assume, the use of the term diazonium salt implies only the particular basic isomer containing pentavalent nitrogen. Further, the term can only properly be used when it is known that the conditions are such that the diazonium form is the one exclusively or predominatingly present. Under sufficiently acid conditions diazo-compounds always assume this structure, and diazo-compounds existing in acid solution or isolated from acid solutions may be taken as existing in the diazonium form, though more than one equivalent of acid may be necessary when negative groups occupy the *ortho* or *para* positions to the diazonium group, and so diminish the basicity. The analogy of the ammonium to the diazonium salts cannot be pushed much beyond common possession of basic properties due to pentavalent nitrogen, for in the manner of their reactions the two classes diverge widely,[18] and Hantzsch preferred to compare the diazonium radical to a complex alkali metal. For example, before Hantzsch's proposals were made, Goldschmidt had already discovered that the pure salts are electrically dissociated in solution into two ions,[19] and later Bamberger pointed out how strongly positive the radical must be, because even compounds in which the benzene nucleus carries negative substituents are such strong bases that they form salts with strong acids which are neutral in solution in water and not hydrolytically dissociated.[20] Hantzsch found the degree of ionic dissociation to be about the same as that shown by potassium or ammonium salts. He compared, moreover, the electrical conductivities of solutions of metallic salts with complex ammonium salts and diazonium salts, finding such complete analogy that the basic idea of the diazonium radical has never since been questioned. The large number of double salts which have been described also bear witness to the presence of a radical able to act in combination with other ions in the same way as a metallic ion.

Bamberger, although it was he who had first emphasised the positive nature of the diazonium radical, objected to a thorough-going comparison with the alkali metals because, he said, it cannot be denied that the properties of the diazonium salts are altered, sometimes more, sometimes less, by every substituent attached to the aromatic nucleus,[21] whereas an alkali metal is an invariable entity. But this argument is not valid, because a distinction must be drawn between the effects due to compensations of internal strains set up by substituents and the general behaviour of the remaining valency by which the radical maintains contact with outside anions, and it is in respect of the general behaviour of this valency that the analogy with the alkali metals subsists. Indeed, Robinson, in discussing the electronic theory of organic reactions, has remarked on this point, for the diazo-compounds react by acceptance of electrons, and thus a nitro-group in the *para* position to the diazo-group must, by drawing electrons within the molecule towards itself, induce a greater readiness to accept electrons from external sources by the diazo-group, thus explaining the greater reactivity of *p*-nitrodiazo-benzene compared to diazobenzene.[22]

On the other hand, Schoutissen has marshalled evidence which shows that in its behaviour to its fellow-substituents within the benzene ring the diazonium group acts as a powerfully negative group. Benzene-diazonium sulphate remains unattacked by nitric acid even in strong sulphuric acid solution, deactivation of the *ortho* and *para* positions thus demonstrating its negative influence.[23] As another instance, tetrazotised *p*-phenylenediamine can couple once in strongly acid solution with a phenol, but the second coupling will not take place until the mineral acid has been removed. Now, the power to couple in acid solution is only possessed by diazo-groups, to which nitro-groups stand both *ortho* and *para* (see p. 104). Hence tetrazotised *p*-phenylene-diamine in acid solution must have the structure N≡N— —N=N·X,

and the diazonium group must be as effective in its negative influence as two nitro-groups.[24] Schoutissen has also made benzaldehyde-*p*-diazonium sulphate, and this condenses in the cold with benzene to form triphenylmethane-*p*-diazonium sulphate. Here again only where the aldehyde group is activated by a strongly negative group, as in *p*-nitro-benzaldehyde, will this reaction occur.[25]

If the analogy of the diazonium salts with the ammonium salts and the alkali metals is to be complete, then a diazonium hydroxide must exist analogous to ammonium hydroxide or the caustic alkalis. But treatment of the diazonium salts with alkalis brings about far more

N

deep-seated changes than the liberation of the required hydroxide, and an hydroxide having the structure $\overset{\text{Ar·N·OH}}{\underset{\text{N}}{\vert\vert\vert}}$ has never been isolated, nor can it be certain that it has been obtained free from isomers in solution.   To obtain this hydroxide Hantzsch acted on a pure diazonium chloride in dilute aqueous solution at 0° with a slight excess of moist silver oxide.[26] For example, benzenediazonium chloride (0·7 g.) is dissolved in water at 0° (50 c.c.) and fresh moist silver oxide (0·8 g.) mixed with ice added. After thorough shaking, the solution from which the silver chloride has been filtered is found to be strongly alkaline. Coupling with β-naphthol is instant, and the solution darkens rapidly even at 0°.   Hantzsch and his co-workers have carried out extensive researches which have demonstrated the existence of diazonium hydroxides in solution by conductivity experiments.[27] They found the affinity constant of benzenediazonium hydroxide at 0° to be seventy times that of ammonium hydroxide, while the effects of substituents in the ring have been closely studied.[28]

The Normal Diazotates.   Unless such special methods as those described by Hantzsch are employed, internal rearrangement sets in as rapidly as the hydroxide is liberated by the action of alkali on an acid solution of a diazonium salt, as is shown by the increasing speed with which coupling will occur if a phenol is present. The diazonium salt is changing into that one of the isomeric diazo-compounds which occupies the middle zone in the table of metamorphosis, and which, unlike the diazonium form, possesses the capacity to couple completely and rapidly. Diazo-compounds showing this reaction can therefore be assigned to the class of the normal diazo-compounds unless very strong evidence to the contrary can be adduced. Change from the diazonium form to the normal diazo-form is never clear-cut, but it is an equilibrium the position of which is dependant on internal conditions as represented by substituents and external conditions as represented by acid concentration and temperature. The equilibrium is not one directly between the diazonium salt and the normal diazo-compound, but between the ions of the dissociated hydroxides :—

$$
\begin{array}{ccccc}
\underset{\text{N}}{\overset{\text{Ar·N·X}}{\vert\vert\vert}} & \rightleftharpoons & \underset{\text{N}}{\overset{\text{Ar·N·OH}}{\vert\vert\vert}} & & \text{Ar·N}\!=\!\text{N·OH} \\[4pt]
& & \updownarrow & & \updownarrow \\[4pt]
& & \underset{\text{N}}{\overset{\text{Ar·N}^{+}\text{OH}^{-}}{\vert\vert\vert}} & \rightleftharpoons & \text{Ar·N}\!=\!\text{N·O}^{-}\ \ \text{H}^{+}
\end{array}
$$

The suggestion has been made by Hantzsch that in the case of certain diazonium halides the simpler equilibrium can exist in the solid state :—

$$
\underset{\text{N}}{\overset{\text{Ar·N·Hal}}{\vert\vert\vert}} \quad \rightleftharpoons \quad \text{Ar·N}\!=\!\text{N·Hal}
$$

This assumption can explain the peculiar characteristics of some of the diazonium halides which separate from solution as coloured crystals, whereas the corresponding oxygen acid salts, such as the nitrate, are colourless.   The expectation is reasonable that a compound containing a halogen co-valently linked to tervalent nitrogen will be coloured and unstable, *e.g.* nitrogen trichloride. Hantzsch examined a series of twenty-four compounds derived from six diazonium ions in which the basicity was continuously reduced by loading the benzene ring.   These six diazonium ions were then combined with chlorine, bromine, iodine, and thiocyanate ions, with the result that the colour of the salts continuously deepened as the basicity of the diazonium ion and the acidity of the acid ion fell.   The explosive properties increased in the same order.[29]   Hantzsch and Euler then found that strong cooling caused almost complete decolorisation, the colour returning with return to a higher temperature.   Wherever this reversible change of colour with temperature is found, it is associated with tautomeric change in the molecule, and accordingly Hantzsch offered the further suggestion that the above equilibrium is influenced by temperature, passing over to the coloured azo-form as the temperature rises.[30]

While this explanation may be the true one where these unstable diazo-compounds are concerned, it cannot be the explanation of the cause of colour in all the numerous cases known where colourless bases give rise to stable coloured diazonium salts.   Morgan and his co-workers found diazonium salts from many acylated *p*-diamines to be coloured, particularly those from benzoyl-1 : 4-naphthylenediamine, and concluded from their inquiry that the structure of the diazonium group remains unaltered and the colour arises from increasing complexity of the aromatic nucleus.[31]

In contradistinction to the strongly basic diazonium salts, the diazo-compounds, both normal and *iso*-, are weak acids concerning the constitution of which there is as yet by no means general agreement among chemists.   The normal diazotates, and still more the normal diazo-hydroxides, of the benzene and naphthalene series are so unstable that they are not easy to examine, and the fact that the hydroxides are acidic is best shown in the anthraquinone series, where both the α- and β-diazonium hydroxides can be made in solution from the diazonium sulphates by the action of barium hydroxide.[32]   The freshly made solution of the diazonium hydroxide is alkaline, but becomes acidic in a few minutes as the free diazonium hydroxide re-arranges to the normal diazo-hydroxide.   Hantzsch and Gerilowsky observed the same change to occur when one equivalent of alkali is added to diazotised sulphanilic acid :— [33]

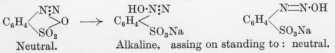

$$C_6H_4 \Big\langle \begin{matrix} N\colon N \\ SO_2 \end{matrix} \Big\rangle O \longrightarrow C_6H_4 \Big\langle \begin{matrix} HO\cdot N\colon N \\ SO_3Na \end{matrix} \qquad\qquad C_6H_4 \Big\langle \begin{matrix} N\colon\colon N\cdot OH \\ SO_3Na \end{matrix}$$

Neutral.   Alkaline, assing on standing to : neutral.

The diazohydroxides can take part in reactions involving either the hydrogen atom or the hydroxyl group. The metal salts, unstable and hydrolytically dissociated, are the result of reaction in the acidic form, but as far greater energy loss occurs when the hydroxyl group is eliminated, their commonest reactions are with substances from which the necessary hydrogen atom can be acquired to permit the elimination of water. The products of such reactions are neutral, non-ionised, and insoluble in water, unless water-solubilising groups are present elsewhere in the molecule. In fact, they are typical co-valent organic substances, so much so that at one time Hantzsch proposed for all such derivatives of the diazo-compounds that the term " diazo " should be dropped and the cyanides, sulphonates, and similar compounds should be called azo-compounds, e.g. azocyanides, azosulphonates, and from that time he employed this nomenclature in his writings.[34] The proposal is logical (and had also been made by Blomstrand), but it has never overcome the inertia of tradition which fights shy of naming as an azo-compound a substance such as a labile diazocyanide which is still capable of coupling with a phenol. As a result of this conservatism the possibility of confusion arising from the use of the term diazo-compound, both as a generic term and as a name for certain specific molecular species—namely, the normal and isodiazo-compounds—has never been removed. There is also want of agreement as to the name to be applied to the diazohydroxides. English usage since 1903 has adhered fairly consistently to the name diazohydroxide, which is therefore used in this book; but more logical writers have sometimes used the term " hydrogen diazotate," while the Germans consistently use the term " diazohydrate " for the same substance.

The Diazo-Oxides. Mention has already been made of these substances in several places, and it will be remembered that they result from the diazotisation of o- and p-aminophenols, sometimes directly, sometimes by the action of alkali on a diazo-compound. They are never formed from m-aminophenols, but they are formed by the elimination of ortho or para substituents in certain diazo-compounds, while a typical diazo-oxide is also formed by 1 : 8-aminonaphthol.

They are quite obviously not diazonium salts, as heretofore described, because they are sparingly soluble in water, non-ionised, coloured, and couple only very slowly. There has never been any question that they are internal condensation products formed by loss of water between the diazohydroxide and phenolic groups :—

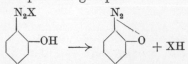

For this reason they are often called diazo-anhydrides, especially in

German writings, though the context usually leaves no doubt that Bamberger's substances of the same name are not in question.

At least three possible constitutions come into consideration for the derivatives of aminophenols free from acidic groups, while a fourth can be imagined when sulphonic or carboxylic acid groups are present. The four forms are :—

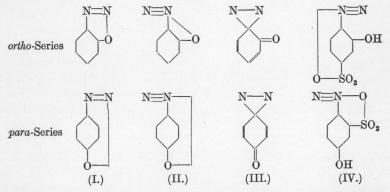

ortho-Series

para-Series

(I.)   (II.)   (III.)   (IV.)

Bamberger was the proposer of the internal diazo-oxide structure I,[35] while Hantzsch and Davidson and also Klemenc put forward the diazonium structure II.[36] The quinonoid form III was suggested by Wolff,[37] but the possibility of IV was ruled out by Morgan and Tomlins,[38] who showed that this compound is actually produced when 4-amino-phenol-6-sulphonic acid is diazotised, and that the true diazo-oxide is only formed when the internal diazonium salt is acted upon by one equivalent of alkali. Wolff's quinonoid structure can also be eliminated because such a structure cannot be assumed by the derivative of 1 : 8-aminonaphthol, so the decision must lie between structures I and II. Morgan and Porter,[39] in a critique of Klemenc's arguments for the diazonium structure, rejected it, mainly on the ground that there is no reason why the m-diazonium oxides should not exist, and they entirely failed to find any evidence of such compounds. Besides, if the diazonium group is present, a strong tendency to double salt formation would be expected, but any such tendency is absent. Battegay and Schmidt,[40] in discussing the structure of the diazo-derivative of 1-amino-2-naphthol-4-sulphonic acid, further remarked that the diazonium group, a strongly basic group, could not exist in the same molecule with a free sulphonic acid group, and that if the structure IV is untenable, the diazonium structure must be likewise untenable. The upshot of the process of elimination is that Bamberger's internal diazo-oxide structure is left, and having been accepted both by Morgan and by Battegay and Schmidt, has been used throughout this book.

The diazosulphides, formed from the aminothiophenols, possess a structure entirely analogous to that of the diazo-oxides.[41]

The *iso*Diazotates.—The consideration of the constitution of the normal diazo-compounds cannot be divorced from a parallel consideration of the *iso*diazo- or stable diazo-compounds, the second and ultimate result of the change wrought on diazonium salts by the action of alkalis.   The core of the controversy as to the constitution of the diazo-compounds has been centred in the relationship of the normal to the *iso*-form, and of the latter to the primary aromatic nitrosamines.   As the *iso*diazo-compounds are so much more stable than the normal salts, so the parent *iso*diazohydroxides might be expected to reach a sufficient degree of stability to permit their isolation and examination.   This has been attempted several times by Hantzsch and his co-workers, but never with unequivocal success, as the instability of the products has prevented isolation in a state of analytical purity.   The place to be allotted to the primary aryl nitrosamines, $Ar \cdot NH \cdot NO$, which are isomeric with the diazohydroxides, has proved difficult, but there has been a considerable measure of agreement that neither of the diazohydroxides can have this structure, as it represents a substance which presumably should be neutral and incapable of direct salt formation.   Consequently if such substances have ever been obtained, they must have arisen by isomerisation of an acid form which can combine with a metal cation.[42] This has militated against an influential school which accepted the face-value of the evidence that the metal salts of the *iso*diazohydroxides might have the constitution of nitrosamine salts, $Ar \cdot NM \cdot NO$.   A larger number of chemists mistrusted and set aside evidence pointing in this direction, the cause for distrust being that while alkylation of the sodium salt of " Nitrosamine Red," $NO_2 \cdot C_6H_4 \cdot N_2 \cdot ONa$, gives the *N*-ether, similar treatment of the silver salt gives the *O*-ether.   Less ambiguous appeared the result of the acetylation by acetic anhydride of alkaline solutions of diazobenzene.   Here v. Pechmann and Frobenius obtained a 30% yield of nitrosoacetanilide, $Ph \cdot NCOMe \cdot NO$, a fact from which they were led to declare that in cold moderately alkaline solutions of diazobenzene a metal salt of the constitution $Ph \cdot NM \cdot NO$ exists.[43] Indeed, it was the view of v. Pechmann that just as an equilibrium exists between the diazonium hydroxide and the diazohydroxide, so another equilibrium, determined by the concentration of alkali, exists between the salts of the normal diazohydroxide and the *iso*-form, which he regarded as the nitrosamine.[44]   In some cases, *e.g.* *p*-nitro-diazobenzene, a small concentration of alkali will move the equilibrium completely in favour of the *iso*-form, and so quickly that the normal metallic diazotate is unknown; in others a high concentration and the application of heat are necessary.   Generally, change in the alkali concentration is not followed by rapid change in cold aqueous solution, which may be used as an explanation why *iso*diazo-compounds couple so slowly, but if heated, as in the technical process for developing prints, or dissolved in alcohol, coupling can be rapid. As will be seen later, Hantzsch taught that this direct explanation was not a true account of the mechanism of the change, which, though often proceeding spontaneously from normal to *iso*diazotate, in the reverse is accomplished more circuitously, the metal always being attached to oxygen. It might be remarked that heating with 75% caustic alkali is a drastic means of inducing a spontaneous change, and is much more reminiscent of the conditions employed to force a weakly acidic nitrogen atom, as in carbazole, to form a salt. Be that as it may, v. Pechmann and Frobenius' view was disturbed when Bamberger said that alkaline hydrolysis of nitrosoacetanilide gave the normal diazo-compound, whereas the slowly coupling *iso*diazotate would naturally be expected according to the equation :—

$$Ph \cdot N(COMe)NO + NaOH = Ph \cdot NNa \cdot NO + NaOAc \ ^{45}$$

This result may have been due either to the nitrosoacetanilide reacting in its tautomeric form or to change of the *iso*diazotate first formed to the normal diazotate. Hantzsch explained it in the case of nitrosobenzanilide as proceeding through addition and subsequent scission.[46]

The foregoing gives an idea of what were some of the loose pieces of the jigsaw puzzle which framers of theories essayed to piece together, and explains why there have been put forward such a variety of proposals for the constitution of the diazo-compounds, since avoidance of the nitrosamine structure for the metal salts of the *iso*diazotates entails propounding some other less obvious structure which will explain the differences of the normal and *iso*diazo-compounds.

The stage is now set for a review of these theories, but before proceeding further, the issue can be much clarified by setting out in tabular form the various structures and names which have been put forward from time to time (see Table XXII, p. 184). This list is not exhaustive, for, as the text bears witness, other authors have contributed a quota of ideas on particular points, but those set out here are the most comprehensive hypotheses covering the whole field.

The Theory of Hantzsch.

Pride of place must be given to Hantzsch, not only for the break-away from current thought which marked his original contribution, but also for the resource with which for nearly forty years he sought experimental proof in defence of his thesis. In 1895 he published a classic paper in which he compared the diazo-compounds with the oximes, the properties of which had been proved by Werner and himself to be due to the existence of stereoisomerides made possible by the immobile C=N bond, thus :—

$$\begin{array}{ll} Ar \cdot C & \\ \parallel \quad cis\text{-Form.} & \\ HO \cdot N & \end{array} \qquad \begin{array}{ll} Ar \cdot C & \\ \parallel \quad trans\text{-Form.} & \\ N \cdot OH & \end{array}$$

TABLE XXII

Constitutions Proposed for the Isomeric Diazo-Compounds

Investigator :	Hantzsch.	Bamberger.	Brühl.	Armstrong. Robertson.	Cain.	Angeli.	Sarkar.
Basis of Theory :	Stereo-isomerism.	Structural Isomerism.	Optical Properties.	Colour.	Quinonoid Tautomerism.	Reactions of Azoxy-compounds.	Electronic Theory of Valency.
Diazonium Salts :	$ArN{:}N$ / Cl	$ArN{:}N$ / Cl	$ArN{:}N$ / Cl		(quinonoid structures)		$[Ar{\cdot}N\overset{+}{:::}N{\cdot}]{\cdot}X^{-}$ $[Ar{\cdot}N\overset{+}{:\rightleftharpoons:}N]X^{-}$
Normal Diazo-hydroxide :	*syn*-Diazo-hydroxide. $ArN\!\!\parallel$ / HON	$ArN{:}N$ / OM or $ArN{\cdot}N{\cdot}H$ / O or $ArN{:}NH$ / O	$Ar{-}N\triangle O$ with H ; $Ar{-}N\triangle O$ with M	Labile Diazo-compounds. $ArN{\cdot}SO_3M$ / N $ArN{\cdot}OM$ / N	$N{:}N{-}OH$	Ar / $O{:}N{:}NH$; Ar / $N{:}N{:}O$ / H	$Ar{\cdot}N\overset{\rightarrow}{:}N{:}$ / X
*iso*Diazohydr-oxide :	*anti*-Diazo-hydroxide. $ArH\!\!\parallel$ / NOH	$ArN{:}N{\cdot}OH$	$ArN{:}N{\cdot}OM$	Stable Compounds. $ArN(OH)NH(OH)$ / $ArN{-}NH$ \ O $ArNH{\cdot}N(OH)$ $ArNH{\cdot}NO$	$ArN{:}N{\cdot}OH$ $ArN{:}N{\cdot}OM$	$ArN{\cdot}N{\cdot}OH$	$Ar{\cdot}{\cdot}N{:}\ddot{N}{::}\ddot{N}{\cdot}{\cdot}X$
Neutral Isomers :	Nitrosamine. $ArNH{\cdot}NO$						

M = atom of a monovalent metal or its equivalent.

Hantzsch reared the whole of his theory from the fundamental proposition that the difference between the oximes and the diazo-compounds lies merely in the substitution of nitrogen for carbon, and that the series of normal and *iso*diazo-compounds must be derived from two stereoisomeric diazohydroxides. Hantzsch called the two possible stereoisomers the "*syn*"-form and the "*anti*"-form, representing the two parent hydroxides thus :—

Ar·N
‖   "*syn*"-Diazohydroxide.
HO·N

Ar·N
‖   "*anti*"-Diazohydroxide.
N·OH

Angeli has also left a record that he discerned the possibility of the same explanation independently of Hantzsch, but he never followed it up.[48]

Inspection of the two forms given above soon permits decision as to which should represent the reactive normal diazo-compound and which the stable *iso*diazo-compound. The *syn*-form must represent a molecule likely to be rendered unstable by internal strain, whether arising from the mere mass of the two nuclei compelled to lie close together or from the effects of chemical attraction or repulsion between them. The *syn*-configuration, therefore, corresponds to the normal diazo-compounds, while the *anti*-form represents the *iso*-diazo compounds in which the strain has been relieved by the acquisition of sufficient space for each nucleus and increase of the separating distance has diminished electro-chemical effects. Since energy is dissipated in the relief of strain, it follows that the *anti*-form must be at a lower energy level than the *syn*-form, from which it thus differs by lower reactivity and lower sensitivity to agencies such as heat and shock. A further corollary is that the change from *syn*- to *anti*-form should take place with evolution of heat.

While the coupling reaction is the most easily applied way of ascertaining whether a given diazo-compound belongs to the *syn*- or *anti*-series, Hantzsch put forward other means of differentiation. The two forms differ in the manner of their decomposition, a fact which can be explained by supposing that the molecules suffer partition as shown by the dotted lines.

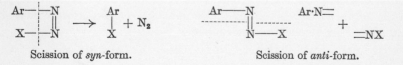

Scission of *syn*-form.   Scission of *anti*-form.

If the above premise is granted, those labile diazocyanides which afford the aryl nitriles must have the *syn*-form, while the stable forms which cannot be decomposed in this way must be the *anti*-diazo-compounds. An example of the typical decomposition of the *anti*-diazo-compound is provided by the oxidation of benzene *iso*diazotate to nitrosobenzene, a reaction represented by Hantzsch :—

$$\begin{array}{c} Ph{\cdot}N \\ \| \\ N{\cdot}OH \end{array} + O = PhNO + NOH$$

Since the *syn*-form alone is active, it is fundamental to Hantzsch's theory that the reactions of the diazonium compounds must be indirect, proceeding through the intermediate formation of the *syn*-diazo-compound, and he accordingly adopted the following scheme, which represents the general reaction as occurring by a particular mode of addition from which the requisite *syn*-form alone can result by scission :— [49]

$$\begin{array}{ccc} Ar & R & \\ | & | & \\ N{\equiv}N + & | & \longrightarrow \\ | & | & \\ X & H & \end{array} \quad \begin{array}{cc} Ar & R \\ | & | \\ N{=}N \\ \overset{+}{XH} \end{array}$$

As examples of this generality, the formation of *syn*-diazotate, *syn*-diazosulphonate and *syn*-diazocyanide were shown occurring thus :—

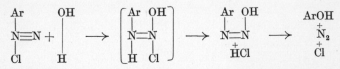

$$\begin{array}{cccccc} Ar & OH & SO_3K & CN & Ar & OK\ or\ (SO_3K)\ or\ (CN) \\ | & | & | & | & | & | \\ N{\equiv}N + & | & or & | & or & | & \longrightarrow & N{=}N \\ | & | & | & | & & \\ NO_3 & K & K & K & & + KNO_3 \end{array}$$

In certain cases Hantzsch had to recede from the view that all reactions take place through the *syn*-diazo-form. The point came up in connexion with the mechanism of the decomposition of diazonium compounds in acid solution. In consistence with the theory, Hantzsch at first treated the decomposition as a special case of the general theory :—

$$\begin{array}{cc} Ar & OH \\ | & | \\ N{\equiv}N + & | \\ | & | \\ Cl & H \end{array} \longrightarrow \left[\begin{array}{cc} Ar & OH \\ | & | \\ N{=}N \\ | & | \\ H & Cl \end{array}\right] \longrightarrow \begin{array}{cc} Ar & OH \\ | & | \\ N{=}N \\ \overset{+}{HCl} \end{array} \longrightarrow \begin{array}{c} ArOH \\ \overset{+}{N_2} \\ \overset{+}{Cl} \end{array}$$

Later, however, he adopted the simpler explanation that the diazonium salt itself breaks down directly.[50] The thermal measurements of Hantzsch and Davidson [51] had already supplied evidence that the rearrangement of a diazonium hydroxide to a *syn*-diazotate may be accounted for by a simpler mechanism :—

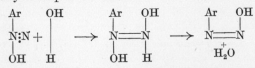

$$\begin{array}{cc} Ar & OH \\ | & | \\ N{:}N + & | \\ | & | \\ OH & H \end{array} \longrightarrow \begin{array}{cc} Ar & OH \\ | & | \\ N{=}N \\ | & | \\ OH & H \end{array} \longrightarrow \begin{array}{cc} Ar & OH \\ | & | \\ N{=}N \\ \overset{+}{H_2O} \end{array}$$

Thus the theory supplied an answer to the very pertinent question of how the *syn*-form and not the *anti*-form could invariably be the first product of reaction or re-arrangement of a diazonium salt, and further showed how the diazonium salts could resemble ammonium salts in the salt-forming power of their pentavalent nitrogen atom, yet differ in the manner of their decomposition.   The stability of the ammonium salts depends on the nature of the acid radical, the more acid the radical the greater the stability of the salt, hence the greater stability of ammonium chloride as compared with ammonium carbonate.   On the other hand, much evidence has already been brought forward to show that the stability of diazonium salts is independent of the anions of strong acids, and so, not being accountable by hydrolytic action, must needs be explained by the active intervention of a second substance.

There are cases where a diazonium compound or a diazo-compound undergoes a reaction which results in the formation of more than one product, the best known being that with alcohol, which can lead either to phenol ethers or hydrocarbons, according to the substituents in the aromatic ring.   The addition hypothesis first explained this as being due to differing electrochemical attractions affecting the addition of the alcohol.   With aromatic nuclei positively substituted phenol ethers are the main product, because addition occurs thus :—

$$\begin{array}{ccc} \overset{\displaystyle Ar}{\underset{\displaystyle Cl}{\overset{|}{\underset{|}{N \vdots N}}}} + & \overset{\displaystyle OAlk}{\underset{\displaystyle II}{|}} & \longrightarrow \quad \overset{\displaystyle Ar\ \ Alk}{\underset{\displaystyle ClH}{\overset{|\ \ |}{N\!=\!N}}} \quad \longrightarrow \quad \overset{\displaystyle ArOAlk}{\underset{\displaystyle \overset{+}{ClH}}{\overset{+}{N \vdots N}}} \end{array}$$

With strong negatively substituted nuclei, *e.g.* tribromobenzene, the opposite pole of the alcohol molecule is attracted, and so addition occurs in the opposite sense to the above, thus :—

$$\begin{array}{ccc} \overset{\displaystyle Ar}{\underset{\displaystyle Cl}{\overset{|}{\underset{|}{N\!\equiv\!N}}}} + & \overset{\displaystyle H}{\underset{\displaystyle OC_2H_5}{|}} & \longrightarrow \quad \overset{\displaystyle Ar\ \ H}{\underset{\displaystyle ClH + MeCHO}{\overset{|\ \ |}{N\!=\!N}}} \quad \longrightarrow \quad \overset{\displaystyle ArH}{\underset{\displaystyle HCl + MeCHO}{N\!\equiv\!N}} \end{array}$$

The formation of ethyl hypochlorite may be intermediate in the oxidation of the alcohol.

Hantzsch originally interpreted this reaction as proceeding through the *syn*diazo-compound, but later had misgivings as to the correctness of this view, since the reaction occurs with equal facility in strongly acid solution.   It must therefore be possible for the diazonium salt to react directly with the alcohol, and in his later explanation Hantzsch utilised measurements which have shown the angles between the valency bonds of oxygen in alcohol to be 96°, and assumed that the reaction is initiated by appropriate addition of the alcohol to the diazonium salt :— [52]

$$\begin{array}{c} \overset{\displaystyle Ar \cdot N \equiv N \quad OEt}{\underset{\displaystyle Cl \qquad\qquad H}{\diagup \qquad \diagdown |}} \quad \longrightarrow \quad ArOEt + N_2 + HCl \end{array}$$

If Ar is substituted by powerful negative groups, then the primary attraction, represented by the dotted line, acts in the opposite way :—

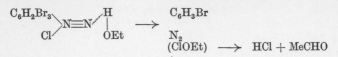

If Hantzsch's theory of the constitution of the diazo-compounds is correct, it follows that every diazo-compound can exist in three isomeric forms, diazonium, *syn*-, and *anti*-diazotates.   Hantzsch has been able to cite but few cases proving his theory up to the hilt, and its present wide acceptance has been achieved more by careful co-ordination of many facts all pointing in the same direction.   In building up this body of evidence he sought the chief support from three classes of compounds :—

1. The diazocyanides.

2. The diazobenzenesulphonic acids, $\overset{O----\rceil}{\underset{O_2S \cdot C_6H_4 \cdot N \vdots N.}{|}}$

3. The diazosulphonates, $Ar \cdot N = N \cdot SO_3K.$

Further support has come from other quarters, even from opponents, while Hantzsch himself has been compelled to record more than one negative result.

A brief *résumé* of this evidence and of Hantzsch's views on the primary arylnitrosamines will now be given followed by some account of the criticisms to which the theory has been subjected.

The Diazocyanides.—In describing the reactions of the diazo-compounds it has been remarked that when they react with cyanides in aqueous solution coloured precipitates result, and that two modifications, labile and stable, of such diazo-compounds can usually be shown to exist.   Their physical properties and reactions show that they cannot be diazonium compounds, and Hantzsch therefore said they were the *syn*- and *anti*-diazocyanides, formed according to the general principles of his theory in the way mentioned above.   Accordingly, it was to be expected that colourless, highly-ionised diazonium cyanides should be capable of existence, and the diazonium radical being a compound alkali metal, such cyanides would resemble an alkali cyanide.   A clue to their existence was discovered when it was found that diazonium chlorides treated with silver cyanide give, in addition to the insoluble yellow diazocyanide, a soluble colourless double cyanide with silver cyanide.[53] Alkali cyanides cannot be used for this reaction because their invariable accompaniment by hydroxyl ions causes isomerisation of any diazonium cyanide formed to the diazocyanide.   Since hydrocyanic acid is so weak an acid, difficulty was experienced in finding a case where a solid salt could be isolated, but eventually by evaporating *p*-anisol diazonium hydroxide with excess hydrogen cyanide *in vacuo* at room temperature a double cyanide was obtained of the constitution :—

$$MeO \cdot C_6H_4 \cdot N_2 \cdot CN \cdot HCN \cdot H_2O$$

This was found to have the properties expected of a diazonium salt, being a colourless crystalline solid ionised in aqueous solution, and giving the typical yellow precipitate of the diazocyanide when treated with alkali.[54] Hantzsch could therefore point to a family of three isomers as demanded by his theory :—

MeOC$_6$H$_4$·N⫶N   MeOC$_6$H$_4$·N   MeOC$_6$H$_4$·N
      | ‖   ‖
     CN   NC·N   N·CN

Diazonium cyanide.   *syn*Diazocyanide.   *anti*Diazocyanide.

The achievement afforded strong support for the stereochemical theory.

There are only two other cases in which the complete family of the three expected isomers can be isolated in the solid state (p. 190), and unfortunately there is little possibility of the existence of many more. In the first place, hydrocyanic acid occupies an anomalous place among the acids, and has given rise to discussion as to its structure which has only of recent years received a satisfactory explanation on the electronic theory.[55] Acids stronger than hydrocyanic acid afford only the stable diazonium salt; with weaker ones only the diazocompounds exist. Only strongly positive substituents in the benzene ring are favourable to the diazonium cyanide, so that when the diazocyanides of *p*-anisol or *ψ*-cumene are dissolved in water, the equilibrium concentration of the diazonium cyanide can reach quite a considerable value :— [56]

MeOC$_6$H$_4$·N   MeOC$_6$H$_4$·N≡N   MeOC$_6$H$_4$·N≡N$^+$ $^-$CN
     ‖   ⇌ | ⇌
   NC·N   CN

Nevertheless the most weakly negative of substituents influence the equilibrium so greatly in favour of the diazo-forms that, in general, it is only the *syn*- and *anti*-diazocyanides which can be isolated.

The Isomeric Diazobenzene Sulphonic Acids.—Owing to its insolubility, the inner anhydride of diazobenzene-*p*-sulphonic acid had long been known before Hantzsch confirmed for it the diazonium structure which had previously been mooted by other workers :—

Moreover an *iso*-salt had been prepared by Bamberger by the usual method of heating with excess caustic alkali before Hantzsch had published his theory. The normal or labile isomer necessary to complete the family of isomers was prepared by Hantzsch and Gerilowski by acting on diazotised sulphanilic acid with aqueous caustic alkali at 0°.[57] Both the sodium and potassium salts were made, the former as white needles crystallising with four molecules of water, the latter anhydrous and passing more easily into the iso-form. For purity and ease of preparation this is by far the most satisfactory family of isomers. The complete family of potassium salts is also known in the case of diazo-benzene-o-sulphonic acid.[58]

The normal salt of diazobenzene-p-sulphonic acid showed the properties such as coupling with β-naphthol, readily losing nitrogen, and having an alkaline reaction due to its weakness as an acid and consequent hydrolytic dissociation. Conductivity measurements were made of both salts in aqueous solution, and the disodium salt of the iso-form gave values agreeing well with those of other sodium salts of dibasic acids. The normal salt gave values which showed the acid to be weaker than the acid giving rise to the iso-salt, while both gave three ions. Accordingly Hantzsch regarded these facts as evidence that the isomerism of the two diazotates is spatial, and represented their constitutions by the structures :— [59]

$$NaO_3S \cdot C_6H_4 \cdot N \atop \| \atop NaO \cdot N \quad syn\text{-Form.} \qquad\qquad NaO_3S \cdot C_6H_4 \cdot N \atop \| \atop N \cdot ONa \quad anti\text{-Form.}$$

Against this it should be noted that in the same paper Hantzsch and Gerilowsky reported that the synoximes are stronger acids than the antioximes. Angeli in regard to this matter has pointed out that of the two cinnamic acids, that which has the carboxyl group nearer to the phenyl radical is a stronger acid than that which has the carboxyl group turned away, i.e.
$$Ph \cdot CH \atop \| \atop HO_2C \cdot CH$$
is more acidic than
$$Ph \cdot CH \atop \| \atop CH \cdot CO_2H.$$
This fact is in agreement with the order of acidity of the oximes, and that the syndiazotate appears to be anomalous in being less acidic than the antidiazotate.[60]

The Isomeric Diazosulphonates.—The diazosulphonates are known only in the two modifications, the preparation and properties of which have been already described (see p. 93). No substance having the properties to be expected of a diazonium salt of sulphurous acid has ever been discovered to complete the family of isomers. When Hantzsch discovered the labile form, he brought these compounds forward as evidence of the stereoisomerism of the diazo-compounds, and he represented their formation in solution from the diazonium chloride as taking place thus :—

$$\begin{matrix} Ar & K \\ | & | \\ N\equiv N & + & SO_3 \\ | & | \\ Cl & K \end{matrix} \longrightarrow \begin{matrix} Ar & SO_3K \\ | & | \\ N=\!=\!=N \\ \overset{+}{KCl} \end{matrix} \; syn\text{-Salt.} \longrightarrow \begin{matrix} Ar \cdot N \\ \| \\ N \cdot SO_3K \end{matrix} \; anti\text{-Salt.}$$

The following facts were the basis for his assertion that the two salts are stereoisomers :—

1. The more deeply coloured isomer has the power to couple with β-naphthol, and on standing in solution changes to the stable form, which cannot couple, and must therefore be a member of the *anti*-series. Therefore the labile coloured form is the *syn*-isomer.

2. Conductometric determination showed the salts of both series to dissociate in solution into two ions, the *syn*-salt in addition giving evidence of hydrolytic dissociation.

3. The measurements of absorption spectra, made first by Dobbie and Tinkler and later repeated by Hantzsch and Lifschitz, showed the absorption curves of both labile and stable diazosulphonates to be the same, and it could therefore be argued that their molecular structure must be the same. The same identity of the absorption curves was also found in the case of the labile and stable diazocyanides already mentioned, but the absorption spectrum of the diazonium cyanide was quite different.

Mention might be made here of the fact that the absorption curves of the normal and *iso*diazobenzene hydroxides were found to have very differently shaped curves, though, as parent hydroxides of both the cyanides and sulphonates, identical absorptions would be expected. Dobbie and Tinkler were therefore forced to the conclusion that the normal and *iso*diazotates are structural isomerides, and further that the resemblance of the curve of the *iso*-salt to phenylmethylnitrosamine appeared to support the formula originally proposed by Schraube and Schmidt. The work of Hantzsch and Lifschitz confirmed the findings of Dobbie and Tinkler in respect of these differences in the absorption spectra.

The Oxidation of *p*-Chlorodiazobenzene Cyanide (Bamberger). —The work of Bamberger in 1912 [61] came too late to be a definite support in the early days when Hantzsch was striving to make good the footing of his theory, but the firmness of its establishment was marked when a former opponent found in it the most adequate means to explain his results.

When the labile *p*-chlorodiazobenzene cyanide is oxidised by hydrogen peroxide in ether, the reaction products are dependant on the conditions. In the presence of magnesium carbonate the main resultant is *p*-chloronitrosophenylhydroxylamine, $Cl \cdot C_6H_4 \cdot N <^{NO}_{OH}$, while *p*-chlorophenylazoformamide is a by-product. If oxidation is carried out in presence of caustic soda the relationships are reversed, but in the latter case the result cannot be due to conversion of the labile cyanide to the stable cyanide, because the latter can be demonstrated to be unattacked by hydrogen peroxide in ether. Bamberger, therefore, partly by analogy with some of his previous work on the oxidation of the oximes and partly by a process of reasoning he did not make clear, suggested that the oxidation of the diazocyanides is analogous to that of the diazotates and oximes which he represented :—

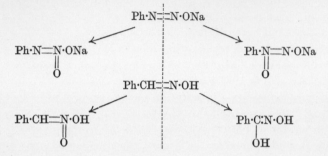

Though the above shows the resemblance between the diazo-compounds and the oximes, as postulated by Hantzsch, it does not explain, except by inference, how the facts of the oxidation of the labile *p*-chlorodiazobenzene cyanide prove that the cyanide in question has the *syn*-structure.

The *iso*Diazotates and the Primary Arylnitrosamines.— Beside the question of the constitution of the normal and *iso*diazotates Hantzsch concerned himself with the relationship between the *iso*diazotates and the primary arylnitrosamines. Hantzsch described how this relationship, which is not evident in the *iso*diazo-salts, fixed as they are as *anti*-compounds, becomes evident when attempts are made to liberate the free hydroxide. He held the opinion that as soon as the metal is replaced by hydrogen a labile molecule results, setting up the equilibrium :—

$$\underset{\text{N·OH}}{\overset{\text{Ar·N}}{\|}} \rightleftharpoons \underset{\text{NO}}{\overset{\text{Ar·NH}}{|}}$$

The equilibrium can move so that the nitrosamine is the only form, and the nature of the aromatic nucleus determines which way movement shall go. Engler supplied experimental evidence along these lines in the naphthalene series.[62]

The criteria Hantzsch employed to decide which of the two isomers was in hand were the following, from which it is evident that they are widely different in character :—

*iso*Diazohydroxides are electrolytes of acid reaction with definite affinity constants, forming salts with dry ammonia and reacting directly with phosphorus and acyl halides.

Primary nitrosamines are non-conductors, without action on indicators, without measurable affinity constants, and non-reactive at room temperature with phosphorus and acyl halides. They are *pseudo*-acids—that is to say, they will combine with an alkali, but only after undergoing tautomeric change to give a neutral salt—the *anti*diazotate.

It follows, therefore, according to Hantzsch, that as the nitrosamines are not acids, the metallic *iso*diazotates cannot possess the nitrosamine constitution.

These generalities were supported by experiments with the sodium salt of *p*-nitro*iso*diazobenzene and the potassium salt of *p*-bromo*iso*-diazobenzene.[63] These experiments, in which conductometric measurements played a considerable part, left much to be desired owing to the difficulty of preparing material in a state of purity, and Hantzsch again returned to the attack with an experimental study of eight cases. Only in two cases could both the *iso*diazohydroxide and the nitrosamine be prepared. Moreover, among the other examples he unfortunately included 1-diazo-2 : 4 : 6-tribromobenzene, from which by the action of cold weak alkali followed by acid he obtained a well-defined crystalline derivative of neutral reaction, which he took to be the nitrosamine, but which Orton showed to be the stable internal diazo-oxide :—

one bromine atom being easily detached by the weakest alkali.[65] In his spectroscopic researches with Lifschitz the case of *p*-nitrodiazobenzene hydroxide was studied afresh, when the substance was found to give a different absorption spectrum from a solution of the neutral substance believed to be the nitrosamine; but it must be remembered that at that date the colour changes which can be brought about by electron drift within a molecule by different solvents was not understood, and a change in structure was considered to be proved. Hantzsch wrote a summary of the evidence, direct and indirect, for the existence of the equilibrium

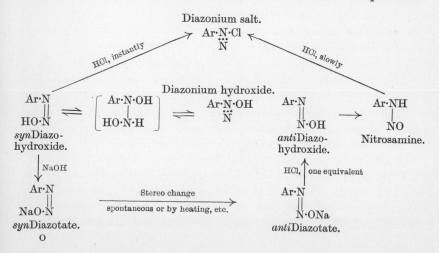

between the *iso*diazohydroxides and the nitrosamines,[66] but this aspect of his theory has failed to carry wide conviction, particularly after the doubt cast by the work of Orton.   It is also unfortunate that the primary arylnitrosamines have not been prepared by any other route, so that an equilibrium with the *iso*diazotates cannot be approached from that side.   Hantzsch, however, never departed from this viewpoint, and it is incorporated in the classic tabular scheme, which is reproduced on the preceding page and shows, according to his theory, the relationships of the isomeric diazo-compounds.[67]

Criticisms of the Theory of Hantzsch.

As has been remarked, Hantzsch has secured a wide measure of recognition for his theory, not by any incontrovertible proof, but by the accumulation of small pieces of evidence, and also possibly because the basic idea bears the stamp of *prima facie* probability.   But for all his work the theory does not stand so secure as, for instance, that of the position isomerism of the benzene derivatives, nor the stereoisomerism of the oximes which was proved by Mills and Bain.[68]   Opponents have not been lacking, but, the evidence being piecemeal, the attack has likewise been necessarily suffused and unable to gain a decisive victory. Nevertheless note must be made of these objections because they represent points which require clearing up or presenting in a new way.

Opponents who supported the theory of the structural isomerism of the normal and *iso*-diazo-compounds pointed out that Hantzsch had by no means taken account of all the possibilities of isomerism among the diazosulphonates and diazocyanides, because the groups $-SO_3H$ and $-CN$ can themselves exist in isomeric forms.   The cause of this is now known, for they are both typical tautomeric dyads, the tautomerism being due to a semi-polar double bond, so that two different electronic configurations yield the same ion, but the isomerism of the diazo-compounds is shown in the solid state in non-ionised compounds.

Bamberger suggested that the facts as touching the diazosulphonates can be explained just as well by supposing the two salts to be :—

$Ph \cdot N{=}N \cdot O \cdot SO_2K$ $Ph \cdot N{=}N \cdot SO_3K$
Potassium diazobenzenesulphite.   Potassium diazobenzenesulphonate.
Normal or *syn*-salt.   *iso*- or *anti*-Salt.

Claus reached the same conclusion,[69] though he reached it from the belief that normal potassium sulphite is $KO \cdot SO_2K$.

On purely chemical grounds quite as good a case can be made for the constitution proposed by Bamberger and by Claus as for those of Hantzsch.   In view of the known instability of the azo-group when attached to oxygen, as in the oxygen analogues of the diazoimino-compounds, the diazosulphite structure would explain the power of the normal isomer to couple with phenols as against the loss of that power in the stable form in which the azo-link is directly attached to sulphur. A much more vulnerable alternative was suggested by Blomstrand and by Bamberger—namely, that the normal diazosulphonates are diazonium compounds, $\begin{array}{c} Ar \cdot N \cdot SO_3K \\ \| \\ N \end{array}$. Hantzsch replied to this that a diazonium sulphonate would dissociate into three ions in aqueous solution, $Ar \cdot N_2^+$, SO_3^-, K^+, by analogy with potassium sulphite, and also that, as benzenediazonium salts with colourless anions such as SO_3^- are colourless, whereas the normal diazosulphonate is red, it must be an azo-derivative, and cannot be derived from the diazonium isomer. The only unchallenged item is the spectroscopic evidence, and this must tell heavily on the credit side of Hantzsch's account. In the state in which the matter now rests, finality cannot be considered as reached, nor will it be possible to regard it as settled beyond doubt until the sulphur atom has been cleared of responsibility. It may be noted here that the debate on the isomerism of the inorganic sulphites shows a curious resemblance to that of the diazosulphonates.[70]

Hantzsch's interpretation of the chemistry of the diazocyanides had to meet a similar line of attack to that delivered on the diazosulphonates. Orton suggested that the structures of the two forms are :—

$Ar \cdot N \equiv N \cdot NC$ *syn*-Compound. $Ar \cdot N \equiv N \cdot CN$ *anti*-Compound.

Hantzsch has given reasons why it is improbable that any of his cyanides are *iso*cyanides,[71] but has never given formal proof of this contention, while his opponents have never taken the trouble to prove the converse.

Because of the inherent possibility of isomerism in molecules containing cyanide and sulphite radicals, v. Pechmann examined the benzenediazosulphones $Ph \cdot N_2 \cdot SO_2 \cdot Ph$ prepared from diazobenzene and benzenesulphinic acid (see p. 48). He could find no evidence of isomerides, nor did Hantzsch and Singer, while Hantzsch and Dybowski proved that a supposed case of isomerism in the diazothiosulphonates had no basis in fact. Hantzsch said that the failure to find the expected isomers is because such compounds can exist only in the *anti*-form, which is almost certainly true, because they are really azo-compounds. According to his general scheme for the reactions of diazonium compounds Hantzsch represented the reaction thus :— [72]

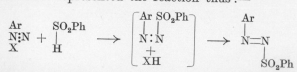

Nevertheless the situation remained a stalemate, for no progress had been made towards proving the existence of the diazosulphones in the *syn*-form.

Hantzsch used the power to couple with phenols as the distinguishing mark of the *syn*diazo-compounds as compared with the *anti*diazo-compounds, though he admitted that the latter do couple, albeit much more slowly. Coupling always takes place through the diazotate even when the diazonium salt is employed, for the action of alkali produces the *syn*diazotate, so that the whole process is represented :—

$$
\begin{array}{l} \text{Ar} \\ | \\ \text{N}\!\equiv\!\text{N} \;+ \\ | \\ \text{Cl} \end{array}
\begin{array}{l} \text{OH} \\ | \\ \\ | \\ \text{K} \end{array}
\longrightarrow
\begin{array}{l} \text{Ar} \;\; \text{OH} \\ | \qquad | \\ \text{N}\!\!=\!\!\text{N} \end{array} + \text{HAr}'
\longrightarrow
\left[\begin{array}{l} \text{Ar} \;\; \text{Ar}' \\ | \qquad | \\ \text{N}\!\!=\!\!\text{N} \end{array} \right] + \text{H}_2\text{O}
\longrightarrow
\begin{array}{l} \text{Ar} \\ | \\ \text{N}\!\!=\!\!\text{N} \\ | \\ \text{Ar}' \end{array}
$$

No *syn*azo-compound has ever been detected, for it is always the *anti*azo-compound which appears, a result which is not surprising when one considers the strain which would exist in a molecule such as the one depicted in brackets. For steric reasons the *syn*azo-compound is probably incapable of existence, and, if formed, must go over at once into the *anti*-form, but then the difficulty arises of finding an adequate reason as to why the coupling of the *anti*diazotate, which already possesses the final orientation, should be so much impeded. (Concerning the shape of the azobenzene molecule see p. 103.)

The foregoing is a special case of the general form, of which several examples have been given, by which Hantzsch represented the reactions of diazonium salts which lead to *syn*-derivatives, or through them to more stable end-products. This mode of representation goes much further into the mechanics of reaction in solution than is warrantable, because it postulates not only an addition reaction by an undissociated molecule, but also postulates that only one particular manner of collision results in reaction. In his last discussion on the reaction of alcohol with diazonium compounds, Hantzsch has himself referred to this representation as empirical, but because the spatial configuration of the resultant is pre-determined, the assumption of some such condition cannot be escaped. The theory as it stands provides no means of predicting why other modes of reaction should not be possible. For instance, in the case of the diazosulphonates, if, with Hantzsch, potassium sulphite is assumed to be symmetrical, then there is no reason why the *anti*-salt should not be produced in the reaction :—

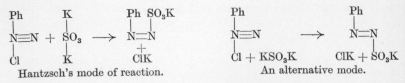

Hantzsch's mode of reaction.   An alternative mode.

If reaction occurs between free ions, there is still less reason why the collisions should not produce equal parts of the isomers, supposing the structure of the diazonium ion in solution is accurately represented.

Hantzsch has, of course, used these alternatives to explain the differing action of alcohol on diazonium compounds, and he was alert to apply to the problem any new knowledge as to the actual shape of molecules and the possible effect of such shape on reaction. Nevertheless we remain at present without knowledge as to what forces regulate the reactions of diazonium salts, so that only a derivative oriented in a particular way can result. It must be recorded that the problem has not escaped attention, and Swientoslawski has put forward an explanation as to why only one isomer makes its appearance, basing his hypothesis on the idea that the tervalent nitrogen united by a double bond can be " deformed," becoming more acidic thereby, and so giving rise to a stereoisomer of the compound containing the undeformed atom.[73] He arrived at this conclusion from his long-continued thermochemical researches among oximes and diazo-compounds. As the " deformed " atom is the more acidic, it is the one present in the *iso*diazotates, and Swientoslawski represents the isomeric diazohydroxides thus :—

Ar·N═N·OH Normal diazohydroxide.

$$\begin{array}{l} \text{Ar·N} \\ \;\;\| \;\;\; \textit{iso}\text{Diazohydroxide.} \\ \text{HO·N} \end{array}$$

the atoms marked in heavy type being " deformed " and having lost a plane of symmetry. It can be seen that a third isomer, the *anti*diazohydroxide of Hantzsch, should appear, but Swientoslawski says the forces between the aryl nucleus and the hydroxyl group prevent such an isomer from coming into existence. Under the fire of criticism by Hantzsch and others,[74] Swientoslawski has enlarged on his hypothesis,[75] but until he announces the cause of the deformation of the nitrogen atom and the mode of operation of this force, his explanation really gets no further than that of Hantzsch, which, even if cruder, is more serviceable. Brady's work, in which he showed a relationship between dissociation constant and stereoisomerism among oximes, may prove a pointer in the right direction,[76] but diazohydroxides are so unstable that dissociation constants for both normal and *iso*-forms have only been determined in the case of diazobenzene-*p*-sulphonic acid. Moreover, until stereoisomers are proved by the method of resolution to exist among the diazo-compounds, analogies with the oximes may prove of little value, for which reason the recent demonstration by Meisenheimer that the oximes previously considered to belong to the *trans*-series are in fact members of the *cis*-series and *vice versa*, has not been reflected by any change of view as to the configurations of the *syn*- and *anti*-diazo-compounds.

The possibility remains that in the fullness of time the daring postulates of Hantzsch may after all prove correct, and may take their place in the long line of inspired guesses which have so notably advanced the science of chemistry.   In the meantime they remain an invitation to further inquiry, and they have been discussed here at some length because they will form the background from which the next advance is made.

The Theory of Bamberger.

In his efforts to elucidate the problem of the constitution of the diazo-compounds Bamberger studied their chemical reactions and attempted syntheses which would give unequivocal evidence of structure, whereas Hantzsch applied the technique of Ostwald and the physical chemists to supplement chemical studies by physical measurements as a means to inquire more deeply into the processes by which the final products were reached.   In dealing with compounds so labile as the diazo-compounds, Bamberger was at some disadvantage, a disadvantage which was accentuated because he did not start from such a solid and firmly held basic hypothesis as did Hantzsch.   Consequently, although he contributed much to the knowledge of the reactions of the diazo-compounds, he changed his opinions as to their constitution more than once, and finally became converted to Hantzsch's way of thinking.[77] It might be said that it was he who compelled Hantzsch to hammer out his theory of the stereoisomerism, because in alliance with v. Pechmann and Frobenius he represented the school which held that the diazotates are structural isomers.   He accepted Blomstrand's constitution for the diazonium compounds having been largely instrumental in its rehabilitation, though for some time he held that diazonium hydroxides combine directly with cations to form the metallic diazotates.[78]

The nitrosamine structure for the *iso*diazotates has always been the obvious choice of the believers in structural isomerism, while the structure $Ar \cdot N = N \cdot OH$ has been equally obvious for the normal diazotates.   Bamberger at first supported that school which drew its chief argument from the facts of the acetylation of alkaline diazo-solutions and the formation of hydrazones in coupling reactions.   He then toyed with the idea that diazotisation consists first in the formation of phenylnitrosamine $Ph \cdot NH \cdot NO$, which, being unstable, rearranges to the normal diazohydroxide.[79]   But as a result of attempts to determine the constitution of the *iso*diazotates by synthesis he was led to alter his view.   He devised the synthesis of diazo-compounds from nitrosobenzene and hydroxylamine :— [80]

$$Ph \cdot NO + H_2NOH \longrightarrow Ph \cdot N = N \cdot OH + H_2O$$

and though his product coupled instantly with α-naphthol, he considered that only traces of the normal compound had been formed, and he therefore gave the above constitution to the *iso*-form.   When he used arylhydroxylamines in place of hydroxylamine itself he obtained azoxy-compounds :— [81]

$$Ar \cdot NO + OHNH \cdot Ar \longrightarrow Ar \cdot N \overset{O}{=\!\!=} N \cdot Ar + H_2O$$

but admitted that no definite evidence as to the structure of the *iso*diazo-compounds had been obtained. Much later Hantzsch represented Bamberger's synthesis as giving the normal diazo-compound by an additive reaction :— [82]

$$Ar \cdot NO + HNH \cdot OH \longrightarrow Ar \cdot N \!\!\begin{array}{c} OH \\ NHOH \end{array} \longrightarrow \left[\begin{array}{c} Ar \cdot N \cdot OH \\ | \\ OH \cdot N \cdot H \end{array} \right] \longrightarrow \begin{array}{c} Ar \cdot N \\ \| \\ HO \cdot N \end{array} + H_2O$$

Were the normal and *iso*diazo-compounds different structurally some differences in their behaviour to reagents would be expected. Bamberger said that the production of diazo-anhydrides from normal diazotates, but not from *iso*diazotates, is proof of a structural difference, and he represented the substances at first as diazonium ethers, and then as diazonium diazotates :—[38]

$$\begin{array}{c} Ar \cdot N \cdot O \cdot N \cdot Ar \\ \| \quad \| \\ N \quad N \end{array} \quad or \quad \begin{array}{c} Ar \cdot N \cdot O \cdot N \!=\! NAr \\ \| \\ N \end{array}$$

Further, he claimed that differences exist in respect of reduction and treatment with acid chlorides,[84] but Hantzsch was unable to find any such difference on repeating the work.[85]

Undoubtedly Bamberger's most subtle attempt to come at the structure of the *iso*diazo-compounds was his synthesis from *o*- and *p*-hydroxybenzylaniline.[86] These substances yield nitrosamines which are hydrolysed by treatment with very dilute caustic soda, and the reaction should proceed according to the following scheme :—

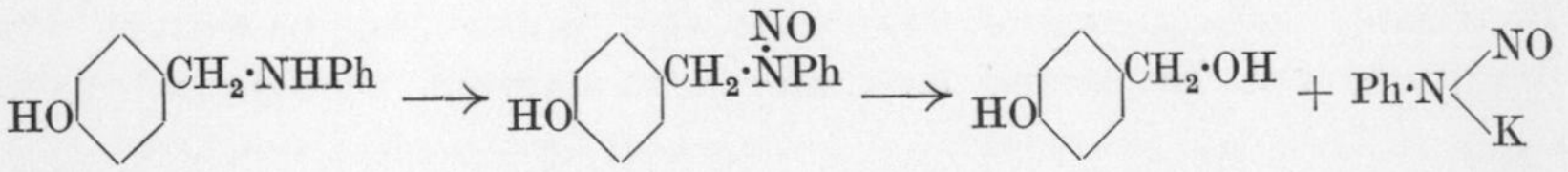

$$HO \!-\!\!\bigcirc\!\!-CH_2 \cdot NHPh \longrightarrow HO \!-\!\!\bigcirc\!\!-CH_2 \cdot \overset{NO}{N}Ph \longrightarrow HO \!-\!\!\bigcirc\!\!-CH_2 \cdot OH + Ph \cdot N \!\!\begin{array}{c} NO \\ K \end{array}$$

He considered that the evidence pointed to the formation of an *iso*diazotate, $Ph \cdot N = N \cdot OK$, and therefore that the substance $Ph \cdot N \!\!\begin{array}{c} NO \\ K \end{array}$ had only a very transitory existence. The scheme for the relationships of the diazo-compounds which he published is that of his mature judgment on the experiments before conversion to the stereochemical theory, and it is given here because recently renewed attention has been paid to the possibilities of such constitution. He represented the sequence of changes brought about in diazonium salts by increasingly alkaline conditions thus :—

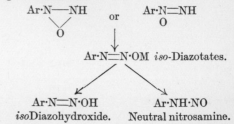

$$Ar \cdot \underset{\underset{N}{\|\|\|}}{N \cdot X} \longrightarrow Ar \cdot \underset{\underset{N}{\|\|\|}}{N \cdot OH} \longrightarrow (Ar \cdot N_2 \cdot OH)(Ar \cdot N_2 OM)$$

Normal diazohydroxides and diazotates of unknown structure which it is suggested might be such as :—

Ar·N——NH \quad or \quad Ar·N=NH

Ar·N=N·OM *iso*-Diazotates.

Ar·N=N·OH \qquad\qquad Ar·NH·NO
*iso*Diazohydroxide. \qquad Neutral nitrosamine.

The impression left on the mind of the reader of Bamberger's papers is that an excellent experimental technique produced results which were not sifted by the application of sufficiently rigid criteria nor supported by any strongly-held theoretical view.

The Theory of Brühl.

Where direct chemical evidence had failed to give an answer to the vexed question of the diazo-compounds, it cannot be surprising that some investigators sought to apply purely physical means, and the conclusions brought forward by Brühl must be noted briefly, because, though entirely different from any yet suggested, they were at least backed by a rigidly logical argument.[87]

There is a body of evidence to show that the refractive index of a substance is the sum of the specific atomic refractive indices of its components. These indices in turn vary with the type of bond uniting the atoms. If the various values of the indices are known and the refractive index of a substance the constitution of which is in question is also known, then a process of summation will afford information as to the nature of the valency bonds present in the molecule.

Brühl's measurements supported the Blomstrand diazonium constitution, but he parted company with current thought when he represented the normal diazohydroxide as $\underset{H}{\overset{Ar}{>}}N\underset{O}{\overset{N}{<}}\Big|$, forming metallic diazotates by attachment of the metal atom to nitrogen by direct replacement of the hydrogen. He emphasised the close relationship of the nitrosoacylarylides to the normal diazotates, and showed the hydrolysis of nitrosoacetanilide thus :—

$$\underset{MeCO}{\overset{Ph}{>}}N\underset{O}{\overset{N}{<}}\Big| + NaOH = MeCO_2 Na + \underset{H}{\overset{Ph}{>}}N\underset{O}{\overset{N}{<}}\Big|$$

He was led to these configurations because he found the nitrogen in diazo-compounds to give high values for its specific refractive index, and therefore he was compelled to adopt formulæ to accommodate the high number of valency bonds indicated.

He believed the *iso*diazohydroxide to be structurally different from the normal diazohydroxide, and to have the azo-form, $Ar \cdot N = N \cdot ONa$, with the metal attached to oxygen. He also examined a *p*-nitrodiazo-benzene methyl ether, and concluded it to be a member of the *iso*-series.

The Theory of Armstrong and Robertson.

Like the preceding theory, the one which now comes under consideration was based by its authors on a physical property of the diazo- and azo-compounds—that of colour. Their hypothesis as to the constitution of the diazo-compounds was, indeed, but a part of a general discussion as to the relation of colour to chemical constitution.[88] The underlying fact of the whole superstructure was the yellow colour of benzeneazoethane, $Ph \cdot N = N \cdot Et$, a substance discovered by Fischer. Now, paraffin radicals, being saturated, cannot be in any way responsible for colour, and accordingly the colour of " phenyldiazoethane," as Armstrong and Robertson called Fischer's compound, must be due to the aromatic nucleus plus the azo-link, $Ph \cdot N = N -$. It follows, therefore, that all substance containing this group must be coloured, while it cannot be part of colourless substances.

Since the majority of diazo-salts are colourless, Armstrong and Robertson were content to adhere to the Blomstrand constitution, and they went further by adopting it, as Bamberger had done, tentatively, for the normal sulphonates and cyanides. They represented the transformation from the normal to the *iso*-form as proceeding through a coloured hydrate, and both these latter compounds were *ex hypothesi* held to contain the azo-link :—

$$\underset{N}{\overset{Ar \cdot N \cdot SO_3K}{|||}} \longrightarrow \underset{N \cdot OH}{\overset{Ar \cdot NH \cdot SO_3K}{|}} \longrightarrow Ar \cdot NH(OH) = N \cdot SO_3K \longrightarrow Ar \cdot N = N \cdot SO_3K$$

To accommodate the metallic diazotates they went back to Bamberger's discarded opinion, and proposed the diazonium form for the normal metallic salts, since these are colourless, and a roundabout intervention of hydration akin to that invoked by Hantzsch, to reach the old nitrosamine constitution, $Ar \cdot NK \cdot NO$, for the metallic *iso*-diazotates. The action of alkali on a diazonium salt thus came under the scheme :—

$$\underset{N}{\overset{Ar \cdot N \cdot OH}{|||}} \longrightarrow \underset{N \cdot OH}{\overset{Ar \cdot NH \cdot OH}{|}} \longrightarrow Ar \cdot N = N \cdot OH$$

The latter compound would be coloured, and therefore its existence is forbidden, but it can be supposed to hydrate in either of two ways, and the colourless hydrates can be resolved again to give two isomeric and indistinguishable isomeric nitrosamines :—

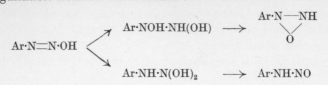

If the above reasoning really represents the truth, then the whole basis of the theory of Hantzsch is swept away, as the authors pointed out. They classed the coloured salts described by Hantzsch as mixtures of diazonium salts with azo-compounds; they pointed to the unsatisfactory analytical figures of some of Hantzsch's compounds and to the absence of any stereoisomers of azobenzene, and concluded that the whole theory was misconceived.

That consideration of colour can give useful information as to the constitution of chemical individuals cannot be denied. Hantzsch himself used it as an argument as to the structure of the double salts of copper salts with diazo-salts. But such considerations cannot settle the question of the constitution of the diazo-compounds offhand in three brief pages of print, and it is hardly necessary to do more than indicate the ways in which the theory of Armstrong and Robertson was attacked. Hantzsch [89] quickly quoted examples of undoubted azo-compounds incapable of existing in the hydrazone form, but which are nevertheless colourless, e.g., the azo-*iso*butyric derivatives of Thiele, $CRMe_2 \cdot N{=}N \cdot CRMe_2$,[90] and v. Pechmann's nitrodiazo-ester $NO_2 \cdot C_6H_4 \cdot N{=}N \cdot OMe$.[91] Therefore Armstrong and Robertson had no ground for their hypothesis, since substances containing the azo-link are not invariably coloured. Cain [92] also has pointed out that the behaviour of Armstrong and Robertson's radical, $Ph \cdot N{=}N{-}$, varies greatly, according to the nature of the group to which it is attached, and that the colour is no criterion of these variations or of the differences in structure which determine them. Indeed, as noted earlier, Hantzsch's proposal to call all compounds containing the $-N{=}N-$ link azo-compounds had foundered on that very snag.

The question of the relation of the colour and constitution of diazo-compounds has arisen again recently, though in less controversial form. Dilthey and his co-workers in a discussion on heteropolarity have formulated the diazonium salts as carbonium salts $\left[Ar\diagdown\begin{smallmatrix} N \\ \mathrel{\vert\vert\vert} \\ N \end{smallmatrix} \right]^+$ and have given examples showing that the conversion of $[Ar \cdot NH_3]^+$ to $[Ar \cdot N_2]^+$ is always accompanied by deepening of shade.[93]

The Theory of Cain.

The diazotisation reaction, as has been shown, is confined to primary amino-groups attached to an aromatic nucleus or a nucleus having the characteristic internal unsaturation of the aromatic compounds, and in the theories which have been described up to this point the diazo-compounds in all their tautomeric forms have been represented as still containing the unaltered aromatic nucleus. Cain [94] pointed out that some of the difficulties encountered in explaining the behaviour of the diazonium salts might be removed if more account were taken of the aromatic nucleus. For example, there is nothing in either Blomstrand's or Kekulé's formulæ, $\mathrm{Ph\cdot\underset{Cl}{N:}N}$ or $\mathrm{Ph\cdot N{=}N\cdot Cl}$, to indicate by mere inspection that outstanding reaction of the diazo-compounds, the facile loss of all their nitrogen. Now, aniline may have a tautomeric quinonoid form ![NH quinonoid form], through which its oxidation to p-benzo-quinone proceeds, and diazotisation might proceed by the same route, leading thus to an entirely new constitution for benzenediazonium chloride :—

Cain argued that such a constitution would explain the ease with which the nitrogen is lost, for whereas nitrogen attached to an aromatic nucleus by a single bond is held firmly if attached by a double bond, as in quinone chlorimide, ![quinone chlorimide], it is readily given up. On the other hand, as the latter compound has properties analogous to a diazonium salt, and differs only in that the chlorine atom is not ionised, it follows that the diazonium salt almost certainly contains a pentavalent nitrogen atom to which anions are attached. Moreover, the theory fits in with the fact that only those amines capable of existing in a tautomeric quinonoid form are able to undergo diazotisation, and thus explains the non-occurrence of the reaction in the aliphatic series. It was also pointed out that as both *para-* and *ortho*-quinones exist, diazonium salts of the new constitution must also have a second tautomeric form :—

Such an *ortho*quinonoid form would be the only one able to exist in the case of certain heterocyclic diazo-compounds such as those derived from 4-amino-antipyrine and 5-amino-1 : 2 : 4-triazole.[96]   Indeed, the suggestion was taken to the further stage of conceiving a dynamic equilibrium between the *ortho*- and *para*-quinonoid phase.[97]

Among other facts adduced by Cain as being more adequately explained by his theory was the difficult tetrazotisation of *p*-phenylene-diamine, for when one amino-group has been diazotised and the aromatic ring has assumed the quinonoid form, then a C—N bond has to be broken before nitrous acid can react with the second amino-group :—

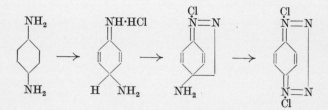

Negative substituents which often prevent tetrazotisation do so by rendering the C—N link too strong to be broken by the conditions of diazotisation.   Such a difficulty cannot arise with benzidine, which behaves as if the two benzene nuclei were separate entities, and so gives a bisdiazonium salt :—

It might be expected that substances possessing this quinonoid structure would be coloured, and in fact coloured diazonium salts are known, but Cain countered criticism by pointing out that the proposed structure is only hemiquinonoid.   In passing, it may be pointed out that Cain was not alone at this time in seeking some such constitution for the diazo-compounds, for Euler suggested the structure :— [98]

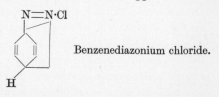

Benzenediazonium chloride.

The normal diazotates are the closest relatives to the diazonium salts, and should possess a constitution entailing the minimum of rearrange-ment in the transition.   Cain represented the diazonium : normal diazo-equilibrium thus :—

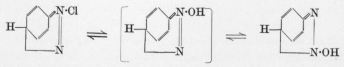

Now, preferential rupture by reagents of the C—N bond as against bonds between two nitrogen atoms was a fundamental postulate of the theory, a postulate which Cain supported by derivation from work of Buchner.[99] That the reduction of the supposed quinonoid diazonium salts leads to hydrazines depended on this postulate, the reducing agent first rupturing the C—N bond and then reducing the —N≡N— bond. Similarly, reagents bringing about conversion of the normal diazohydroxide to the *iso*diazohydroxide would rupture this same weak C—N bond, and conversion would proceed thus :—

This structure for the *iso*diazotates affords an explanation for their more sluggish reactivity as compared with the normal diazotates because they are true aromatic compounds. Moreover, it allows a way out of the difficulty of the *N*- and *O*-ethers, both derivable from the *iso*diazo-salts by permitting a suitable tautomerism, so that the metallic salt can assume the most stable form :—

$$\text{Ph·N}{=}\text{N·OK} \rightleftharpoons \text{Ph·NK·NO}$$

This theory is vulnerable at several points, and Hantzsch was not long in opening an attack of which the leading heads were :—

1. Benzenediazonium salts must be true aromatic compounds, because if they possessed a quinonoid structure they would show the readiness of the quinones to be attacked in the ring by halogens or by oxidising or reducing agents.

2. The postulate of the preferential scission of the C—N bond is unsound, and a compound of the structure advocated for benzene-diazonium chloride would reduce to *p*-phenylenediamine, and not to phenylhydrazine.

3. Both the normal and *iso*diazo-compounds behave as aromatic compounds and their differences are too small to be accounted for by such great differences in structure as proposed by Cain. For instance, there would be great differences in their absorption spectra, whereas such have not been found.[100]

All the above are weighty objections, but in particular number two is the Achilles heel of the theory. Among the negatively substituted *p*-phenylenediamines one cannot easily see why the C—N bond should resist rupture by powerful diazotising agencies, but yet break readily in the coupling reaction. Nor does it appear why the bond should re-form when *iso*diazotates pass back under the action of acids to diazonium salts or normal diazohydroxides. Cain discussed the point, but hardly cleared away all the difficulties.[101] On the question of the absorption spectra Cain supported his views by showing the similarity of the absorption curves of α-naphthalenediazonium chloride with p-quinonediazide.[102] Hantzsch contested the legitimacy of the analogy.[103] Schoutissen has objected to Cain's theory on the ground that it does not fit in with the negative character of the diazonium radical.

Schmidt has made use of Cain's theory to explain some reactions in which the *para* position to the diazonium group is involved, causing diaryls to appear as by-products in the synthesis of the aromatic arsenic acids.[104] But the apparent connection with the *ortho* and *para* positions in the benzene ring can be better accounted for by the electronic theory rather than by envisaging the existence of a quinonoid ring with all the accompanying reactions which the appearance of that structure must entail.

The Theory of Angeli.

The study of azoxy-compounds and their relationship to the diazotates has led Angeli and the Italian school to give support founded on experiment to the constitution put forward tentatively by Bamberger for the normal diazotates.[105]

The essential argument and line of reasoning run as follows : Asymmetric azo-compounds when oxidised give two separate isomeric azoxy-compounds :—

$$Ar \cdot N \dot{:} N \cdot Ar' \qquad\qquad\qquad Ar \cdot N \dot{:} N \cdot Ar'$$
$$\overset{\|}{O} \qquad\qquad\qquad\qquad\qquad \overset{\|}{O}$$

In addition, in certain cases where $Ar = p\text{-}Br \cdot C_6H_4-$ and $Ar' = p\text{-}NO_2 \cdot C_6H_4-$, then two further isomers, which are diazo-derivatives, are also known :—

$$Ar \cdot N \!\!=\!\! N \cdot OAr' \qquad\qquad Ar \cdot N \cdot Ar'$$
$$\qquad\qquad\qquad\qquad\qquad\qquad \overset{|}{NO}$$

Inspection of this group of compounds shows that a close structural relationship exists between the azoxy-compounds and diazo-compounds, a relationship which Bamberger demonstrated by showing that a diazo-compound is produced by mild oxidative scission of p-azoxyphenol.[106] Bamberger's reaction is not sufficiently free from ambiguity to be of value as a means of determining constitution, but Angeli found that benzenediazocarbonamide can be oxidised to benzeneazoxycarbonamide, which hydrolyses in alkaline solution to give a normal diazohydroxide. This reaction is more suitable as a means of fixing the constitution of the diazohydroxide. There are three alternatives for the constitution of benzeneazoxycarbonamide :—

$$Ph \cdot N \!\!=\!\! N \cdot CONH_2 \qquad Ph \cdot N \!\!=\!\! N \cdot CONH_2 \qquad Ph \cdot N \cdot NO$$
$$\overset{\|}{O} \qquad\qquad\qquad\qquad \overset{\|}{O} \qquad\qquad\qquad\qquad \overset{|}{CO \cdot NH_2}$$

The last compound is known, and is the very unstable nitrosophenyl-urea, hence one of the former is the structure fixed for the stable crystalline carbonamide. Therefore Angeli represents as follows the action of aqueous caustic soda on benzeneazoxycarbonamide which affords a liquid showing strongly the reactions of a diazohydroxide :—

$$Ph{\cdot}N{=}N{\cdot}CONH_2 \quad \longrightarrow \quad Ph{\cdot}N{=}N{\cdot}CO_2H \quad \longrightarrow \quad Ph{\cdot}N{=}NH$$
$$\quad\;\; \overset{\|}{O} \qquad\qquad\qquad\quad \overset{\|}{O} \qquad\qquad\qquad\quad \overset{\|}{O}$$

It may be remarked in passing that by a study of the hydrolysis of nitrosoacetanilide Walther was led to formulate the normal diazo-hydroxides as similarly containing pentavalent nitrogen :—

$$Ph{\cdot}N{=}NH \qquad or \qquad Ph{\cdot}N{=}NH{=}O$$
$$\;\;\; \overset{\|}{O}$$

In Angeli's theory the normal diazotates may have either of two structures which contain " twinned double bonds " :—

$$\begin{array}{ccc} Ar & & Ar \\ | & or & | \\ O{:}N{:}NH & & N{:}NH{:}O \end{array}$$

From such a structure their reactivity can be at once inferred, as they show a close resemblance of such active substances as keten and the *iso*cyanates :—

$$H_2C{:}C{:}O \qquad\qquad Ar{\cdot}N{:}C{:}O$$

In Angeli's opinion the formation of the *iso*diazo-compounds is brought about and the reactivity at the same time diminished by the nitrogen passing into the tervalent state :—

$$Ar{\cdot}N{=}NH$$
$$\quad\;\; \overset{\|}{O} \qquad\qquad\searrow$$
$$\qquad\qquad\qquad\qquad Ar{\cdot}N{:}N{\cdot}OH$$
$$Ar{\cdot}N{:}NH{\cdot}O \nearrow$$

Moreover, this constitution for the *iso*diazotates confirms Bamberger's experiments by which *iso*diazotates were obtained by the reduction of both phenylnitroamine and nitrosophenylhydroxylamine :—

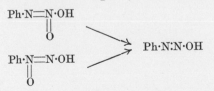

$$Ph{\cdot}N{=}N{\cdot}OH$$
$$\quad\;\; \overset{\|}{O} \qquad\qquad\searrow$$
$$\qquad\qquad\qquad\qquad Ph{\cdot}N{:}N{\cdot}OH$$
$$Ph{\cdot}N{=}N{\cdot}OH \nearrow$$
$$\quad\;\; \overset{\|}{O}$$

This theory is therefore a revival of the view of the normal and *iso*-diazohydroxides as structural isomers. Angeli has explained that the metallic diazotates need not necessarily be directly derived from the above compounds, which are the free diazohydroxides, and are the reactive forms of the metallic diazotates arising from them by hydrolytic dissociation.

At first sight it appears a serious defect of Angeli's theory that the nitrogen in the normal diazohydroxides is pentavalent, arousing the expectation of strong basicity.   Cambi and Szego, however, examined [107] and compared the absorption spectra of diazotates with arylnitrosohydroxylamines and arylnitroamines, and reached the conclusion that though the nitrogen is in fact pentavalent, it is nevertheless in the same condition as in the nitro-compounds and devoid of basic properties. If this should be the case, Angeli's normal diazohydroxides contain a semi-polar double bond :—

$$\overset{\text{Ar}}{\underset{}{\mid}}\quad\quad\text{or}\quad\quad\overset{\text{Ar}}{\underset{}{\mid}}$$
$$\text{O}{\Leftarrow}\text{N:NH}\quad\quad\quad\text{N:NH}{\Rightarrow}\text{O}$$

It would be interesting if further evidence could be adduced for this view.

So pronounced a structural difference between the normal and the *iso*diazotates cannot but be shown in different reactions, and a number of illustrations have been forthcoming.   Nitrohydroxylamine was found by Bigiavi [108] to be without action on the *iso*diazohydroxide, but when this reagent is added to a normal diazohydroxide vigorous reaction occurs, and nitrosobenzene can be isolated from the resinous product. Free " nitroxyl " is assumed to be the active agent :—

$$\underset{\overset{\|}{\text{O}}}{\text{Ph·N:NH}} + \text{OHN} = \text{Ph·N:O} + \text{N}_2 + \text{H}_2\text{O}$$

The same chemist explained the change back of the *iso*diazohydroxide to the normal diazohydroxide, a change usually supposed to go through the diazonium form and always requiring a diminution of alkalinity, as being analogous to the Beckmann transformation, oxygen migrating from one nitrogen atom to the other :—

$$\text{Ph·N}{=}\text{N·OH} \longrightarrow \underset{\text{OH}}{\overset{\text{Ph·N:N}}{\mid}} \longrightarrow \underset{\overset{\|}{\text{O}}}{\text{Ph·N:NH}}$$

In short, the metallic salts of the *iso*diazohydroxides are inert like a metallic nitrite, and only exhibit activity when free like nitrous acid.

Angeli has explained how his proposed constitutions can be applied to a number of the well-known reactions of the diazo-compounds. [109]

Diazo-ether formation and coupling are represented as analogous addition reactions, the latter being completed by a rearrangement :—

Ph·N(:O):NH + Alk·OH $\longrightarrow$ Ph·N(OH)·NH·OAlk $\longrightarrow$ Ph·N=N·OAlk + H$_2$O
Ph·N(:O):NH + Ph·OH $\longrightarrow$ Ph·N(OH)·NH·OPh $\longrightarrow$

Ph·N=N·O·Ph $\longrightarrow$ Ph·N=N·Ph·OH

It is to be regretted that he has not included the case of dimethyl-aniline.

The decomposition of normal diazohydroxides by weak reducing agents is explained by the formation of an unstable phenyldi-imide, for if the reduction is carried out by sodium stannite in the presence of benzaldehyde, β-benzoylphenylhydrazine is obtained.[110]

Having such a structure, the mild oxidising properties of the diazo-compounds are explained of which a number of examples were quoted, such as Gutmann's oxidation of arsenite to arsenate :—

$$Ph \cdot N_2 \cdot OH + AsO_3Na_3 = Na_3AsO_4 + C_6H_6 + N_2 \quad [111]$$

From this Angeli concluded that the oxygen is present in the " oxide " form, and from Bigiavi's work above that a normal diazohydroxide can be decomposed by removal either of the imino-group or the oxygen atom :—

$$Ph \cdot N \vdots NH \quad \overset{\text{"Nitroxyl"}}{\longrightarrow} \quad Ph \cdot N \vdots O + N_2 + H_2O$$
$$\underset{O}{\|} \quad \overset{\text{Reduction}}{\longrightarrow} \quad Ph \cdot N \vdots NH \longrightarrow C_6H_6 + N_2$$

As might be expected, the revival of such views revived also the old polemics, and Hantzsch challenged Angeli's interpretation of his reactions at every point. These counter-arguments, in so far as they do not repeat any points previously discussed, may be condensed under the following headings :—

1. That normal metal diazotates have the metal attached to oxygen, and not to nitrogen, as must be the case in a compound of the con-stitution proposed by Angeli. In this the defect of the old nitrosamine formula reappears.[112]

2. The diazohydroxides are weak acids and non-electrolytes dissolving in water by formation of hydroxonium salts, and that therefore the interpretation of the absorption spectra was incorrect.[113]

3. The substance having Angeli's constitution for the normal diazohydroxide would be iminonitrobenzene, and on Angeli's own showing it is formed by the hydrolysis of benzene azoxycarbonic ester, and is the source of the nitrosobenzene and ammonia which ultimately appear :—

$$\underset{O}{\overset{Ph \cdot N = N \cdot CO_2Et}{\|}} \longrightarrow \underset{O}{\overset{Ph \cdot N = NH}{\|}} \longrightarrow Ph \cdot NO + NH_3$$

No diazo-compound has ever been observed to decompose into nitroso-benzene and ammonia, and therefore the supposed intermediate cannot have such a structure as the above. If a diazo-compound does really

P

appear, then the iminonitrobenzene rearranges under the influence of
the caustic alkali :—

$$\underset{\underset{O}{\parallel}}{Ph\cdot N \!=\! NH} \longrightarrow \underset{\underset{ONa}{\mid}}{Ph\cdot N \!\equiv\! N} \longrightarrow \underset{\underset{OH}{\mid}}{Ph\cdot N \!\equiv\! N} + NaOH \longrightarrow PhN \!\equiv\! N\cdot OH + NaOH$$

Hantzsch also maintained that the reaction of normal diazotates with
nitroxyl is better explained as follows :— [114]

$$\underset{\underset{HO\cdot N \quad NH}{\parallel \quad \mid}}{Ph\cdot N \quad O} \longrightarrow \underset{(OHN \!=\! NH)}{\overset{PhNO}{+}} \longrightarrow Ph\cdot NO + N_2 + HO_2$$

4. Normal benzenediazotates are oxidised in alkaline solution, to
salts of phenylnitroamine, or " benzenediazoic acid," $Ph\cdot N \!=\! NO_2M$,
which would be impossible on Angeli's constitution.

5. Angeli's constitution cannot explain the isomerisation of normal
to *iso*diazo-compounds which takes place even in the solid state, as
the change would require the migration of an oxygen atom, whereas,
according to Hantzsch, the change is merely one of position, and so
can take place without the substance being dissolved.[115]

At the present time a considerable body of opinion appears to be
arriving at a view close to that of Angeli, and it may be mentioned
that Franklin, in his monograph on the chemistry of ammonia
as a reaction medium in place of water, looking at the whole matter
from an entirely different angle, uses for diazobenzene the formulæ
$PhN \!=\! {}^\times_\times N^\times \!\!-\!\! OH$ and $PhNH \!-\! {}^\times N^\times_\times \!=\! O$, one nitrogen atom being thus
represented as ammonia nitrogen and the other as nitrous acid
nitrogen.[116]

Diazo-Compounds and the Electronic Theory of Valency.

It is not strictly within the competence of the electronic theory of
valency to settle such a question as the constitution of the diazo-
compound, except to forbid constitutions which overstep its rules, and
hence no compounds to which electronic formulæ cannot be given have
been included in Table XXII.   The value of the theory lies in its power
of indicating the origin of reactivity in molecules and the effect of varied
structure on the reactivity, and in this volume it is from that point of
view that the theory has been invoked.

But on considering the reactivity of the diazo-compounds certain
constitutions may become more probable on the electron theory than
others, and electronic constitutions have been put forward on this basis
by Sarkar.[117]

For the diazonium salts he accepts the established constitution, but
assigns two electronic formulæ which he holds to be indistinguishable, a
point on which the work of Schoutissen (see p. 104) throws doubt.

He rejects Hantzsch's stereochemical theory, holding with Bamberger and Angeli that the normal diazotates, on account of their close resemblance to the diazonium salts, must contain a pentavalent nitrogen atom, but it cannot be agreed that his method of escape from Bamberger's dilemma, that the same hydroxide cannot be both a base and an acid, is a happy one. The instability of the normal diazotates he ascribes to the disproportionate sharing of electrons between the nitrogen atoms which his formula indicates.

In respect of the *iso*diazotates he accepts the constitution of Bamberger, Brühl, Cain, and Angeli, to which he gives an electronic interpretation.

The influence of the electronic theory of valency has created the tendency to regard the molecule of reactive and tautomeric substances as plastic structures adapting themselves to small changes of environment and recording the adaptation by changes in reactivity. Thus Baker, accepting v. Pechmann's diazonitrosoamine forms for the normal and *iso*diazotates, represents the labile system by the symbols :—

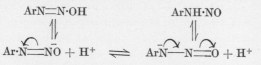

and so gives an explanation, in terms of electronic drift, of the different ethers afforded by different cations.[118]

These attempts to apply the electronic theory of valency cannot be regarded as more than preliminary exercises in the problem, for a full solution must include provisions for explaining the effects of substituents on stability, not only of the metabolic diazotates, but also for diazocyanides, diazosulphonates, and the peculiar problem of their isomerism.

Conclusion.

The reader who has persevered to this point may well feel like the sage who in his youth departed from the discussion of the saints and doctors by that same door wherein he went. Advocates have been found to plead for every constitution for the diazo-compounds which can be devised within the rules of valency. The impression too often left after the perusal of all the ink which has been spilled on the subject is a feeling that it is a decidedly unsatisfactory situation where such contrary arguments can fairly be urged to explain the same observation. A safe deduction from such a state of affairs is that some vital piece of information is missing, and meanwhile the question of the constitution of the diazo-compounds remains unsettled.

That development should pass through such a stage is perhaps inevitable. The polemics of the 'nineties sprang from a scramble of discovery that may fittingly be compared to a gold rush, wherein the several prospectors vie in staking out claims, each hoping to monopolise the largest possible auriferous area. But whereas Nature and man may in time efface all traces of the rude hackings of prospectors, the pages of the *Berichte* for ever enshrine the mementoes and dejecta of the great diazo-stampede, and give some justification for the assertions of those philosophers who have maintained that organic chemistry is not to be ranked among the exact sciences. Doubtless behind the controversy lay the implicit faith that each tautomer had one definite and rigid constitution, whence, if one constitution correctly expressed the facts, all others must be wrong.

To-day the activity of the past has given place to comparative stagnation in the field of investigation of the diazo-compounds among academic chemists, for no one has stepped forward to fill the place made vacant by the death of Hantzsch. The initiative lies very definitely with the industrial chemists who vouchsafe no information as to the theoretical ideas on which they base their work, but from whom the stream of patents relating to manufactures utilising diazo-compounds shows little diminution. The continual reappearance in patent scripts of the nitrosamine constitution for *iso*diazotates indicates, however, that the original view of Schraube and Schmidt still has a following, in spite of all attempts to convert the holders to other ways of thinking. In academic quarters the theory of Hantzsch is generally accepted and used as the vehicle to transmit ideas and express results. Provided this is done with proper reservations as to its limits, this is certainly a convenient usage, and indeed similar reservations pervade all organic chemistry and are implied in our action every time we write the aromatic hexagon.

From whence will come the information which will put the question of the constitution of the diazo-compounds beyond doubt it is impossible to foresee. Direct interest in the puzzle has ebbed at the present time because it does not seem soluble by frontal attack, and the main preoccupation of theoretical organic chemists is with the electronic theory of valency and quantum mechanics. The non-existence of any school devoted to a steady if small volume of research on diazo-compounds is to be regretted. In reading the papers of the great polemical period, one is struck by the broadness of the generalisations drawn from experiments made over a small range of compounds. The score or more of aromatic amines supplied commercially and in a high degree of purity for Ice-Colour work includes a number, particularly for producing blues and violets, which were unknown or scarcely available to the early investigators. Little has been published concerning the diazo-compounds derived from these amines except the shade and fastness of their azo-derivatives. A painstaking examination of their reactions would doubtless produce interesting results, for it must be remembered that it is impossible to argue from analogy beyond the broadest outlines. Every industrial chemist is aware that most discoveries and inventions arise from patient re-working of old lines of research by men inspired with a new idea, equipped with a new tool or new reagents. The elegant paper of Taylor on the constitution of the halides of Methylene Blue as determined by X-rays shows what unsuspected facts can be established even in an homologous series.[119] There exist diazo-compounds which would be sufficiently stable for X-ray examination or examination by the electron diffraction technique, and such examination might establish the configuration of the molecule of the *iso*diazotates and settle whether they are of the diazo- or nitrosamine type. The spectra might also well be re-examined with modern spectrophotometers in the design of which great improvements have been made in the last few years. Certain it is that only by continued efforts utilising both chemical and physical means after the example set by Hantzsch will our knowledge advance to such a point that it will become impossible to make further confusion by setting new theories afloat as casually as has been done in the past.

REFERENCES

[1] Griess, *Phil. Trans.*, 1864, **154**, 667; *Ann.*, 1862, **121**, 257; 1866, **137**, 39.
[2] *Repert. de Chemie Pure*, 1858—9, **1**, 338; *Zeitsch. für Chem.*, 1863, **678**, 511.
[3] Griess, *Ber.*, 1874, **7**, 1620.
[4] Kekulé, "Lehrbuch der Organischen Chemie," II, 717; 1866.
[5] Langfurth, Spiegelberg, *Ann.*, 1878, **191**, 205; 1879, **197**, 305.
[6] Strecker, *Ber.*, 1871, **4**, 786.
[7] Erlenmeyer, *ibid.*, 1874, **7**, 1110.
[8] Blomstrand, *Chemie der Jetztzeit*, 1869, **4**, 272; *Ber.*, 1875, **8**, 51.
[9] E. Fischer, *ibid.*, 1877, **10**, 1331.
[10] Blomstrand, *J. pr. Chem.*, 1897, ii, **58**, 176.
[11] Bamberger, *Ber.*, 1895, **28**, 444.
[12] Hantzsch, *ibid.*, p. 1734.
[13] v. Pechmann, *ibid.*, 1894, **27**, 651.
[14] Walther, *J. pr. Chem.*, 1895, ii, **51**, 528, 581.
[15] Sieber, *Textilber.*, 1927, **8**, 609.
[16] Oddo, *Gazz.*, 1935, **65**, 1105.
[17] Hantzsch and Reddelien, "Die Diazoverbindungen," p. 33.
[18] Hantzsch, *Ber.*, 1900, **33**, 2518.
[19] Goldschmidt, *ibid.*, 1890, **23**, 3220.
[20] Bamberger, *ibid.*, 1894, **27**, 3417.
[21] Bamberger, *ibid.*, 1896, **29**, 446, 564, 608.
[22] Robinson, "Lectures," p. 14.
[23] Schoutissen, *Rec. trav. chim.*, 1921, **40**, 763. See also Griess, *Phil. Trans.*, 1864, **154**, 684.
[24] Schoutissen, *J.Am.C.S.*, 1933, **55**, 4541.
[25] Schoutissen, *Rec. trav. chim.*, 1935, **54**, 97, 381.
[26] Hantzsch, *Ber.*, 1898, **31**, 340. See also Curtius, *ibid.*, 1890, **23**, 3035.
[27] Hantzsch, Davidson, *ibid.*, 1898, **31**, 1612.
[28] Hantzsch, Engler, *ibid.*, 1900, **33**, 2147.
[29] Hantzsch, *ibid.*, p. 2179.
[30] Hantzsch, Euler, *ibid.*, 1901, **34**, 4166.
[31] Morgan, Wootton, *J.C.S.*, 1907, **91**, 1311. Morgan, Couzens, *ibid.*, 1910, **97**, 1691.
[32] Battegay, Béhar, *Bull. Soc. Ind. Mulhouse*, 1923, **89**, 241.

[33] Hantzsch, Gerilowsky, *Ber.*, 1895, **28**, 2002.
[34] Hantzsch, *ibid.*, 1900, **33**, 1556.
[35] Bamberger, *ibid.*, 1895, **28**, 837 footnote.
[36] Hantzsch, Davidson, *ibid.*, 1896, **29**, 1522. Hantzsch, *ibid.*, 1902, **35**, 888; 1912, **45**, 3011. Klemenc, *ibid.*, 1914, **47**, 1407.
[37] Wolff, *Ann.*, 1900, **312**, 119.
[38] Morgan, Tomlins, *J.C.S.*, 1917, **111**, 497.
[39] Morgan, Porter, *ibid.*, 1915, **107**, 645.
[40] Battegay, Schmidt, *Bull. Soc. chim.*, 1927, iv, **41**, 205.
[41] Jacobsen, *Ann.*, 1893, **277**, 219.
[42] Orton, *J.C.S.*, 1903, **83**, 801.
[43] v. Pechmann, Frobenius, *Ber.*, 1894, **27**, 651.
[44] v. Pechmann, *ibid.*, 1892, **25**, 3505.
[45] Bamberger, *ibid.*, 1894, **27**, 914.
[46] Hantzsch, *ibid.*, 1895, **29**, 621.
[47] Hantzsch, *ibid.*, 1894, **27**, 1702.
[48] Angeli, *Gazz.*, 1894, **24**, ii, 369.
[49] Hantzsch, *Ber.*, 1900, **33**, 2517.
[50] Hantzsch, *ibid.*, 1904, **37**, 1084.
[51] Hantzsch, Davidson, *ibid.*, 1898, **31**, 1612.
[52] Hantzsch, *ibid.*, 1930, **63**, 1786.
[53] Hantzsch, Danziger, *ibid.*, 1897, **30**, 2529.
[54] Hantzsch, *ibid.*, 1901, **34**, 4166.
[55] Hammick, New, Sutton, Sidgwick, *J.C.S.*, **1930**, 1876.
[56] Hantzsch, *Ber.*, 1901, **34**, 4166.
[57] Hantzsch, Gerilowski, *ibid.*, 1895, **28**, 2002.
[58] Gerilowski, *ibid.*, 1896, **29**, 1075.
[59] Hantzsch, *ibid.*, 1896, **29**, 743.
[60] Angeli, *ibid.*, 1926, **59**, 1400.
[61] Bamberger, *ibid.*, 1912, **45**, 2054.
[62] Engler, *ibid.*, 1900, **33**, 2188.
[63] Hantzsch, Schümann, *ibid.*, 1899, **32**, 1703.
[64] Hantzsch, Pohl, *ibid.*, 1902, **35**, 2964.
[65] Orton, *J.C.S.*, 1903, **83**, 796.
[66] Hantzsch, *Ber.*, 1912, **45**, 3036.
[67] Sidgwick, " The Organic Chemistry of Nitrogen," p. 271.
[68] Mills, Bain, *J.C.S.*, 1910, **97**, 1866.
[69] Claus, *J. pr. Chem.*, 1894, ii, **50**, 239.
[70] Mellor, " Comprehensive Treatise on Inorganic Chemistry," Vol. 10, 234 *et seq.*
[71] Hantzsch, *Ber.*, 1908, **41**, 3534. Euler, *Archiv. für Chem.*, 1906, **2**, 1.
[72] Hantzsch, Singer, *Ber.*, 1897, **30**, 312.
[73] Swientowslawsky, *Ann. Soc. d'Encour. Sci. Expt.*, 1917, Supp. No. 7; *A.*, 1920, i, 326; *Bull. Soc. chim.*, 1924, iv, **35**, 137 ann.
[74] Hantzsch, *Ann.*, 1931, **491**, 284. Meisenheimer, Theilacker, *ibid.*, 1929, **469**, 144.
[75] Swientowslawsky, *Ber.*, 1929, **62**, 2034; *Ann.*, 1931, **491**, 273.
[76] Brady, *J.C.S.*, **1929**, 946.
[77] Bamberger, *Ber.*, 1912, **45**, 2054.
[78] Bamberger, *ibid.*, 1896, **29**, 457.
[79] Bamberger, *ibid.*, 1894, **27**, 1948.
[80] Bamberger, *ibid.*, 1895, **28**, 1218.
[81] Bamberger, Renaud, *ibid.*, 1897, **30**, 2279.
[82] Hantzsch, *ibid.*, 1905, **38**, 1035.
[83] Bamberger, *ibid.*, 1898, **31**, 2636.
[84] Bamberger, *ibid.*, 1896, **29**, 473; 1897, **30**, 2111.
[85] Hantzsch, *ibid.*, 1897, **30**, 339, 621; 1899, **32**, 1718.
[86] Bamberger, Müller, *Ann.*, 1900, **313**, 97.
[87] Brühl, *Zeit. physikal. Chem.*, 1898, **25**, 577; 1899, **26**, 47.
[88] Armstrong, Robertson, *J.C.S.*, 1905, **87**, 1280.
[89] Hantzsch, *Proc.*, 1905, **21**, 289.
[90] Thiele, *Ann.*, 1896, **290**, 1.

[91] v. Pechmann, *Ber.*, 1894, **27**, 672.
[92] Cain, p. 180.
[93] Dilthey, Blankenburg, Brandt, Hutweiler, *J. pr. Chem.*, 1932, ii, **135**, 36.
[94] Cain, *J.C.S.*, 1907, **91**, 1049.
[95] Morgan, Wootton, *ibid.*, p. 1315.
[96] Forster, Müller, *ibid.*, 1909, **95**, 2072.   Morgan, Reilly, *ibid.*, 1913, **103**, 808.
[97] Orton, Reed, *ibid.*, 1907, **91**, 1561.   Morgan, Micklethwaite, *ibid.*, 1908, **93**, 617; 1910, **97**, 2561.
[98] Euler, *Ber.*, 1908, **41**, 3979.
[99] Buchner, Witter, *ibid.*, 1894, **27**, 868.
[100] Hantzsch, *ibid.*, 1908, **41**, 3532.
[101] Cain, *ibid.*, p. 4189; 1909, **42**, 1209.   Compare Hantzsch, *ibid.*, 1909, **42**, 394, 2137.
[102] Cain, *ibid.*, 1913, **46**, 101.
[103] Hantzsch, Lifschitz, *ibid.*, p. 414.
[104] Schmidt, *Ann.*, 1920, **421**, 168.
[105] Angeli, *Gazz.*, 1921, **51**, i, 35; *Ber.*, 1926, **59**, 1400.
[106] Bamberger, *ibid.*, 1900, **33**, 1957.
[107] Cambi, Szego, *ibid.*, 1928, **61**, 2081.
[108] Bigiavi, *ibid.*, 1929, **62**, 2101; *R.A.L.*, 1929, vi, **9**, 1118.
[109] Angeli, *Ber.*, 1929, **62**, 1924; *R.A.L.*, 1929, vi, **9**, 933.
[110] Angeli, Jolles, *ibid.*, **10**, 141.
[111] Angeli, *Ber.*, 1930, **63**, 1977.   Compare Bamberger, *Helv. Chim. Acta*, 1931, **14**, 242.
[112] Hantzsch, *Ber.*, 1927, **60**, 667.
[113] Hantzsch, *ibid.*, 1929, **62**, 1235.
[114] Hantzsch, *ibid.*, 1930, **63**, 1270.
[115] Hantzsch, Strasser, *ibid.*, 1921, **54**, 655.
[116] Franklin, " The Nitrogen System of Compounds," pp. 290 *et seq.*, Reinhold, New York, 1935.
[117] Sarkar, *J. Indian C.S.*, 1935, **13**, 19.
[118] Baker, " Tautomerism," p. 153 (Routledge, 1934).
[119] Taylor, *Chem. and Ind.*, 1935, **54**, 732.

AUTHOR INDEX

ABRAHAM, 66
Abt, 21
Agfa, 12, 22, 171
de Aguiar, 21
Ahrens, 159
Albanesi, 78
Alcock, 24
Algerino, 101
Altschul, 5, 25
Ambuhl, 123, 138
Ammelburg, 59
Andresen, 164
Angeli, 66, 84, 92, 127, 146, 185, 190
   Theory of, 206–210, 211
Angelico, 66
d'Angelo, 24, 66
Armstrong, 201
Arzberger, 21
Aussig, 44
Auwers, 113

Bachmann, 151
Bader, 51
Badl, 138
Baeyer, 24, 128, 135, 157
Bailar, 146
Bain, 194
Baker, 211
Balz, 37, 156
Bamberger, 12, 16, 25, 26, 60, 61, 81,
    82, 83, 85, 86, 87, 90, 92, 96, 97,
    116, 123, 125, 136, 141, 143, 150,
    176, 177, 181, 183, 189, 191, 194
   Theory of, 198–200, 206, 210, 211
Bär, 106
Bart, 37, 161
B.A.S.F., 9, 38, 56, 58, 59, 87, 88
Battegay, 12, 56, 99, 123, 153, 181, 213
Baudisch, 92
Bauer, 105, 116
Bayer, 12, 21, 25, 39, 99, 123, 128, 160
Becker, 24, 39
Beckh, 138
Beckmann, 156
Beeson, 146
Béhar, 153, 213
Benda, 22, 162
Benedikt, 139
Bergmann, 122
Bergstrom, 89
Bernthsen, 136
Berthelot, 78
Bevan, 164, 167
Beyer, 123

Bigiavi, 77, 208, 209
Binder, F., 37, 132
Bindewald, 122
Binz, 162
Blagden, 155, 158
Blangy, 12
Blankenburg, 215
Blomstrand, 175, 180
Blumberger, 69, 71, 118, 160, 195
Boehler, 12
Boeseken, 62
Borghaus, 21
Börnstein, 160
Borsche, 151
Bradfield, 126
Brady, 197
Brandt, 215
Bressel, 67
Briner, 14
Bromwell, 153
Brühl, 200, 211
Brütsch, 123
Bucherer, 45, 78, 88, 116, 158
Buchner, 205
Bülow, 21, 101, 111, 153
Burawoy, 106
Burdach, 138
Burgess, 64
Burns, 48, 74
Busch, 123, 130
Busoni, 146
Buss, 124
Butleroff, 174

Cain, 63, 67, 68, 69, 71, 146, 152, 176,
   202
   Theory of, 203–206, 211
Calico Printers Association, 123
Cambi, 208
Cameron, 16, 146
Camiglieri, 73
Canzler, 157
Caro, 24, 67, 135
Caspar, 159
Cassella, 9, 22, 34
Castellana, 24
Cauffmann, 146
Chamberlain, 145
Chattaway, 25, 35, 100, 101, 122, 148
Chwala, 24
Ciusa, 171
Claasz, 24, 49, 50
Claisen, 123
Clark, 67

Claus, 10, 94, 194
Clayton, 123
Clayton Aniline Co., 160
Cleague, 22, 34
Clifford, 160
Coates, 165
Conant, 118
Consden, 101
Contardi, 158
Corbishley, 31, 89
Corse, 149
Couzens, 213
Cross, 164, 167
Cumming, 154
Curtius, 81, 83, 141

Dangerfield, 26, 117
Danziger, 214
Dashiell, 152
Davidson 181, 186
Davies, G. R., 17
Davies, J. S. H., 48
Davies, W., 126
Dehn, 74
den Dooren de Jong, 124
Dilthey, 202
Dimroth, 118, 119, 120, 130, 133
Dobbie, 191
Dovey, 48
Dreyfus, 160
Drumm, 62
Dunkel, 151
Dunn, 143
Du Pont, 139
Dutt, 142
Duval, 112
Dybowski, 50, 195

Earl, 128
East, 153
Eber, 12
Eberle, 14
Eble, 133
Ehrlich, 124
Eibner, 146
Eichler, 78
Ekbom, 50, 156
Elion, 13
Elkins, 105
Engel, 122
Engler, 192
Epstein, 22
Erban, 7
Erdmann, 155
Erlenmeyer, 174, 175
Euler, 68, 69, 71, 90, 179, 204
Evens, 146
Ewers, 50
Eynon, 24
Eyre, 54

Faldino, 107

Favrel, 123
Feer, 36, 39, 170
Fernelius, 89, 138
Fierz-David, 109, 120, 142
Filippytschew, 117
Fischer, E., 25, 93, 127, 141, 153, 175
Fischer, O., 26, 96, 97, 105, 116, 139, 201
Fisher, 123
Fletcher, 143
Földi, 38, 161
Forgan, 148
Forster, 100, 133, 142
Franklin, 210
Freese, 143
Freimann, 122
Friedländer, 21, 24, 28, 142, 145
Friedmann, 124
Friswell, 135
Fritsch, 123
Frobenius, 82, 89, 130, 138, 182, 183, 198
Frohlich, 48
Fuchs, 13
Fukushima, 171

Gabriel, 91
Gaess, 59
Garforth, 48
Garland, 133
Garton, 101
Gasiorowsky, 146
Gaspar, 172
Gattermann, 123, 147, 155, 157, 160
Gay, 171
Gebauer-Fulnegg, 115, 143
Gehren, 157
Geigy, 9, 99
Gerilowski, 179, 189, 190
Gerngross, 151
Gibbs, 93
Gipp, 163
Girard, 12
Glogauer, 49
Glutz, 93
Godden, 21
Goldschmidt, 104, 117, 121, 132, 133, 135, 138, 176
Gomberg, 150
Gortner, C. V. and R. A., 102
Gosh, 123
Goske, 136
Graebe, 131, 160
Graham, 146
Grandmougin, 122, 128
Grässler, 51
Gray, 38
Green, 135, 159, 164, 167
Greiner, 67
Griesheim, 88
Griess, 1, 11, 13, 20, 24, 26, 34, 67, 81, 82, 91, 93, 100, 103, 116, 128, 129, 130, 141, 142, 144, 147, 149, 154, 160, 174

Grieve, 98, 149
Griffin, 146
Grippa, 124
Gruhl, 133
Gutmann, 97, 160

Hall, 93
Haller, 153
Hammick, 214
Hantzsch, 15, 16, 19, 21, 23, 26, 35, 49,
    50, 55, 61, 66, 68, 70, 71, 77, 83,
    86, 87, 90, 94, 97, 100, 120, 121,
    126, 135, 143, 146, 147, 153, 155,
    176, 178, 179, 180, 182
  Theory of, 183–198, 199, 202, 205,
    209, 210, 212, 213
Harding, 171
de la Harpe, 77
Harper, 171
Hartley, 102, 160
Hartmann, 118
Hausknecht, 159
Hausser, 68
Hay, 53
Heidelberger, 139
Heilmann, 123
Heinichen, 153
Heller, 92, 116, 122
Henderson, 160
Henriques, 171
Hepburn, 24, 38, 45, 46
Hermanns, 124
Herz, 25
Heumann, 139
Heusler, 138, 157
Hewitt, 123
Hey, 98, 149
Heyden, 162
Hickinbottom, 115
Hidegh, 103
Hill, 122
Hinsberg, 48
Hird, 22
Hirsch, 16, 24, 60, 68, 75, 138, 149, 153
Hodgson, 12, 21, 145, 155
Hofmann, 21
Hofmeister, 153
Hollemann, 156
Holliday, 28
Holm, 133
Horio, 171
Houston, 14
Hubner, 91
Hummel, 170
Hunter, 67, 105
Hutweiler, 215

I.C.I., 9, 38, 51, 96, 122, 123, 139
I.G., 9, 12, 21, 22, 23, 34, 38, 48, 51, 74,
    88, 95, 99, 123, 124, 139, 151, 159,
    162, 172
Ikuta, 19, 26

Indovina, 74, 153, 171
Irschik, 123

Jacobs, 139
Jacobsen, 22, 143, 214
Jäger, 24, 26, 60, 135, 157
Jambuserwala, 123
Japp, 111
Jean, 123
Jennisch, 111, 123
Jochem, 16, 153
Johnsen, 139
Johnson, 14, 122
Jolles, 73, 127, 146, 153
Jonas, 151
Jones, 14
Justin-Mueller, 153

Kacer, 18
Kalb, 162
Kalianoff, 122
Kalm, 163
Kalle, 9, 22, 38, 99, 153, 160, 171
Karrer, 16, 115, 120, 162
Kay, 142
Kaufler, 16
Kekulé, 21, 103, 174
Kenyon, 101
Keppler, 124
Kershaw, 145
Kiefe, 153
Kime, 67
Kinzelberger, 34
Kirner, 165
Kishner, 31
Klason, 160
Klemenc, 181
Klimova, 163
Klingemann, 111
Knapp, 99, 146
Knecht, 13, 70, 75
Knoevenagel, 15, 74
Knorr, 66
Koechlin, 28
Koenigs, 67
Kögel, 169
Kohler, 123
Kolbe, 1
König, 115, 123
Königs, 48, 128
Konink, 12
Korezynski, 159
Kortwright, 146
Kotscheschkow, 163
Krasover, 31
Kraus, 60, 143
Kritscher, 96
Kuchenbecker, 126
Kuhling, 150
Kuhlmann, 57, 58, 139
Kuhn, 106
Kunz, 26, 148

Kunze, 91
Kunzle, 99
Kvalnes, 151

Ladenburg, 21
Lamplough, 74
Landsberg, 160
Lange, 96
Langfurth, 213
Langgurth, 170
Lantz, 46, 123
Lauer, 106
Lauth, 26
Lawson, 21
Lecco, 128
Leichtlin, 124
Lellmann, 35, 155
Lenhardt, 123
Lenz, 157
Leuchs, 171
Leukhardt, 160
Levi, 107
Levin, 26, 31, 48, 89
Levinstein, 22
Ley, 55
Lieb, 162
Liebermann, 123
Lierg, 172
Lifschitz, 191, 193
Limpricht, 128
Ljaschenko, 165
Locher, 151

Madden, 67
Macintire, 149
Mai, 140
Maier, 38, 77, 166
Manchot, 66
Mangini, 142
Mann, 21, 160
Manura, 122
Manzelius, 156
Marriott, 41
Martius, 4
Mason, 105, 113
Maw, 146
May, 38
Mazzara, 122
Mebus, 7
Meisenheimer, 197
Meldola, 24, 52, 53, 132, 153
Merz, 124, 146
Metcalf, 153
Meyenburg, 98
Meyer, K. H., 112, 113, 120
Meyer, M., 92
Meyer, V., 12, 16, 110, 138
Michael, 99
Michaelis, 25, 26, 66, 139
Michel, 142
Micklethwaite, 21, 22, 24, 123, 215
Miller, 106, 138

Mills, 194
Misslin, 11
Mitscherlich, 103
Mitra, 156
M.L.B., 22, 34, 38, 58, 59, 126, 162
Moale, 146
Möhlau, 13, 88, 123, 128, 149
Mohr, 66
Molinari, 133
Morgan, 15, 17, 18, 24, 34, 64, 66, 92,
   107, 138, 139, 146, 179, 181
Morrow, 66
Mounier, 164
Mrozinski, 159
Muhlert, 122
Muir, 154
Müller, E., 159
Müller, J., 98
Müller, R., 215
Muller, 68
Munzer, 123
Murray, 170

Neogi, 156
Nichol, 68
Niementowski, 148
Nietzki, 20
Nesmejanov, 38, 163
New, 214
Nijk, 22, 162
Noelting, 56
Nölting, 21, 132
Nötzel, 122
Norris, 149

Oberst, 146
Oddo, 68, 142, 153, 171, 176
Oehler, 22
Oekonomides, 139
Olivieri, 157
Orloff, 135
Orndorff, 122, 146, 153
Orton, 54, 55, 86, 126, 158, 165, 193, 195
Ostroshinskaja, 77
Ostwald, 198
Overwien, 139

Paal, 96
Pabst, 12
Paden, 114
Palmer, 153
Parkes, 101
Parks, 123
Parsons, 146
Pask, 48
Paterno, 157
v. Pechmann, 49, 81, 82, 89, 96, 111,
   123, 130, 138, 176, 182, 183, 195,
   198, 202, 211
Perkin, F. M., 123
Pernert, 151
Peters, 46

Peterson, 118
Pfitzinger, 128
Pharma Chemical Co., 139
Philips' Gloeilampenfab., 171, 172
Pieroni, 92, 124
Pierron, 139
Pickard, 21
Pinner, 139
Pinnow, 159
Platt, 70
Pohl, 214
Pollack, 115, 143
Popp, 66
Porter, 181
Powell, 171
Power, 146
Pozzetto, 122
Pray, 71

Quilico, 67

Raiford, 146
Ray, 122
Reddelien, xii
Reed, 215
Reid, 22
Reilly, 62, 66, 115, 215
Reinders, 139
Remsen, 146, 152
Remy, 35, 155
Renaud, 142
Reverdin, 53, 77
Rjasanzew, 67
Robertson, 201
Robinson, 121, 177
Rohner, 8, 122
Römer, 127
Rosenhauer, 135
Rostovtseva, 63, 76
Rotter, 142
Rowe, 19, 26, 31, 46, 88, 117
Ruff, 165, 168
Ruggli, 99, 146, 159
Rugheimer, 25
Ruhl, 26

Sachs, 124
Sandmeyer, 154, 155, 157
Sándor, 122
Sandoz, 38, 99, 153
Sarkar, 210
Saunders, 101
Schaarschmidt, 6
Schachnow, 151
Schäffer, 67
Schaffer, 153
Schall, 22
Scharwin, 122
Schering-Kahlbaum, 67
Scheuer, 21
Schiemann, 156
Schiff, 142

Schleissing, 60
Schlotterbeck, 123
Schmachtenberg, 101
Schmidt, C., 81, 82, 87, 191, 212
Schmidt, H., 161, 206
Schmidt, J., 38, 77, 166, 181
Schmidt, M. P., 94
Schmidt, O., 26
Schmiedel, 94
Schmitt, 9, 14, 15, 93, 157
Schneider, 14
Schoen, 169
Scholl, 12, 14, 148
Scholler, 123
Schoutissen, 11, 15, 20, 21, 62, 104, 177, 206
Schraube, 81, 82, 87, 123, 191, 212
Schremann, 55
Schroeter, 39, 40
Schröter, 166
Schultz, 12
Schultze, 91
Schulze, 123
Schümann, 61, 214
Schwalbe, 6, 70, 75
Schwartz, 157
Schwechten, 154
S.C.I., 8, 16, 22, 34, 48, 51, 122, 123, 126, 160
Scottish Dyes, 48
Seide, 67
Seidler, 14, 67
Sekiguchi, 78
Sen, 123
Seyewitz, 164
Sheddon, 146
Shober, 153
Sidgwick, 214
Sieber, 38, 176
Silbermann, 99
Silberrad, 142
Silberstein, 54
Singer, 49, 195
Smiles, 160
Smith, C., 123, 132
Smith, L. I., 114
Smythe, 60
Snow, 69
Spencer, 165
Spiegelberg, 213
Stadler, 160
Stafford, 89
St. Denis, 96, 172
Stein, 165, 168
Stenhouse, 13
Stephens, 59
Stollé, 22
Stolz, 66
Storch, 125
Strasser, 215
Streatfeild, 54, 132
Strecker, 127, 175

Strohbach, 123
Stuart, 102
Stuber, 12
Stursa, 123
Suais, 123
Suizu, 139
Sunder, 10
Supniewsky, 38
Sutton, 214
Suzuki, 62
Swarts, 157
Swientoslawski, 78, 197
Szego, 208

Täuber, 21
Tafel, 138
Tama, 48
Tassily, 62
Taylor, 213
Tepper, 48
Terentiev, 77, 123
Thann and Mulhouse, 39
Thiele, 66, 85, 202
Thomas, 155, 160
Thompson, 70
Tichwinski, 128
Tilden, 138
Tinkler, 191
Tochtermann, 123
Tomlins, 181
Tröger, 50
Tschekalin, 117
Tscherwinski, 5
Tschitschibabin, 67

Uemura, 122
Ueno, 62, 78
Ufer, 172
Ullmann, 131, 147
Unger, 135
Upton, 22
Usines du Rhone, 153

Valentiner, 157
van der Grinten, 171
van Veen, 124
Vaubel, 21, 25, 138
Veinberg, 134
Veley, 117, 124

Vesely, 123, 157
Vielan, 159
Vieille, 78
Vignon, 78
Viktoreff, 41, 70
Vock, 23, 77, 146, 156
Vorländer, 23, 151
Votoček, 157

Wacker, 142
Waentig, 156
Wahl, 46, 123
Walker, 12, 21, 155
Wallach, 9, 135, 157
Wallbaum, 12
Walls, 139
Walther, 128, 155, 176, 207
Waters, 151
Watt, 138
Watts, 132
Wechsler, 59
Weida, 146
Weiler-ter-Meer, 9
Weisz, 67
Werner, 183
Weselsky, 139
Whitehead, 142
Wichelhaus, 67
Wilke-Dörfurt, 38
Wimmer, 139
Winston, 146
Witt, O. N., 9, 13, 40, 56, 122
Wohl, 96, 142
Wojciechowski, 79, 84
Wolff, 116, 181
Wootton, 92, 123, 138, 215
Wormall, 142
Wulz, 136
Wurtz, 174

Yamamoto, 73, 171
Yamashita, 171
Yokojima, 139

Zakrewski, 21
Zeitlin, 142
Zeniseck, 157
Zimmermann, 146
Zincke, 21, 122, 126

SUBJECT INDEX

ABSORPTION spectra of diazo-compounds, 191, 208
Action on diazo-compounds of :—
acetic anhydride, 96
alcohols, 144, 187, 208
amidines, 136
amines, aliphatic, 130
amines, aromatic, 106, 129, 138
ammonia, 130
antimony salts, 160
arsenic salts, 75, 160, 209
arylsulphinic acids, 48
arylsulphonic acids, 39–45
benzoyl chloride, 96
bromine, 100
cobalt thiocyanate, 158
copper, 147
cuprous salts, 147, 148, 154
cyanamide, 138
hydrazines, 141
hydrazoic acid, 142
hydrogen sulphide, 143
hydroxylamine, 140, 158
imines, 138
oximes, 141
quinones, 150
reducing agents, 126, 146, 209
sulphonamides, 39
sulphites, 93
water, 151, 152
Alkyl nitrites, use of, 15
Aminoazobenzene, formation, 108, 135
Amyl nitrite, use of, 15, 130
Anthanthrone, 148
Arylhydrazines, 126
Arylnitroamines, 51
Arylnitrosamines, 192
Arylnitrosohydroxylamines, 51
Arylsulphamic acids, 17, 51
" Azo-ammonium," 176
Azo-compounds, 103, 148
configuration of, 103
endo-, 112
hydrolysis, 117
tautomerism, 106
Azo-guard, 41
Azomercaptans, 143
Azophor Red, 32
Azothiophenols, 143
Azoxy-compounds, 92, 206

Barium nitrite, use of, 8
" Benzene diazoic acid," 125

Calcium nitrite, use of, 8
Carbazole, 131
4-Chlorotoluene diazonium chloride, stability, 43

5-Chlorotoluene diazonium chloride, stability, 42
Clayton Yellow, 159
Coupling, amines, 106
aminonaphthol sulphonic acids, 108, 110
butadienes, 114
diamines, 107
hydrocarbons, 113
1 : 5-dihydroxynaphthol, 105
keto-enol tautomers, 110–112
naphthols, 104
phenol ethers, 112
phenols, 104, 208
polyhydric phenols, 105
proteins, 122
sulphamic acids, 107
Coupling, effect on, of :—
acidity, 104, 110, 118
pyridine, 115
substituents in diazo-compounds, 109
Coupling, migration during, 116
Coupling energy, 115, 117
Coupling reaction :—
ejection of substituents, 115
electron theory and, 121
kinetics, 117
mechanism, 118

Decomposition of diazo-compounds :—
by heat, 68, 75
by light, sunlight, 165
mercury vapour, 166
rate of, 68
Diaryls, formation, 147
" Diazo-," origin of name, 1
Diazoamino-compounds, 4, 128
absorption spectra, 132
constitution, 129, 131, 132
formation, 129
pyrolysis, 131
rearrangement, 134
salts of, 131
scission, 131, 134
uses of, 134
Diazo-anhydrides, 86, 87, 199
Diazoarylsulphinates, 48
Diazoarylsulphonates, 39–48
Diazocarboxylic acids, 92
Diazo-compounds :—
action of nitric acid on, 11, 99, 177
analysis of, 75–77
bromination, 99
chlorination, 99
isomeric constitutions, Table XXII, 184

Diazo-compounds :—
 nitration, 99
 oxidation, 125
Diazo-compounds, explosives, use as, 67
 explosive, 143
 formation, by condensation reactions, 26
 formation, by oxidation, 25
 formation, by scission, 26
Diazo-cyanides, 91
 constitution, 188, 195
 preparation, 91
Diazo-ethers, 89
Diazo-group, replacement by :—
 acetoxy-group, 153
 amino-group, 158
 azimino-group, 142
 bromine, 155
 chlorine, 154
 cyano-group, 157
 fluorine, 156
 halogens, 154
 hydrogen, 144
 hydroxyl, 151, 152
 iodine, 154
 nitro-group, 158
 nitroso-group, 158
 selenocyano-group, 160
 sulphinic acid group, 159
 sulphonic acid group, 160
 thiocyano-group, 157
 thiol-group, 159
Diazohydroxides, 81, 104
Diazoic acids, 125
Diazo-imines, 18
Diazoimino-compounds, formation, 135, 137
 synthetic use, 156
 technical use, 136–138
Diazonium aurichlorides, 34
 borofluorides, 37, 153, 159
 fluorosulphonates, 37
 hydrochlorides, 35
 hydrofluorides, 35
 iododichlorides, 101
 platinichlorides, 34
 plumbichlorides, 35
 tetrachloroiodides, 101
Diazonium nitrate, from sulphonate, 94
Diazonium salts :—
 complex, 34
 constitution, 174–178, 203, 204, 210
 simple, 23, 24
 detection, 77
Diazo-oxides, 7, 180, 193
Diazo-perhalides, 100, 101
Diazo-resins, 153
Diazosulphonates :—
 constitution, 190, 196
 preparation, 93
 uses, 95

Diazotates, anti- and syn-, 185
 differences n- and iso-, 77, 85, 208
 nomenclature, 83
isoDiazotates :—
 application in printing, 88
 constitution, 182, 185, 195, 197, 199, 205, 207, 211
 detection, 77
 preparation, 84, 85
normal-Diazotates :—
 constitution, 178, 185, 195, 197, 205, 207, 211
 detection, 77
 preparation, 83
Diazotisation of :—
 amines, strongly basic, 6
 amines, weakly basic, 10
 p-aminoacetanilide, 18
 aminoanthracenes, 12
 1-aminoanthraquinone, 6
 aminoanthraquinones, general, 12, 14, 15
 aminoazobenzene, 7
 o-aminoazotoluene, 34
 aminobenzaldehyde, 11
 aminobenzoic acids, 9
 p-aminodimethylaniline, 19
 aminodiphenylamines, 8
 4-amino-4'-ethoxydiphenylamine, 19
 4-amino-3-methoxydiphenylamino, 8
 aminonaphthols, 7
 1-amino-2-naphthol-4-sulphonic acid, 7
 aminophenols, 15
 aniline, 15
 benzidine, 6, 16
 bromonitroanilines, 10
 4-chloro-2 : 6-dinitroaniline, 11
 4-chloro-o-toluidine, 5, 40
 diamines, 16, 20
 1 : 5-diaminoanthraquinone, 16
 diaminodisulphamic acids, 17
 4 : 4'-diaminobenzeneazonaphthalene, 17
 dianisidine, 36
 2 : 6-dibromo-4-nitroaniline, 11
 2 : 5-dichloroaniline, 6
 2 : 6-dichloro-4-nitroaniline, 11
 2 : 4-dinitroaniline, 10, 14
 2 : 4-dinitro-1-naphthylamine, 11, 54
 dinitrotoluidines, 10
 3 : 5-dinitro-o-toluidine, 13
 heterocyclic amines, 64
 methyl-p-phenylenediamine, 19
 naphthionic acid, 9
 naphthylamines, 6
 naphthylenediamines, 17
 1 : 4-naphthylenediamine, 20
 2 : 7-naphthylenediamine, 15, 21
 p-nitroaniline, 6, 9, 32
 nitrodiacetyl-p-phenylenediamine, 18
 nitronaphthylamines, 11, 54

Diazotisation :—
    buffered solutions in, 8
    copper salts, effect, 8
    end-point, detection, 5, 10, 14
    failure of reaction, 22
    speed of, 61
Diazotisation of :—
    1-nitro-2-naphthylamine, 55
    picramic acid, 1, 10, 13
    picramide, 11, 14
    stilbene, diamino-, 16
    sulphanilic acid, 9
    tetrabromoaniline, 10, 14
    triaminotriphenylmethane, 16
    2 : 4 : 6-trinitro-5-aminoanisol, 11
    2 : 4 : 6-trinitroaniline, 11
    trinitroanisidines, 53
Diazotisation, methods of, Table I, 2
    direct method, 3
    Griess's method, 13
    inverted method, 9
    Knoevenagel's method, 15
    strong acid solvents, 10
    Witt's method, 12, 64
Diazotypes, 167
Diphenyl, 147
Dispersing agents, aid to diazotisation, 4

Ehrlich's diazo-reaction, 122
Electrolysis, 152, 156

Formazyl, 112
Free radicals, 98, 147

Guaiacol, 152

Ice Colour Bases, Table VI, 31
Ice Colours, 19, 28
Iminonitrobenzene, 209
Indazoles, 85

Naphthalene sulphonic acids, as stabi-
    lisers, 39–44
β-Naphthol-1-sulphonic acid, 45
Nitrazol C, 32
Nitroamines, 125
Nitrobenzenediazonium   chloride,
    stability, 42
Nitrogen tetroxide, diazotisation with,
    14
Nitrogen trioxide, diazotisation with,
    14, 15, 19
Nitrosoacetanilide, 183
Nitrosoacetanilide, preparation, 97
Nitrosoacylarylamines, 96, 200
    speed of decomposition, 98
Nitrosamine Red, 87
Nitrosamines, 81, 82, 192, 200, 202
Nitrosulphonic acid, 12
Nitrosylsulphuric acid, 10, 11, 15, 21,
    22, 32, 34

Nitrosyl bromide, 12
Nitrosyl chloride, 12, 15, 130
Nitrous acid gases, 13, 14
Nitrous acid, oxidising action of, 7
Nitrous anhydride, 14
" Nitroxyl," 84, 208, 209

Paranil A, 40
Para Red, 28, 32, 46
Phenols and phenol ethers, 152, 153
Phenyltriazene, 130
Photography, 167
Photolysis, 165, 166
Phthalazines, 47

Rapid Fast dyestuffs, 88
Rapidasol dyestuffs, 95
Rapidogen dyestuffs, 137
Reactions, classification, 80
Reduction of diazo-compounds :—
    to hydrazines, 126
    to hydrocarbons, 145
Refractivity of diazo-compounds, 200

Sandmeyer reaction, 154–157
Self-diazotisation, 54
Stabilised diazo-compounds, 28 et seq.,
    108, 137
Stabilised diazo-compounds, " Active,"
    30
Stabilised diazo-compounds, " Passive,"
    30, 170
Stability of diazo-compounds :—
    solids, 67
    solutions, 67–74
    solutions, effects of colloids, 71
    solutions, effects of neutral salts on,
        70
    solutions, graph of p_H, v. stability, 72
    solutions in presence of stabilisers,
        41–43
    table of, 69, 70
Substituents, rate of elimination, 54
Sulphazides, 127

Tetrazo-compounds, coupling, 177
Tetrazotisation of :—
    diamines, 19, 20, 21
    2 : 4-diaminophenol, 20
    m-phenylenediamine, 20
    o-phenylenediamine, 21
    p-phenylenediamine, 20, 21
    m-tolylenediamine, 21
Tetrazotisation, by stages, 20
Thermochemistry, 78
Triazenes, 128
" Twinned double bonds," 207

Vacanceine Red, 28

Zinc chloride, double salts, 36